The Plato of Praed Street ——— the life and times of Almroth Wright

by

Michael Dunnill

The ROYAL
SOCIETY *of*
MEDICINE
PRESS *Limited*

©2000 Royal Society of Medicine Press Ltd

1 Wimpole Street, London W1G 0AE, UK
207 E Westminster Road, Lake Forest, IL 60045, USA
http://www.rsm.ac.uk

British Library Cataloguing in Publication Data
A catalogue record for this book is available from the British Library

ISBN 1-85315-477-6

Typeset by Dobbie Typesetting Limited, Tavistock, Devon

Printed in Great Britain by Henry Ling Ltd, the Dorset Press, Dorchester, Dorset

Contents

List of Illustrations

Permission to reproduce sought, where necessary, from the listed source

Cover Illustration

Almroth Wright. (Original in possession of Giles Romanes)

Chapter 1

Figure 1
The Reverend Charles Henry Wright and his wife Ebba in the garden of their house in Wandsworth. (Original in possession of Giles Romanes)
Figure 2
Almroth Wright in his twenties during his time at Cambridge. (Colebrook L. *Almroth Wright*. London: William Heinemann, 1954)
Figure 3
Jane Georgina Wright in 1890 shortly after arriving in Sydney. (Original in possession of Giles Romanes)

Chapter 2

Figure 4
The Royal Victoria Hospital at Netley. It was pulled down in 1967 and now only the chapel, which has been converted into a small museum, remains. (Hampshire County Council, The Castle, Winchester SO23 8UJ)
Figure 5
'Oakhurst', the Wright's house in Netley, in 1895. Wright is standing in the doorway. (Original in possession of Giles Romanes)
Figure 6
Wright in his laboratory at Netley. (The Wellcome Library, 210 Euston Road, London NW1 2BE)

Chapter 3

Figure 7
David Bruce, a photograph taken when he was a Major-general and Commandant of the Royal Army Medical College. (*Journal of the Royal Army Medical Corps*, Keogh Barracks, Ash Vale, Aldershot GU12 5RQ)

Chapter 4

Figure 8
Some of the staff of the inoculation department *circa* 1908. Wright is in the centre with Leonard Noon on his left. Stewart Douglas is on the other side of Wright (only half in the picture). The two figures at the back are John Freeman and Leonard Colebrook. Note the formal dress; Noon wears a black coat and pin-stripe trousers. (The Wellcome Library, 210 Euston Road, London NW1 2BE)
Figure 9
Leonard Noon in the laboratory at St Mary's in 1910. He is smoking, something that is strictly prohibited in a bacteriology laboratory today. At this time he had advanced pulmonary tuberculosis, and he died in 1911. (The Wellcome Library, 210 Euston Road, London NW1 2BE)
Figure 10
A laboratory tea party before the First World War. Wright is listening to Douglas and Fleming while Freeman looks on. (The Wellcome Library, 210 Euston Road, London NW1 2BE)
Figure 11
Wright emerging from the sea in Dorset during one of the laboratory week-end outings. He considered this the best photograph ever taken of him! (Alexander Fleming Laboratory Museum, St Mary's Hospital, Paddington, London W2 1NY)

Chapter 5

Figure 12
A diagrammatic representation of Ehrlich's side-chain theory of antibody production. He postulated that the antibody-forming cell carried a series of receptors in the form of projections or side-chains on its surface. Foreign antigens with the correct spatial configuration attached themselves to the appropriate receptor and the whole became detached and liberated into the serum as an antibody. A new receptor then formed on the cell surface and the process was repeated. (Adapted from Ehrlich P. *Proc Roy Soc* 1900; **66**: 424. The Royal Society, 6 Carlton House Terrace, London SW1Y 5AG)
Figure 13
Wright's method of obtaining blood from the finger and collecting it into glass tubes. The skin of the finger was sterilised and then pierced by the sharpened glass tube (a). The open end of the tube was then placed at the edge of the drop of blood, which entered the tube by capillary attraction (b). The tube was not placed in the centre of the drop of blood as this resulted in blood rising up on the outside of the tube. (From Wright AE. *Technique of the teat and capillary glass tube*. London: Constable, 1912)
Figure 14
A collection of Wright's blood tubes in which blood has clotted, the clots having retracted and separated from the clear yellow serum. Some empty tubes and some capillary tubes, one with

attached rubber teat, can be seen on the right of the picture. (Alexander Fleming Laboratory Museum, St Mary's Hospital, Paddington, London W2 1NY)

Figure 15
(a) Neutrophil polymorphonuclear leucocytes in the peripheral blood. These are capable of ingesting, ie phagocytosing, bacteria. (b) Macrophages, which can also ingest bacteria and foreign particles into their cytoplasm. The two smaller cells on the left of the picture are lymphocytes. (Professor K Gatter, John Radcliffe Hospital, Headington, Oxford OX3 9OU)

Chapter 6

Figure 16
Major Greenwood, one of the founders of medical statistics. (Dunhill M. *Medical Dictators*. London: Keynes Press)

Chapter 7

Figure 17
Cartoon from *Punch*, 1913. The caption reads: 'History in the Making: the unchivalrous Sir Almroth Wright denying his identity to a fair caller at the fire-proof retreat where he is retiring after the nervous strain of writing "The Unexpurgated Case against Female Suffrage"'. (*Punch*, Trevor House, 100 Brompton Road, London SW3 1ER)

Chapter 8

Figure 18
The casino at Boulogne converted into No.14 British Military Hospital. Wright had to walk through these wards each day to the laboratory. (Photograph courtesy of the Imperial War Museum, Lambeth Road, London SE1 6HZ)

Figure 19
The laboratory above the casino; it had previously been the fencing school. (Photograph courtesy of the Imperial War Museum, Lambeth Road, London SE1 6HZ)

Figure 20
Wright in the uniform of a full colonel at the laboratory bench. (The Wellcome Library, 210 Euston Road, London NW1 2BE)

Figure 21
The glass model of a shrapnel wound devised by Fleming. Organisms placed in the spiked outpouchings were unharmed by antiseptics. (Colebrook L. *Almroth Wright*. London: William Heinemann, 1954)

Figure 22
A group outside the casino in Boulogne. Seated are Wright and Harvey Cushing; standing are Colebrook, Roger Lee and Alexander Fleming. Cushing and Lee were in charge of the surgical and medical divisions of the Second Harvard University Unit, which took over some of the wards in the casino in 1916. (The Wellcome Library, 210 Euston Road, London NW1 2BE)

Chapter 9

Figure 23
General Sir Alfred Keogh, director general of the Royal Army Medical Corps 1914–18. (The Wellcome Library, 210 Euston Road, London NW1 2BE)

Chapter 10

Figure 24
Sir Walter Morley Fletcher, The first Secretary of the Medical Research Council. (Medical Research Council, 20 Park Crescent, London W1N 4AL)

Figure 25
The visit of the Prince and Princess of Montenegro to the inoculation department on 24 October 1929. The Mayor and Mayoress of Paddington (Mr and Miss Snell) and the Town Clerk, Mr Abbiss, are on the left of the picture, the Prince and Princess in the centre and Wright in the background. The others are unidentified. (Alexander Fleming Laboratory Museum, St Mary's Hospital, Paddington, London W2 1NY)

Chapter 11

Figure 26
Lady Wright in 1920, holding her grandson. (Original in possession of Giles Romanes)

Figure 27
'Southernwood', the house built by Wright at Farnham after the First World War. (Original in possession of Giles Romanes)

Figure 28
Almroth Wright and his brother, Major-General Henry Wright. (Original in possession of Giles Romanes)

Figure 29
The visit to Buenos Aires in 1931. From left to right: Mr Bliss, John Freeman, Mildred Bliss, Wright, an unknown Argentinian and Berkeley Moynihan. (The Wellcome Library, 210 Euston Road, London NW1 2BE)

Chapter 12

Figure 30
Visit of Queen Elizabeth on 9 August 1944 to St Mary's. Wright and the Queen are standing next to each other. Lord Moran's head can just be seen appearing over the left shoulder of the Queen. (Alexander Fleming Laboratory Museum, St Mary's Hospital, Paddington, London W2 1NY)

Figure 31
Wright in his garden at 'Southernwood' shortly before his death. (Original in possession of Giles Romanes)

Preface

On 3 May 1947 a small gathering assembled at Golders Green crematorium to pay their last respects to a distinguished medical scientist. An extraordinary character, Almroth Wright had been a major force in medicine since the late 19th century. The friend of statesmen and men of letters, he was more than the conventional doctor. His private life was tumultuous; he separated from his wife, had numerous women friends and developed a passionate but unrequited attachment to the wife of a wealthy American diplomat. Yet few were there that day to pay tribute to this major figure in British public life; within ten years of his death both the man and his work, which had laid the foundation for much in modern medicine, were largely forgotten or ignored. It is social historians who now tend to remember him, and this for his eccentric opinions on women: notoriously, he insisted women were intellectually inferior to men and should be denied the suffrage.

The period between Wright's birth in 1861 and his death in 1947 witnessed a revolution in medicine. In the 1860s acceptance of the germ theory of infectious disease still lay in the future. Diseases such as diabetes mellitus and pernicious anaemia presented insoluble enigmas; puerperal fever was a dreaded complication of childbirth; infant mortality was high and death from infection in childhood all too frequent. For all its attendant pomp, surgery was hazardous and life-threatening, except for the simplest procedures. Within the next fifty years there was an eruption of knowledge in bacteriology and, after much opposition, the gradual acceptance of the microbial origin of infectious disease. Elucidation of the nature of the body's defence against infection and methods of enhancing it were discovered and resulted in the birth of the new science of immunology. In these advances Wright played a seminal role.

At the beginning of the 20th century infection was the major cause of death in Europe and the United States. Typhoid, pneumonia, and staphylococcal and streptococcal infections far outweighed degenerative arterial disease and cancer as causes of mortality, particularly among the young. There was no specific treatment. Yet there was hope both of prevention and treatment in the use of newly developed vaccines. In the last years of the 19th century Wright, when he was professor of pathology at the Army Medical School at Netley, produced a vaccine against typhoid fever which had a dramatic effect in reducing mortality from this disease in the British Army in India and elsewhere. Typhoid accounted for more deaths than enemy bullets in the Boer War; yet, following the introduction of preventive inoculation, after considerable and surprising resistance on the part of the army authorities, the incidence in the 1914–18 war was negligible.

Wright extrapolated from his experience with typhoid and made vaccines against numerous other common infections. He considered that it should be possible to employ vaccines not only in prevention but also in treatment of established infection. In this he was gravely mistaken but, in the absence of any other specific treatment, vaccine therapy assumed great popularity among both the medical profession and the lay public. He manufactured his vaccines at St Mary's Hospital, Praed Street, where he was appointed as bacteriologist in 1902 and where he remained until 1946.

Wright had neither the time nor the inclination to devote to marketing of these products. In 1908, however, he approached the well-known pharmaceutical company Parke Davis and reached an agreement with them whereby they undertook to market the vaccines and share the proceeds from their sale with his laboratory. This agreement was renewed at intervals until the advent of the National Health Service in 1948. The money so derived provided the basis for the establishment of the inoculation department at St Mary's Hospital. The sums involved were substantial — though no accounts remain — because they allowed Wright not only to pay himself and the salaries of his medical and technical staff but also to finance purchase of equipment. Some money was used, too, for compassionate purposes, supporting widows and children of staff who had died. There thus was formed a major self-financing unit in a London teaching hospital, largely supported by a pharmaceutical company and independent of the hospital authorities: a situation that would not be allowed in the centralised and publicly regulated structure of health administration that obtains today. The department was to make a major contribution to 20th-century medicine it was here that Alexander Fleming discovered penicillin.

Relations with Parke Davis generally remained on a cordial footing during the 40 years that the agreement was operative. Indeed, such was the respect in which Wright and his department were held that in 1923 Parke Davis requested that the testing and bottling of their own therapeutic sera, which until that time had been undertaken in Cambridge, should be carried out in the inoculation department. Throughout the time of their association Wright wrote a series of prospectuses for Parke Davis, advertising the vaccines and instructing in their administration. Many of the transactions between Wright and the company were carried out on the latter's behalf by a Mr T Maben; when Maben celebrated his golden wedding anniversary, the department gave him a substantial gift. The advent of sulphonamides in the mid-1930s, however, resulted in a drop in the sales of vaccines. The consequent uncertain financial situation led to discussions with Parke Davis as to the possibility of securing for the department a greater proportion of the revenue. Negotiations were conducted between Fleming and Sir Max Bonn, a merchant banker, on behalf of the department with a Mr Ernest Pope representing the company. No firm conclusion was reached at this time (June 1939) and the catastrophe of war engulfed all parties within a few months. The emergence of penicillin as a therapeutic agent in 1942 further reduced the sales of vaccines, and by the end of the war their use in treatment had largely been abandoned.

Yet at the beginning of the 21st century some second thoughts may be permitted. The concept of giving a vaccine to stimulate the natural defences of the body following infection is not, after all, so bizarre. Rabies vaccine has been administered after the patient has received a dog bite. More recently, hepatitis B vaccine is given before symptoms and signs of disease are manifest. There are increasing efforts to treat those infected with the human immunodeficiency virus along the same lines. Increasing resistance of infecting organisms to antibiotics has generated renewed enthusiasm for prophylactic vaccines against infections. Future historians will look back on the partnership between Wright and Parke Davis as the starting point for this new and significant area of therapeutic endeavour.

Wright's work on immunology, which also included reconciliation of the competing theories of cellular and humoral immunity, constituted only one of his achievements. It can be claimed that he founded the discipline of clinical pathology and was among the first to realise the importance of the laboratory both in diagnosis of disease and in monitoring its treatment. At St Mary's Hospital he established a department that became world-famous for its research and innovative techniques. He insisted that pathologists should be granted equal status with physicians and surgeons on the hospital staff. His compelling personality inspired intense devotion in his junior colleagues. Among these was not only Alexander Fleming but also Leonard Colebrook, who played a major role in improving treatment of puerperal fever and in transforming the management of burns.

Wright was a man with a wide acquaintance outside the world of medicine. He numbered among his intimate friends Bernard Shaw, Arthur Balfour and Lord Moulton; the last-named was said to be the cleverest man in Britain. He was firmly of the belief that the government should finance medical research and his letter to the press in 1905, followed by lobbying of his political friends, bore fruit in the formation of the Medical Research Committee, later renamed the Medical Research Council. That he did not play a more prominent role in the subsequent organisation of that body was due to the outbreak of the Great War. It was in this conflict that he made what some consider his greatest contribution to medicine, when he demonstrated the immense harm done to wounds by indiscriminate use of antiseptics. Wright, always greatly moved by human suffering, was prepared to go to any extreme to improve the lot of the wounded soldier. In propounding his views he clashed once more with the Army authorities, not only over wound treatment but also over the organisation of the Royal Army Medical Corps. He went over the heads of the generals and approached his political friends. His views were finally accepted but never fully acknowledged.

He was by nature blunt-spoken and enjoyed nothing so much as fierce argument. Tactful in expressing his opinions he was not, and this frequently gave offence. As with many men of genius some of his ideas were hare-brained, as in his over-enthusiastic claims for vaccine therapy. His attitude to statistical methods was equally wrong-headed, and this led to a famous polemical confrontation with Karl Pearson, the leading biomathematician of the day.

Wright's unpopularity among members of the medical profession can be attributed not only to his argumentative nature but also to his contempt for the Harley Street ethos at a time when the West End private practitioner was regarded as the fount of medical wisdom. Wright was a clever man; fluent in French, German, and Spanish as well as the classical languages, with an extensive knowledge of European literature — he was able to remember 250,000 lines of poetry. Clever men, particularly if they do not conceal the fact, are often unpopular. But Wright was loyal to his staff and friends and that loyalty they returned in full measure. When his pupil and colleague Alexander Fleming received an honorary degree from Harvard University he said of Wright that he was 'one of the great men of this world whose work as a pioneer has never been sufficiently recognised'. This book, which explores Wright's work in relation to medical conditions and opinion in the early part of the 20th century, attempts to redress the balance. It has been written with the general reader in mind and technical terms have been kept to a minimum, while essaying to do justice to the underlying scientific basis of Wright's work.

This biography owes its origin to a remark made by Gwyn Macfarlane. He had just completed his definitive work on Alexander Fleming and suggested there was a place for a new assessment of his mentor, Almroth Wright. There have been two previous biographies. The first by Leonard Colebrook, published in 1954, was a eulogy by a close friend. The second by Zachary Cope in 1966 was written in praise of vaccine therapy and was more critical — it was Cope who coined the phrase 'Plato of Praed Street'. I have drawn freely on these works but neither of them had the benefit of material now available in the Public Record Office (PRO), the Contemporary Medical Archive Centre (CMAC) at the Wellcome Institute, the archives of Trinity College, Dublin and the manuscript collection at the British Library. These reveal much that is new, particularly with regard to the management of the wounded in the First World War.

Acknowledgements

This book could not have been written without the constant help and advice of my friend Philip Waller. To him I owe an enormous debt but any historical error in the text is my own, while any virtue must be ascribed to him. His wise counsel has been invaluable.

Kevin Brown, the archivist at St Mary's Hospital, has proved a source of much help and encouragement in guiding me through the various records of that hospital and medical school. The extraordinary jumble of records of the Royal Army Medical Corps, which has been brought into some logical order by the sterling work of Shirley Dixon, lately of the Contemporary Medical Archive Centre, have provided valuable source material. Julia Shepperd and all the staff of that department have been extremely helpful. Michael Holroyd kindly let me see correspondence between Wright and Bernard Shaw. Various Irish members of Wright's family were traced by Mark Curthoys. I have had the benefit of conversing with Dr Keith Rogers who worked with Wright before the war; I am grateful to him and his wife for their hospitality. The late Lawrence Biddle entertained me with reminiscences of John Freeman, a close colleague and friend of Wright. Information about the department at St Mary's was given me by Sir Robert Williams; both he and Professor Bill Noble were able to enlighten me about the life of Leonard Colebrook. Peter Lawrence told me of his memories of Wright's close friend Grizel Hartley. Some details concerning the Royal Victoria Hospital at Netley were supplied by Patrick Kirkby. Valuable information concerning life in Australia at the end of the 19th century was generously sent to me by Robert Dingley and Professor Bruce Warren.

Certain of my long-suffering friends have read all or part of the typescript during preparation of this book and have given freely of their time and advice. I mention only the following: John Carey, Kevin Gatter, Simeon Gordon, Winifred Gray, Roger Highfield, Gail Simmons, John Potter and David Weatherall.

I wish to express my gratitude to Giles Romanes for his encouragement when I was contemplating embarking on this work, for sharing his memories of his grandfather with me, and to both him and his wife for their hospitality.

Finally, this book would not have been published without the generous support of Parke Davis and the help of Peter Richardson,

Tanya Thomas, Jean Macqueen and the publications department at the Royal Society of Medicine.

M S Dunnill
June 2000

Abbreviations

BOM: Minutes of the Board of Management, St Mary's Hospital
Br Lib MSS: British Library Manuscript Collection
CMAC: Contemporary Medical Archives Centre, Wellcome Institute
PP/COL: personal papers of Leonard Colebrook held at CMAC
PRO: Public Record Office, Kew
TCD: Archives of Trinity College, Dublin

Chapter 1

An Evangelical Upbringing

Almroth Wright was descended on his father's side from stern Ulster Protestants.[1] A member of Cromwell's Northern Army in Ireland was Captain James Wright who had charge of Golagh in County Monaghan; and from him were descended the Wrights of Floraville, Donnybrook, County Dublin. Almroth Wright's paternal grandfather, Edward Wright, was a distinguished barrister who, having received a doctorate of laws at Trinity College, Dublin, practised on the North-East Circuit. Yet of greater significance was his enthusiastic membership of the Evangelical Alliance. He had four sons: the eldest became professor of botany at Trinity College and the youngest entered the army, but the other two were ordained. The elder of these was Charles H H Wright, Almroth's father, a man of exceptional intellectual ability. From his earliest days he appears to have been a fanatical evangelical Protestant with beliefs based on a literal interpretation of the scriptures. While still at school he wrote letters to the press advocating the Protestant cause and had to be restrained by his father, who was irritated by his presumption. His abomination of Roman Catholicism was apparent even at this early age and, together with the Rev Florence McCarthy (a man), he attempted to convert the Catholics of Donnybrook. Unfortunately the subjects of his attention appear to have been equally dedicated and he so infuriated them that after speaking at a meeting he had to leave by a side door in order to avoid a lynching. A crowd then pursued him, threatening to throw him in the river Dodder should he have the temerity to address them again.[2] In fact he did just this, but the Catholics apparently admired his courage and did not carry out their threat. He did not escape entirely, however; 'a bigoted virago' by name Mrs Ryan kept a pail of dirty water to empty over him every time he passed her house.

Academically Charles Wright was distinguished, showing a particular aptitude for languages and, as befitted a future clergyman, theology. Admitted to Trinity College in 1852, he collected prizes in Hebrew, Arabic, Irish and philosophy, graduating BA with first-class honours in 1857 and in divinity the following year. Even during his

1

undergraduate days, while on country walks he would distribute tracts to fruit-pickers and agricultural labourers, recording these activities in 'an intensely spiritual diary'. Although for many years he was to be a parish priest, he retained his academic interests writing extensively on biblical criticism; and he was widely acknowledged as a scholar of great linguistic ability. In 1878 he gave the Bampton Lectures in Oxford on 'The prophesies of Zachariah', and in 1882 he was a candidate for the professorship of Hebrew at Cambridge. In collaboration with GT Stokes, professor of ecclesiastical history in the University of Dublin he published in 1887 *The writings of St Patrick, Apostle of Ireland'*. Silvester records in his memoir of Charles Wright that a copy was sent to Mr Gladstone and 'an appreciative reply was received'.

Charles Wright was ordained in Ripon Cathedral by Bishop Robert Bickersteth in April 1859 and appointed curate to an old friend of his father, Dr Blackwood, vicar of Middleton Tyas in Yorkshire. Living with Dr Blackwood and his wife were two young girls, Emma and Ebba Almroth. The Almroth sisters were from a distinguished Swedish family. Their father, Nils Almroth, was director of the Swedish Royal Mint and professor of chemistry at the Royal Military School at Marieburg near Stockholm.[3] Their grandfather had been a doctor of medicine and a member of the Medical Council. Nils Almroth had died on 31 October 1852. In 1853 there was an outbreak of cholera in Stockholm and at the invitation of a M Trottet, a French Protestant clergyman of a strongly evangelical persuasion, Ebba went to Lausanne for a few weeks until the epidemic was under control. She returned there with her sister in 1854 to stay in a house owned by a Madame Vinet, the widow of 'a well-known author'. They were enthusiastic attendants at the local Protestant prayer meetings, and at one of the first of these there was a collection for people living in the north of Sweden who were being subjected to religious persecution. This both annoyed and surprised the sisters as they were unaware of any religious intolerance, and they so informed an English couple who had been at the meeting. These were the Rev Dr Blackwood and his wife, Lady Alicia Blackwood, with whom they struck up a close friendship. Lady Blackwood was concerned for the welfare of the two young girls living on their own and invited them to come and stay in England. This invitation they accepted and went to live with the Blackwoods in Ventnor, Isle of Wight.

They did not stay there long. Florence Nightingale's call for nurses to tend the sick and wounded during the Crimean War was answered by the Blackwoods and both the Almroth girls accompanied them, sailing for Asia Minor on 6 December 1854. Blackwood was appointed chaplain to the hospitals in Constantinople and Scutari and the ladies enrolled as nurses. Miss Nightingale was doubtful if they understood the nature of the work when they volunteered to go where they might be of greatest use but, when satisfied on this point, she appointed Lady Alicia and her party to attend the women and children who had accompanied the army.[4] These camp-followers had been sent down from Varna and were accommodated in cellars beneath the hospital. Cecil Woodham Smith[5] describes the conditions under which more than 260 women and infants were living: 'Soldiers' wives, widows and prostitutes were crowded together, men from the Depot were forced to live with their wives in a room containing 50 or 60 other persons, a soil pipe drained into the corner of one cellar, drinking was incessant and the place was a pandemonium of drunkenness, cursing and swearing.' Ebba Wright later wrote of their experiences: 'The doctors and nurses were nearly driven to distraction in order to find room even to lay down the sick and dying on the floor . . . Food was scarce and the only thing we had to offer to the poor wounded men was grapes.'[6] The weather was not good and frost-bitten fingers and toes were common, with many of the digits becoming gangrenous and dropping off. At one stage there was an average of 80 funerals a day. Even under these conditions their evangelical mission was always to the front of their minds, with Blackwood distributing religious tracts to the wounded. Ebba was often mistaken by the soldiery for Florence Nightingale, to whom she bore a superficial resemblance. At the end of the war the party toured the battlefields of the Crimea.

On their return to England Blackwood took the living of Middleton Tyas. Today this is a quiet, well-kept village one mile east of the Great North Road at Scotch Corner. It was not always so. The countryside surrounding the village is rich in minerals. In the 18th century copper was discovered nearby and this brought some prosperity and an increase in population.[7] Much of the mining took place on glebe land and the vicars became wealthy. Today the church is approached down a long tree-lined avenue set half a mile from the village, and it is surrounded by grass-covered mounds, the remains of spoil from the mines. These mines were nearing the end of their best days when the Blackwoods arrived but it was still a profitable living and enabled the incumbent to employ two curates. Blackwood used his wealth to good purpose, building and staffing a school which is in use to this day. In spite of the mining, and the proximity of the main London to Edinburgh road, the village was isolated and peopled by rough uneducated folk who seldom ventured into neighbouring communities. Ebba records that boys were punished on occasion by putting ropes round their necks and attaching them to each other. During the years that Blackwood held the living all this changed, and he and his curates gave the village children an excellent education. As well as English grammar and literature there was Euclid and, for one and three quarter hours a day, Latin. Every afternoon the girls occupied themselves with sewing.

It was into this parish that Charles Wright came as curate in 1859. After what must have been a whirlwind courtship he married Ebba — and the other curate, H W Bagnell, married her elder sister Emma. Both Wrights shared the same spiritual aims, exhibiting a fervent Protestant zeal: both referred to Roman Catholics as perverts. The honeymoon was spent in Scotland, but clearly this was no time for conventional relaxation and on the Sunday Charles Wright preached a sermon on the pier at Arrochar.

During the next three years, while at Middleton Tyas, they had three sons. Eric Blackwood Wright, who was to become Judge of the Supreme Court of Trinidad, was born on 1 March 1860, followed by Almroth Edward on 10 August 1861, and on 1 November 1862 by Charles Theodore Hagberg, who in later life was Librarian of the London Library. At this time Charles Wright not only gave weekly lectures on Bunyan's *Pilgrim's progress* to the parishioners, but also published *The book of Genesis in Hebrew with a critically revised text, various readings and critical notes* as well as a grammar of the Irish language. With a rapidly expanding family it was important for Wright to obtain a more permanent position with an increase in salary. He and his wife had aspirations in the missionary field but to his chagrin he was rejected by the Church Missionary Society on medical grounds. What these grounds were is not recorded but they cannot have been based on accurate clinical observation as he lived to the age of 73 years.

Frustrated in his missionary ambitions, he applied for the post of English chaplain at Dresden, then described as 'the Florence of Germany'. There were 11 candidates and Wright was successful, being supported by the British ambassador and most of the congregation. The Wrights with their young family arrived in Dresden on Wednesday 29 April 1863, a time when the city appeared at its best with the streets lined with lilac trees coming into bloom. They were to remain there five years, during which two more sons were born to them: Henry, who was commissioned into the Royal Engineers and rose to become a Major General, and Ernest, the only son to follow his father into the church.

There was little money. Charles's stipend was £180 a year and, although Ebba had a little of her own, there was no scope for extravagance. Almroth in later years when referring to another described his being 'brought up in scholastic surroundings and comparative poverty — in other words in a combination of circumstances eminently favourable to the development of the life of the mind.' The words were also true of his own upbringing.[8] In these liberated days it is difficult to imagine the life of a Victorian evangelical household. Prayers were held every morning before breakfast accompanied by readings from both the Old and the New Testament. Grace was said before every meal and there were more prayers in the evening. Even on a holiday Sunday was strictly observed as a day of worship; the blinds were drawn, sombre clothing worn and the day devoted to prayer and the scriptures. To the end of his days Almroth was able to quote at length from the Bible. In this Calvinist atmosphere fulfilment was to be found only in reading of the scriptures. The narrowness of this existence associated with a harsh arrogance might well have had a disastrous effect had Almroth been an only child. Mercifully, the presence of four brothers ensured some lightheartedness and horseplay. As in many such families the final effect on the offspring was the reverse of that intended by the parents. Only one boy, the youngest, went into the church. It would seem that Charles Wright was behaving against his natural instincts, because he

Figure 1
The Reverend Charles Henry Wright and his wife Ebba in the garden of their house in Wandsworth.
(Giles Romanes)

was possessed of cheerful and genial qualities that he did his best to suppress. In his journal he warned himself about 'the necessity for spiritual watchfulness in the midst of social converse' and reprimanded himself for 'being too prone to flippancy and nonsense'.

The children during this period in Dresden and later in Boulogne were not sent to school but were educated largely by their parents. Ebba was proficient in Latin and Greek as well as having some knowledge of Hebrew. Occasional tutors were employed but, although the classical side of their education was exemplary, mathematics does not appear to have featured strongly in their curriculum. This may have influenced Almroth in later years, when his hostile views on statistical methods gained him notoriety.

Life in Dresden was not without excitement for the Wright family. In 1866 war broke out between Prussia and Austria. Saxon troops were mobilised and ordered to join the Austrian army. Mrs Wright and the children were on holiday at Schandau, and Charles Wright brought them back to Dresden where preparations were in hand for reception of Prussians, who entered the town unopposed immediately the Saxons had retired. A proclamation was made declaring a state of siege and the citizens ordered to supply provisions for the occupying troops. Mrs Wright has left a description[9] of what followed. At about 4 am one day in July they awoke to the sound of bells ringing and, looking out of the windows, saw the street filled with soldiery. The householders were ordered to prepare breakfast for troops seated along the roadside and in the gardens. Cans of coffee and baskets of bread were supplied. The Prussians were well-behaved and the citizens grew friendly with their conquerors. The Wrights entertained some cheerful Rhinelanders and, true to their calling, started to distribute tracts among them only to find 'many were Christians'. Some of them they had even met in connection with the British and Foreign Bible Society. One recognised Charles Wright and lamented that Germans were fighting Germans but said, 'We feel the Prussian cause is the cause of God. We can fight for the Protestant against Popery.' This nicely chimed with Wright's beliefs: he was said by the Dean of Canterbury, Henry Wace DD, to have devoted the greater part of his time to the work of active opposition to Roman doctrine and practice. Yet, despite his vigorous opposition to Catholicism, Wright can have borne little personal malice, certainly at this stage of his career, as he became friendly with the local priest who exchanged kisses with him when they met — an action that astonished the young Almroth.

After breakfast the Prussians moved on and for two days all was quiet. Then early one morning, Uhlans were seen galloping through the cornfields behind the Wrights' house; more Prussians filled the town and soldiers knocked on their door to warn them that an attack was imminent. Trenches were dug, cannon were brought into the streets and the family, who were eating breakfast at the time, were ordered to evacuate the house leaving all their belongings behind. This must have caused considerable alarm as there were five children, ranging from seven years to six months in age, two nurses and a deaf and dumb maid, Catherine, inherited from Charles Wright's mother; the children showed no fear, however, and indeed every sign of enjoying the situation. The party numbered ten in all and went to a friend's house in the centre of town but were moved on from there by the police to high-priced lodgings where they stayed until, on 26 June, they managed to escape to England. They returned on 26 August, the war having lasted only six weeks, to find that soldiers had been quartered in their house and that the Wrights had to bear the cost of their maintenance. Happily the Prussians had been well-behaved, taking off their boots before entering the house and smoking only in the garden.

When peace was restored, life was not easy for Charles Wright. There were high churchmen among his congregation who objected to his evangelical style of preaching and found offensive his refusal to turn towards the altar during the creed. Furthermore, in deference to a strong American element among his flock, he introduced a prayer for the President of the United States. A minority of the congregation appealed to the bishop of London, who sent out a second chaplain giving 'his episcopal sanction to a church schism'. Fortunately, in 1868 the Colonial and Continental Church Society invited Wright to take the chaplaincy at Holy Trinity Church in Boulogne. This he accepted and, after being presented with a service of silver plate by the faithful among his congregation, the family left for France.

Boulogne at that time was a sink of iniquity. Not only was it a refuge for bankrupt members of the English upper classes, but it had a shifting maritime population who frequented the numerous brothels and bars near the port. Together with the Wesleyan minister, Joseph Gaskin, Wright established the 'British Sailors' Institute'. It provided rooms in which the sailors 'could read, write, spend a quiet evening and have religious services on Sunday and, as opportunity served, during the week'. Surprisingly, perhaps, it appears to have been a successful venture. At first it occupied the second floor of some old Napoleonic barracks rented from the town authorities but these had to be vacated during the Franco-Prussian War in 1870.

Charles Wright appears to have been quite unbending in his Protestant fervour. He was particularly intolerant of any sexual lapse.

An entry in his diary, quoted by James Silvester in his memoir, records a visit to a brothel. Wright had called on Gaskin: 'Met a Mrs R— there who said she was begged to ask me to bury a Mr S— who had died last week in a fit of intoxication, he being a confirmed drunkard. As Mrs. S— desired that I would call I visited the house, having obtained important information from Mr Gaskin as to the nature of the inmates. Met there Mrs N— and Miss N— and the father of Mrs S—. After a long conversation I stated I could not bury with full Church of England burial service the poor man. Mrs N— approved of my resolve; the others tried to induce me to change my mind, but for many reasons public as well as private affecting the parties themselves, I refused. I had, however, an opportunity of speaking plainly on conversion and of sexual sins of which I had come to suspect the parties to be guilty.' Almroth was to revolt against his father's views on sexual matters just as he did against literal interpretation of the Bible.

The change of home and country did not allow the Wright family to avoid armed conflict: after a year in their new surroundings, the Franco-Prussian War broke out. The year 1871 found them tending wounded German prisoners in Calais, where they distributed bales of blankets obtained from Count Bernstorff, the Prussian Ambassador in London. Conditions under which the NCOs and privates were kept were appalling. There were 450 Germans in the arsenal at Fort Neuilly with only one blanket each during a severe winter. Only one pump in the yard was available for their ablutions. It was during this period that the family became very unpopular as the French thought they were in communication with the Germans — which of course they were, though not in a military sense. They were shouted at in the streets, and they even had difficulty in holding a Protestant service for the Germans. Matters were not made easier by the Wrights having a German governess. At Dunkirk the prisoners were in even worse conditions than in Calais. When they complained that the prison was more suitable for a den of wild beasts they received the reply, 'The Germans are wild beasts and the place suits them perfectly.' Exposing themselves to considerable danger, the Wrights managed to smuggle two soldiers out of the prison, one of whom was a brother of the German governess, and secrete them in their house in Boulogne.

In spite of these disturbances they were able to build a new Sailors' Institute. This was achieved through the generosity of the widow of the Rev F W Hope, who himself had endowed Oxford University with the Hope professorship of zoology. Mrs Hope now gave a considerable sum to the Sailors' Institute that almost defrayed the cost of the new building, in the Boulevard Daunou. This remained in use for many years; interestingly, it housed soldiers when Almroth was working in his bacteriological laboratory set up in the Casino a few doors away during the Great War. Yet Charles Wright was not popular, mainly because of his continual virulent attacks on Roman Catholics. He declared, 'In the pulpit I have attacked and shall continue to attack all false doctrines, especially those of the Church of Rome.' It was thus something of a relief when in November 1874 he exchanged with the Rev C Beauclerk, the incumbent of St Mary's Belfast.

The elder boys were sent to the Belfast Academical Institution. Colebrook[10] records that Almroth said of his time there that he acquired a good basis of Greek and Latin and of general knowledge. His great gift was a prodigious memory. He claimed to have memorised and retained more than quarter of a million words of poetry as well as large sections of the scriptures. His was an intensely inquisitive mind, and relations with his parents, especially his father, became increasingly strained as he questioned the literal acceptance of the scriptures upon which Charles Wright insisted. When Almroth refused to take at face value such tenets of the Christian faith as the Virgin Birth or the Resurrection his father would pound the table with his fist. Physically the two were dissimilar, the father being a small man whereas Almroth was tall, big-boned and described by his friend William Bulloch as almost an acromegalic[11] — a condition of pathological gigantism due to excessive production of growth hormone by the pituitary gland.

In 1878 Almroth entered Trinity College, Dublin to read for an arts degree in modern languages. Four years later he graduated with first-class honours and the gold medal. The demands of the curriculum cannot have been too great, or perhaps his grounding in language and literature in the home environment had been very thorough — he was fluent in French, German and Spanish — because he seems to have been able to begin the study of medicine at the same time.[12] In any event he qualified in medicine in 1883, being highly placed in his year. His medical studies were greatly influenced by J M Purser who was professor of medicine but whose leanings were towards experimental physiology. He was an advocate of the scientific approach to medical practice with logical analysis applied to careful and accurate observation. He dismissed, correctly, much of the then current therapeutics as useless. Undoubtedly he had a profound effect on Wright and steered him towards the experimental approach to medical practice.

Immediately after qualifying in medicine Wright was undecided on his future career. He went to the professor of literature, Edward

Dowden, for guidance. Dowden gave Charles Lamb's advice, 'Literature is a good stick but a poor crutch', adding, 'So if I were you I would go on with medicine. It is the finest possible introduction to life, and, if you have got the gift to write afterwards, it will give you an invaluable background'.[13]

Opportunities for learning research methods in Britain at this time were very limited, in contrast to the great schools in France and above all in Germany. Aided by recommendations from Purser, and possibly from his uncle, Percival Wright, professor of botany at Trinity, he obtained a travelling scholarship worth £100. He used this money to visit Leipzig, where there was a distinguished school of physiology presided over by Ludwig and where Cohnheim, one of the founders of experimental pathology, worked. It was here that he met an Englishman, L C Wooldridge, who was investigating blood coagulation, a subject that was to form the basis of some of Wright's earliest papers.

The money was soon exhausted and he returned to England. The absence of any suitable research grants or fellowships prompted him to apply for a law studentship worth £200 a year. This he was awarded and, although he never qualified in law, the time it allowed him for study enabled him to pass the competitive examination for the Higher Civil Service — just. There were ten places and he was twelfth on the list but three candidates withdrew and thus he obtained the last place. It is noteworthy, in view of his polemical encounters with statisticians in later years, that he chose not to take the papers in mathematics but took instead natural sciences, moral sciences and French language and literature. At last he was assured of a salary. Appointed in 1885 to a clerkship in the Admiralty he found he had time on his hands, the work being undemanding. This allowed him to spend the early hours of the morning and the late afternoons and evenings researching into medicine.

Here luck favoured him, as he was able to use the facilities offered by the Brown Institution. The Brown Animal Sanctuary Institution, to give it its full title, was founded in 1871 on the proceeds of a charitable trust established under the will of Thomas Brown.[14] He left the sum of £20,000 for 'investigating, studying, and without charge beyond immediate expenses, endeavouring to cure maladies, distempers and injuries any quadrupeds or birds useful to man may be subject to'. Brown died in 1852 and the interest on the capital was allowed to accumulate for a period up to 15 years but if after 19 years the Institute had not been established the money was to go to the University of Dublin. The will was unsuccessfully disputed by the University and the next of kin. Fortunately financial aid came from Dr Burdon-Sanderson, a wealthy physician in private practice who was in 1874 to take the chair of physiology at University College, London. and to end his days as Regius professor of medicine at Oxford. The Institution was founded on a site in the Wandsworth Road, bought for the purpose by a Mr John Cunliffe in 1871. Burdon-Sanderson agreed to provide £4000 of his own money on condition he became the first professor superintendent.

The laboratory provided 'hotel' facilities for research workers and was unique in Britain in so doing. Equipment was meagre — it was not until 1900 that £50 was provided for purchase of a microscope — and most of it was brought into the Institution by the itinerant workers, whose research projects had to be approved by the committee of management on the recommendation of the superintendent. Successful applicants, in addition to providing their own apparatus and materials, paid ten shillings a week in advance towards the upkeep of the laboratory.

During Wright's period at the Institute Victor Horsley was the superintendent and Wright assisted him in his studies of thyroid disease by cutting and staining histological sections. Wooldridge had returned from Germany and Wright also worked with him once more on blood coagulation. At this time it was believed that clotting of blood was due to a property of the red blood cells. Wooldridge was the first to point out that this was not so, and that the factors concerned with initiating and producing blood clots were in the plasma. Indeed he succeeded in identifying two of the many factors concerned — fibrin and fibrinogen — and was considered by Horsley as a brilliant and original research worker. Tragically he died young leaving a widow who married Starling, later to become a distinguished physiologist. Unkindly, a contemporary remarked 'I have heard of many reasons for getting married but never in order to get at the notebooks of your predecessor!' Wright maintained an interest in coagulation and later was responsible for one notable advance (described in Chapter 2) but before he could pursue the subject he moved again.

After Burdon-Sanderson, Dr Charles Roy had been appointed superintendent, but in 1884 he was elected to the newly established chair of pathology at Cambridge. In May 1887, Roy persuaded Wright to go to Cambridge, where he was offered the post of demonstrator in the pathology department; he gave up his clerkship at the Admiralty and moved to the Fens. This should have been ideal. He was already showing that technical skill which was later to bring him fame with the publication of his book *The technique of the teat and capillary glass tube,*

Figure 2
Almroth Wright in his twenties during his time at Cambridge. (London: William Heinemann, 1954)

resonant of the string and sealing wax era in physics in the nearby Cavendish Laboratory. Unfortunately Roy did not prove the perfect supervisor. He was a morphine addict and suffered from some form of psychiatric disorder. The early manifestations of this were apparent by the time Wright arrived in his department but were to take on a more severe form later. Roy's life ended miserably, as described by G S Wilson[15]: 'His last three years were clouded by a nervous breakdown, probably as a result of his addiction to morphine. After giving the same lecture three times (*during the same course*) he had to be replaced. He went prematurely grey and died in a fit on 4th October 1897.' Wisely, Wright transferred to the physiology department, where the professor was Michael Foster.

Foster was at the height of his powers and had a large department where the main research interest was directed towards neurophysiology. The son of a surgeon, after a distinguished undergraduate career, he started his professional life as a general practitioner, but at the age of 31 he transferred to the physiology department at University College, London under Sharpey. After this his promotion was rapid; he succeeded Huxley as Fullerian professor at the Royal Institution in 1869 and a year later left for the chair at Cambridge. Here he established a department notable for its teaching of practical physiology. Foster was the first to introduce practical classes into the undergraduate curriculum — a feature that spread rapidly through the medical schools of the western world. He wrote a standard textbook that went into six editions. Yet his main interests appear to have been directed towards academic administration. He was a leading light in founding the Physiological Society and the *Journal of Physiology*, became secretary of the Royal Society and was elected liberal MP for the University of Cambridge from 1900 to 1906. His *métier* was thus teaching and organisation, rather than original research. No doubt, as with many of those with great powers of organisation and administration, an original and rebellious personality such as that of Wright did not endear itself to him. This was unfortunate, because although Foster himself did not prosecute research, he was active in encouraging others. Among those who were working in his laboratory at this time was Henry Head, who was studying the relationship between emotions and visceral reflexes; later he was to do distinguished work on nerve regeneration. He and Wright became friends and this stimulated Wright's interest in the physiological control of the emotions, a subject whose philosophical implications were to occupy him during the last half of his life. Wright would say in later years, 'the soul is the complex of the viscera'.

Meanwhile Wright had entered Trinity College and took the tripos examination; much to his disgust he was placed in the second class. The reason for his relative failure is not recorded but there is no doubt that at this time (as in later years) he displayed, particularly to those that did not know him well, an insufferable arrogance and a certain contempt for the opinion of those who did not agree with him. In spite of many statements he made to the contrary he seldom acknowledged that he might be mistaken in any of his firmly expressed views. In later years he admitted, 'I could never say a modest thing in all my life.' While this may not have mattered when he was once established, it was not something to recommend him to his superiors when he held a subordinate position. He claimed that the respectability and conventional ways of Cambridge were anathema to him and he determined to leave. On departing that University he told an elderly lady that he was going away until people took him at his own valuation.

In spite of his indifferent results in the tripos he obtained a scholarship from the Grocers' Company that allowed him to visit

Figure 3
Jane Georgina Wright in 1890 shortly after arriving in Sydney. (Giles Romanes)

Germany once more, on this occasion Marburg, where he further increased his knowledge of morbid anatomy and histology with instruction from von Recklinghausen. From here he went to spend some months studying physiological chemistry under Seyler in Strasbourg. He returned to England in 1889 a known maverick, an awkward and argumentative character, yet one acknowledged as possessing an original mind. It was on 8 January of this year that Wright married.

The events surrounding his courtship are obscure but while in Cambridge he had met Jane Georgina Wilson, described as a beautiful and accomplished lady. She was Irish and the daughter of Robert Mackay Wilson of Coolcarrigan, Kildare and was two years older than Wright. The marriage took place from the home of Lady Alicia

Blackwood at Box Moor House in Bovingdon, Hertfordshire, the ceremony being performed at St Lawrence Church by his father. The Wilsons were a wealthy family but the fiercely independent Almroth felt that he had to provide support from his own resources by finding remunerative employment. This was not straightforward, because Wright was a difficult character destined all his life to be a member of the awkward squad. Word may well have passed around and the combined verdict been pronounced, as with Lord Lundy: 'Go out and govern New South Wales'. Whatever the reason, his name was put forward by Michael Foster as a suitable person for the post of demonstrator in physiology at the newly established medical school in the University of Sydney. He was accepted and sailed with his wife at the end of 1889 to take up his appointment.

There were at that time three medical schools in Australia. The oldest, Melbourne, had been founded in 1862, Adelaide had followed in 1882 and Sydney in 1883. Australia looked to Scotland rather than England for its founding fathers in medicine. In England many of the medical schools were independent foundations, usually associated with London hospitals and often having only tenuous connections with a university. Many practitioners did not have degrees and their qualifications were diplomas granted by the Royal Colleges. In the 19th century medicine in Scotland had a more academic and experimental basis and was firmly linked to the universities. Of these Edinburgh was outstanding in having a distinguished school of physiology. It was thus to Edinburgh that Sydney looked for a suitable man to establish their medical school. They found him in T P Anderson Stuart. Stuart had had a brilliant undergraduate career, qualifying top of his year with first-class honours in 1880, and proceeding to obtain the MD with Gold Medal in 1882. He won numerous undergraduate prizes and was regarded as the most outstanding product of the Edinburgh medical school for many years. Even so, it was somewhat surprising that he was recruited by the University of Sydney only three years after qualifying and appointed to the combined chair of anatomy and physiology.

He arrived to find facilities that were primitive in the extreme. The medical school was accommodated in four damp unplastered rooms and there were no facilities for lectures or lecturers. A curriculum had to be devised. Only four students arrived for the first year. Yet Anderson Stuart was a man with remarkable energy and ambition. Handsome and tall, he was the son of a prominent businessman and it seems he brought business sense and acumen to the task of founding the new school. By 1885 he had the plans finished and in 1889, when

Wright arrived, the buildings were completed and there was an intake of 70 students.

Wright's sojourn in Sydney was not entirely happy. Both he and Stuart had strong personalities and did not suffer fools gladly. In 1890 a separate chair of anatomy was founded, and Stuart retained the chair of physiology with Wright as his assistant. Years later Robert Scott Skirving[16] was to recall that neither understood the other: 'One, Wright, was a genius, an original thinker and a discoverer, deeply learned in language, literature and poetry with personal qualities both provocative and endearing. Stuart had great, very great abilities could learn anything well and was a master organiser. If he had followed science, as Wright did, he might have accomplished much on a smaller scale than that which his brilliant demonstrator Wright did. But the needs of a new school and conditions of life in Australia took all his energy and craft and push and forced him to devote himself, sometimes unpleasantly so, to forming, organising and set going a really big successful school of medicine . . . Probably Stuart was jealous at times or envious of his remarkable assistant and never realised that he might be making life unpleasant to this witty, learned, unconventional Irish Scandinavian.'

Wright was not alone in finding Stuart difficult. In being the driving force behind what was eventually to become a world class medical school he trod on many toes and made many enemies. Stuart's biographer states, 'he was not always willing to give full consideration to the opinions of others'[17] — a criticism that could as easily have been, and indeed was, applied to Wright. Neither man had an easy domestic life. Stuart's first wife died from an overdose of morphia and many considered he was morally responsible, though he was cleared of the suspicion that he had any direct involvement because he was staying with Scott Skirving at the time.

It was during this period that Wright's own marriage began to falter. In later years, complaining of his wife's attitude towards him, he said that it was in Australia that she started to 'reprobate' him — a favourite term of his to imply condemnation or censure. In the same year that she married, Jane Georgina had to endure the six-week voyage to Australia which in those days, with interminable intervals between ports, tried the patience of the young couple. Almroth was not always an agreeable companion; uninterested in social life, he insisted on long periods of solitude for thinking and reading. During such a voyage passengers occupied the intervals between meals with quoits, shovel board or deck billiards while in the evenings many played poker; others drank themselves to the verge of delirium tremens.[18] None of these diversions held any attraction for Wright or his wife. Brought up in a household where it was accepted that women occupied a subservient position to men, his attitude towards Jane was not as sympathetic as she might have expected. The claustrophobic cabin life did not help. 'That glance across the wedding cake when loving eyes meet is not the same at breakfast time across the shredded wheat' was proving all too true. The fact that Jane was pregnant added to her tribulations.

The Sydney that greeted them on their arrival had experienced two decades of economic boom. Although much of the living accommodation was primitive by English standards many of the public buildings — the Lands Department, General Post Office and Sydney Town Hall — were grand edifices in the most opulent Victorian style. The population was expanding rapidly; by 1891 it reached 383,283.[19] There were difficulties in providing an adequate infrastructure for such a young city, where beer was considered safer to drink than water.[20] By the time the Wrights arrived the problems of the water supply and sewerage system, both of which had been highly unsatisfactory in the 1860s and 1870s, had been largely resolved.[21] Public health measures had been hampered by Dr George Fredrick Dansey, the City Health Officer, who was a miasmatist and did not believe in the germ theory of disease.

The docking of a ship with English passengers at this time was taken as a cue for celebration by the hospitable and kind-hearted citizens. There was much feasting, drinking of champagne and speechmaking in honour of the new arrivals — described by George Sala, a notable travel writer of the time, as 'a brilliant and chaotic dream', but more like a nightmare to the virtually teetotal Wright and his pregnant wife. On 27 November 1889 she gave birth to a son, Edward Mackay. She endured a tumultuous labour and the boy was born handicapped with a club foot and some form of spina bifida. He was to require constant nursing care and, later on unable to go to school, was educated privately. Jane may have attributed her son's disabilities to the trauma of the long sea voyage while carrying the child. Disillusioned by the helplessness of the medical profession to alleviate his condition she turned to alternative medicine, an act calculated to alienate her scientifically minded husband.

Jane Wright had come from a genteel Anglo-Irish family and the harsh conditions and sometimes rough manners of the inhabitants of a country then barely a hundred years old did not appeal to her. Matters were not improved by the lack of domestic staff. Women were in short supply in this land of upward social mobility. Marriage provided an easy way in which a maid could desert her mistress and ascend the

social ladder. A contemporary writer, R E N Twopeny, wrote:
'Because there was a paucity of ladies, and the majority of gentlemen
had but the choice between marrying beneath them or not at all . . .
one constantly hears of the sons of clergymen and army officers
marrying the daughters of grocers and farmers who were quite recently
day labourers.'[22] Women were almost certain to move up the social
scale because of the numerical imbalance between the sexes.[23] The
very limited supply of women for domestic service was not improved
by the idea of servitude, in this radically democratic new country, being
repugnant to the young Australian-born girls who even preferred
factory work. The consequence of this lack of help in the home was
that Jane, who had been used to plentiful servants, found herself in
common with other ladies in Australia having to cook the family
dinner. Almroth's indifference to food and his constant habit of being
late for meals or missing them altogether proved an added irritation.
The one consolation was that food of good quality was cheap.

Wright was totally absorbed in his work, indifferent to his
surroundings and neglectful of the niceties of family life. Jane was
lonely and found few friends of her own class. In any case categorising
individuals as members of one class or another was difficult. Few
millionaires 'made a splash'[24] and a great many wealthy gentlemen
neither 'dressed up or lived up to their incomes'.[25] The ladies who
tried to befriend her were rebuffed and were inhibited from further
acquaintance by the constant bickering between husband and wife. She
seems to have done little to smooth his path and mollify ruffled feathers
brought about by Wright's somewhat abrasive manner. Yet he did
establish some lifelong friendships, notably with Scott Skirving,
although Mrs Wright and Scott Skirving developed an intense dislike
for one another. He thought her unsuited to be the mate of a genius,
but also understood that her role could never have been an easy one. In
his opinion 'although they parted brass rags' — they did not do so until
just before the Great War — they should have made it up.

In those days Wright was acknowledged as a brilliant lecturer —
towards the end of his life he became too verbose — and he made a
deep impression on many of his pupils 'who had the wisdom to
appreciate his personal charm and teaching and who realised they had
met a star'.[26] Among these was A E Mills, who became professor of
medicine at Sydney. In contrast, Alexander McConnell, who became
one of the best surgeons in Australia and known as a wise old serpent,
described Wright as 'just a garrulous Irishman who lived on tea and
buns and said queer things that made no sense'. Throughout his life
Wright was to antagonise surgeons. He despised the ethos of the

surgeons of those days who, often having little training in scientific methods and thought, believed in the maxim that if there was disease cut it out. Wright, on the other hand believed in mobilising the body's natural defence mechanisms and lacked the patience, or desire, tactfully to explain his point of view but instead indulged in acrimonious polemicism.

In the department of physiology the task of organising the teaching with the limited facilities available occupied most of his days leaving little time for research where lay his main interests. He published nothing while in Sydney, but continued to investigate blood coagulation and the problems of diabetes mellitus — projects he had begun in England with Wooldridge. The strains at work and at home together with the need for an increase in salary determined him to return to England. Jane was pregnant again and, in January 1891, the Wrights came back to London. Their second son, Leonard Almroth Wilson, was born on 31 March and mercifully had no physical defects.

In 1890 the Royal Colleges of Physicians and Surgeons had opened some research laboratories in a building on the Embankment and it was there, in 1891, that Wright found temporary employment. He remained for over a year continuing his work on blood coagulation. The position was unsatisfactory for a young man with a growing family. His wife had money of her own and he earned a little in private practice, but it was not enough to maintain the standard of life to which his wife aspired. The superintendent of the laboratories was a pathologist, German Sims Woodhead, who ten years later was elected to the chair of pathology at Cambridge. He had strong military connections and became civilian adviser on pathology to the Army. It is thus not surprising that he should be asked for his views concerning the appointment of a pathologist to what was one of the largest hospitals in Europe, the Army's Royal Victoria Hospital at Netley. He recommended Wright.

Notes

1 Silvester JA. *Champion of the faith: a memoir of the Rev Chas H H Wright DD*. London: Chas J Thynne, 1918.
2 Ibid p5.
3 Wright EJD. *Sunbeams on my path*. 2nd edn. London: James Nisbet & Co, 1900.
4 Blackwood A. *A narrative of personal experiences and impressions during a residence on the Bosphorus throughout the Crimean War*. London: Hatchards, 1881.
5 Woodham Smith C. *Florence Nightingale* p181. London: Book Club Associates, 1972.
6 Wright EJD *Sunbeams on my path*. 2nd edn p33. London: James Nisbet & Co, 1900.
7 Kurdi A. *A North Yorkshire village: Middleton Tyas*. Chester-le-Street: Casdec Ltd, 1988.
8 Colebrook L. Diaries. Contemporary Medical Archives, Wellcome Institute.
9 Wright EJD. *Sunbeams on my path*. 2nd edn p69 *et seq*. London: James Nisbet & Co, 1900.
10 Colebrook L. *Almroth Wright: provocative doctor and thinker*, p6. London: William Heinemann Ltd, 1954.

11 Ibid p3.
12 In the 19th century Irish medical education, like that in Scotland, was university-based whereas in England it was largely confined to hospital schools in London.
13 Colebrook L. *Almroth Wright: provocative doctor and thinker*, p11. London: William Heinemann Ltd, 1954.
14 Wilson GS. *J Hyg Camb* 1979; **82**:155.
15 Wilson GS. *J Hyg Camb* 1979; **83**:171.
16 Skirling RS. Letter to Colebrook. Contemporary Medical Archives, Wellcome Institute, 1954.
17 See the *Centenary book of the University of Sydney*. Sydney: Sydney University Press, 1984.
18 Sala GA. *The land of the golden fleece* (Dingley R, ed) p31. Canberra: Mulini Press, 1995.
19 Fitzgerald S. *Rising damp, Sydney 1870–90* p18. Melbourne: Oxford University Press, 1987.
20 In the Balmain police court a case of drunkenness was dismissed because the accused pleaded that the water was unfit to drink so he drank beer. *NSW Parliamentary Reports* **17**:196.
21 Clark D. Worse than physic: Sydney's water supply 1788–1888. In Kelly M, ed. *Nineteenth century Sydney: Essays in urban history*. Sydney: Sydney University Press, 1990: 54–65.
22 Twopeny REN. 1883 *Town life in Australia* p108. London: Penguin Press, 1973.
23 Fitzgerald, S. *Rising damp, Sydney 1870–90* p172. Melbourne: Oxford University Press, 1987.
24 Sala GA. *The land of the golden fleece* (Dingley R, ed) p45. Canberra: Mulini Press, 1995.
25 Ibid.
26 *Centenary book of the University of Sydney*. Sydney: Sydney University Press, 1984.

Chapter 2

Netley

The building of the Army Medical Hospital at Netley near Southampton was the direct consequence of public outcry concerning the lamentable medical arrangements that existed during the Crimean war. The army invaliding hospitals in England, and especially those at Chatham and Fort Pitt, were an acknowledged disgrace. Florence Nightingale is usually credited with being the moving force behind the new hospital. In fact a broad front of concerned individuals and groups, medical people, politicians and others were together pressing for reform. This included Queen Victoria herself. As early as 5 March 1855 — Florence Nightingale did not return to England until July 1856 — the Queen was writing to Lord Panmure, Secretary of State for War, protesting vigorously about conditions at Chatham hospital and putting the case for a new building on another site.[1] A captain in the Royal Engineers, R M Laffon, was charged with finding a suitable location within reach of the sea and preferably near the naval stations at Portsmouth or Plymouth. Together with a medical colleague, Dr Mapleton, nominated by Andrew Smith, director general of the Army Medical Services, he undertook the search.[2] After taking advice from Sir James Clark, the Queen's physician, a site near Hamble on Southampton Water was chosen.

It could not be considered ideal. The ground was marshy and there was a sewage outfall nearby. Despite these drawbacks, on 27 January 1856 a committee was appointed by Lord Panmure to prepare plans. There was much discussion as to whether there should be one building or a series of pavilions. The committee eventually gave its blessing to a single building designed by Mr Mennie, surveyor of the Royal Engineers Department in Pall Mall. The Queen saw and approved the plans on 18 April 1856, agreed that the hospital should bear her name and on 19 May, in the presence of the Mayor and corporation of Southampton, laid the foundation stone. The ceremony was accompanied by all the pomp of parades, military bands and 21-gun salutes. These did not proceed without mishap: one of the guns of

HMS *Hardy* went off prematurely, blowing two seamen to bits and injuring several others. This catastrophe, which might have been taken as an ill omen, did not prevent the assembled company enjoying their banquet in a specially erected marquee.

Trouble started when the plans were shown to Florence Nightingale, 'that unleashed free-lance elemental force'[3], back from the Crimea and a national heroine. She strongly disapproved of the whole scheme. The site was wrong, she preferred Aldershot; she disliked the single building and advocated the pavilion system, and criticised the nine-bedded wards for being too small for maintaining 'discipline'. She had considerable influence and, when staying with Palmerston for Christmas 1856, convinced the Prime Minister that it would be best to pull down what had already been put up and to start again. This would have cost £70,000 and, not unnaturally, Lord Panmure refused to sanction this. There were undoubted defects. One of the most notable was that the building was constructed back to front with the long corridor, instead of the wards, facing Southampton Water. Even more serious were defects in ventilation — none was provided for the water closets. The floors, constructed of wood rather than encaustic tile, were always damp. At the suggestion of Sidney Herbert[4], the engineer Douglas Galton was consulted and he improved the ventilation system, but the hospital was never a comfortable place. Eventually it opened in March 1863, having taken over seven years to build and costing well over £300,000.

The Royal Victoria Hospital, as it was named, presented an imposing sight when viewed from Southampton Water. It was one of the largest hospitals in the world, having at one stage over a thousand beds. Externally it had an Italian style, possibly due to Prince Albert's influence. A plinth of Cornwall granite supported the main structure, which comprised a mixture of purple bricks and Portland stone. There were two main three-storey wings, each 600 feet long and 70 feet high, while a four-storey central block contained the chapel. The main corridor, which ran the length of the entire building, was 1420 feet long. There was a grand central staircase and the main hall was used as a museum. Double columns of Portland stone flanked the entrances to blocks A and B, and the central block was surmounted by an ornamental belfry tower. Situated at the rear of the hospital, but separated from it by a wooded valley, was a large cemetery; at some remove from the main building there was also a lunatic asylum.

A school for medical officers in the army had been mooted for some time but lack of both enthusiasm and finance had combined to delay the project. In May 1857, following Florence Nightingale's agitation after

Figure 4
The Royal Victoria Hospital at Netley. It was pulled down in 1967 and now only the chapel, which has been converted into a small museum, remains. (Hampshire County Council)

the medical disasters of the Crimea, a Royal Commission, presided over by Sidney Herbert, was appointed to inquire into the 'Sanitary Conditions of the Army and into the Organisation of Military Hospitals and the Treatment of the Sick and Wounded'. This commission recommended formation of a school to instruct medical officers in emergency surgery for wounds, hygiene, transport of the wounded, tropical diseases and other subjects that were not then part of the curriculum in undergraduate medical schools. The idea met with some opposition from members of the profession, who pointed out that there were professors of military surgery in Edinburgh and Dublin, and also, as always, from the Treasury on the grounds of expense. The delay was disappointing and Florence Nightingale wrote on 29 November 1858 to William Aitken, who was to become the first professor of pathology, sympathising with his frustration at the delay in establishing the school — 'But I do not entertain the least doubt of the school being carried . . . Dr Aitken is wrong in attributing the blame of delay to Mr Herbert . . . It is three weeks post from the War Office to the Horse Guards — literally not metaphorically . . . I saw Mr Herbert's letter to General Peel last week urging him to begin it at Chatham.'[5] And this is what happened. The school was established at Fort Pitt, Chatham while Netley was under construction, although characteristically no provision had been made at Netley for a medical school in the original plans.

On 1 April 1860 the senate of the medical school was constituted. Florence Nightingale took a keen interest and appears to have played a major part not only in the establishment of the school, but also in its administration and nominations to the senate and founding chairs. The first course for 29 officers on probation for the British army and 14 for the Indian army started on 2 October 1860. There were many teething problems due to lack of equipment.

In 1863 the school was transferred to Netley and the sixth course for medical officers — there were two a year — began on 15 April. Since there had been no specific provision for accommodation the school took over a large ward on the second floor of A block, which was converted into a lecture room, rooms for the professors and their secretaries, and a library. Laboratories for hygiene and pathology were in a low building near B block.[6] The school was in the Royal Victoria Hospital but not of it, being governed by the independent senate responsible directly to the War Office and Secretary of State. The senate consisted of the principal medical officer at Netley, the professors, the director general of the Army Medical Services Department and the president of the Medical Board at the India Office. Florence Nightingale had a dominant role in the appointment of the four professors, astonishing in view of her sex and the fact that, although a public heroine, she had no official standing. Yet her influence was extraordinary; she even vetoed the appointment of Sir John Hall as director general of the Army Medical Department.[7] The first four professors were all colleagues from her sojourn in the Crimea, Sir Thomas Longmore, Sir Ranald Martin, A E Parkes and William Aitken. Parkes held the key post of professor of hygiene and Aitken was made professor of pathology. Both Parkes and Aitken were civilians and were appointed for life. The others, who were in the army, were given five-year appointments in the first instance.

Aitken had met Florence Nightingale in 1855 when he had been asked by Lord Panmure to go to the Crimea with Professor R D Lyons, of the Catholic University of Dublin, to investigate the diseases filling the hospitals. This resulted in a report to Parliament as a Blue Book in 1856. Aitken occupied the chair of pathology at Netley from 1860 to 1892. A morbid anatomist of the old school, he was described as performing post-mortem examinations with admirable precision. Although friendly with Florence Nightingale, such qualities did not always excite her unqualified admiration. Thus on 25 July 1860, after his appointment and before the move to Netley, she wrote in a letter to him:

'Pathologists are apt to get into the way of considering the main end of such a school to be that of making good pathological preparations. But if the Chatham School produces many good pathological preparations, you must report it to the Statistical Congress as bad. Pathology is doubtless essential, but the aim of our Army School is the prevention of disease, not the record of the harm disease has done.'[8]

Dr Parkes was her favourite and he became an outstanding authority on preventive medicine, publishing the *Manual of practical hygiene* that established his international reputation. His influence was such that officers from Germany, Russia and the United States came to attend his courses.[9]

Yet the school did not always prosper. This was in part due to difficulty in filling vacancies in the Army Medical Department. Pay was poor and conditions of service unsatisfactory, involving long tours of duty overseas without leave and little or no opportunity to keep up with advances in medicine. Another factor was chronic underfunding. In order to enter the service candidates, after qualifying in medicine, had to take an entrance examination; because of the poor pay and conditions, the British Medical Association actively campaigned against young doctors entering for this. The quality of candidates appears to have been low; thus in 1864 eight out of fourteen failed and a leading article in the *BMJ* asked: 'How comes it that gentlemen who have passed their examinations at our Colleges of Surgeons are so often found unfit to perform the duties of army surgeons?'[10] There was considerable dissatisfaction with the denial of rank to medical officers, and with their inferior pay, conditions of service and pensions when compared with combatants. At one stage there were said to be 200 vacancies for medical officers in the army and only seven applicants.[11] The situation was so bad that the Presidents of the Royal Colleges of Physicians and Surgeons, together with the President of the Medical Council had an interview with the Commander-in-Chief, the Duke of Cambridge. It was reported of the Duke that he had two stereotyped answers to every statement that was urged:

'That point, gentlemen, is a matter of discipline; the army lives and breathes through discipline, discipline is its soul and essence; and that other point, gentlemen, is finance. We must above everything maintain discipline and your demands interfere with discipline; therefore they cannot be listened to. As to the other point we cannot touch it; the Chancellor of the Exchequer holds the purse strings of the country, and what you ask is really all a money question. You must go to the Exchequer about that.'[12]

The national press at this time also reported the concern of the Queen with regard to medical care in the army, a concern that persisted throughout her life. The proximity of Netley to Osborne allowed her to pay frequent and often unexpected visits. On the morning of 8 May 1863 she decided to inspect the hospital that afternoon and insisted on seeing the quarters provided for the wives of patients. These she pronounced entirely unsatisfactory.[13] She returned nearly a year later and found that conditions had improved with construction of a row of cottages at the rear of the hospital.[14]

The administration of the hospital was subject to severe criticism by the medical profession. The governor and commandant of the hospital was a major-general who was aided by an assistant commandant, a regular army major, an adjutant, a regular captain and a captain of orderlies, as well as numerous non-commissioned officers and other ranks. None of these was in any way connected with medicine and all were regulars on secondment. The medical officers, including the principal medical officer and the professors, were subordinate to them a matter that was to cause considerable friction with Almroth Wright in years to come. A leader writer in the *BMJ* considered that to place a major-general '. . . at the head of a hospital, and to make him the supreme authority in its administration, is such a palpable absurdity that it requires only to be stated.'[15]

Despite several such protests the system continued and recruitment to the Army Medical Service remained abysmally low. As Table 2.1 shows, there were no candidates at all in 1869 and 1870, and on two further occasions (1872–73 and 1878–79) an entire year passed without any men coming forward.[16] In the early years the death rate in the Service was high, and this must have acted as a deterrent to recruiting.

Conditions in the medical school did not help. On 18 October 1886 the Duke of Cambridge declared himself 'satisfied with all he had seen at the Royal Victoria Hospital, Netley.'[17]. The leader writer in the *BMJ* reacted to this verdict with some astonishment and drew attention to the lack of space available for laboratory work; this had led to the division of classes into two sections, with the consequence that the men had only two months of instruction instead of four. The senate of the medical school had submitted plans for increased accommodation on many occasions which had been 'approved' but when the time for implementation arrived the proposed vote was struck out of the estimates. The importance of the school in providing instruction in those subjects not adequately covered in the curriculum of the undergraduate medical schools — war wounds, tropical diseases,

Table 2.1

British Army Medical Service

Session	Date	Candidates gazetted	Subsequent casualties			Still on active service 1.9.1880
			Deaths	Registrations	Half-pay	
1	Winter 1860	29	7	5	4	13
2	Summer 1861	18	6	2	1	9
3	Winter 1861	No candidates		Twenty medical officers attended		
4	Summer 1862	18	4	2	1	11
5	Winter 1862	27	7	4	0	16
6	Summer 1863	15	1	1	3	10
7	Winter 1863	33	6	5	1	21
8	Summer 1864	39	10	4	1	24
9	Winter 1864	71	17	15	6	33
10	Summer 1865	38	11	2	3	22
11	Winter 1865	16	2	0	1	13
12	Summer 1866	25	5	1	1	18
13	Winter 1866	21	4	3	0	14
14	Summer 1867	25	6	2	1	16
15	Winter 1867	46	12	6	3	25
16	Summer 1868	38	2	3	0	33
17	Winter 1868	21	3	4	1	13
18	Summer 1869	No candidates for Army Medical Department				
19	Winter 1869	No candidates for Army Medical Department				
20	Summer 1870	No candidates for Army Medical Department				
21	Winter 1870	No candidates for Army Medical Department				
22	Summer 1871	36	3	4	1	28
23	Winter 1871	14	0	2	0	12
24	Summer 1872	12	0	0	0	12
25	Winter 1872	No candidates for Army Medical Department				
26	Summer 1873	No candidates for Army Medical Department				
27	Winter 1873	10	0	0	1	9
28	Summer 1874	16	1	0	1	14
29	Winter 1874	16	0	0	0	16
30	Summer 1875	3	0	1	0	7
31	Winter 1875	14	1	4	0	9
32	Summer 1876	No candidates for Army Medical Department				
33	Winter 1876	33	2	1	0	39
34	Summer 1877	17	3	3	0	11
35	Winter 1877	24	1	1	0	22
36	Summer 1878	19	1	1	0	17
37	Winter 1878	No candidates for Army Medical Department				
38	Summer 1879	No candidates for Army Medical Department				
39	Winter 1879	71	0	0	0	71
40	Summer 1880	34	0	0	0	34
Totals	40	804	115	76	30	583

hygiene, selection of sites for field hospitals and transport of the sick and wounded from the battlefield — was obvious, but the government refused to provide adequate finance for training. A further source of discontent was the inadequate living quarters for surgeons on probation. Twenty of them 'were distributed in mean lodging houses in the neighbouring village, to the prejudice of their discipline, to their extreme inconvenience and exposed to the chance of typhoid from insanitary surroundings . . . would the government treat young men going through Sandhurst, or the Staff College in this fashion?'[18]

Undoubtedly the school did not receive the recognition that was its due considering that it was the model for similar schools in Germany and the United States.[19] In 1887 Knox, the accountant general to the War Office, suggested that it be abolished; this though the annual cost was only £4,250, with the government of India paying a large proportion of this sum. The possibility of closure remained a very real one and more than a year later it was still being considered by the government as a measure of economy, only now it was supported 'upon the expressed opinion of many who have passed through the curriculum, that the training at Netley is of little practical utility.'[20] The *BMJ* acknowledged that there was some substance in this criticism and that the course of instruction 'follows too closely upon lines of an ordinary medical school, and that the authorities have failed to realise the true objects the institution was intended to subserve, namely, to superadd to a complete civil education a special training for an army medical career.'[21] It was pointed out that this was an argument for reform rather than abolition. Unfortunately the latter course was rendered more likely following the threat by the government of India to withdraw its financial support and to give initial training to candidates for the Indian Army Medical Service training in the Presidency civil hospitals in Calcutta, Madras and Bombay and their attached medical schools. Yet the Netley school had been in the forefront of preventive medicine both in the United Kingdom and, through the work of Ranald Martin and Alexander Parkes, in India. By July 1890 the question of officers entering the Indian Medical Service was resolved and they continued to receive preliminary instruction at Netley. The school's finances were now assured.

The reservations expressed by the writer of the *BMJ* article concerning the curriculum at Netley may well have been related to influence exerted by Aitken. He was the last of Florence Nightingale's original nominees, a civilian and appointed for life and, while all the other professors were army officers seconded for a period of five years, his position in the school was a source of resentment. He was a man of limited vision. Post-mortem examinations were performed with precision, specimens were mounted and a descriptive catalogue of such specimens compiled. Such services, admirable though they were, failed to satisfy the needs of army pathology where the new science of bacteriology was revealing the causes and possible control of diseases at an astonishing rate, particularly in the field of tropical medicine. Aitken did not include these subjects in the curriculum. He had a flourishing medico-legal practice and even wrote a book entitled *Post mortem examinations at coroner's inquests.*[22] In recent years he had been in poor health and in 1888 an assistant professor had been appointed. This was David Bruce.

At the time Bruce was 33 years old, a regular officer in the Army Medical Service and already distinguished in scientific research. He had qualified in 1881 and in the following year went into general practice in Reigate; here he met his wife, Mary Elizabeth Steele, who subsequently became his partner in all his researches. Practice was not to his liking and he joined the army in 1883, and within a year found himself stationed in Malta as medical officer to the armed forces guarding the vital Mediterranean sea routes to Suez and India. Many of the soldiers forming the garrison were rendered ineffective by a mysterious febrile illness that went under the name of 'Malta fever'. Its onset was often but not always sudden, with chills, severe rigors and profuse sweating at night. In the morning the men awoke in sodden bedclothes but with a normal temperature and, at least in the initial stages, their outward appearance was normal even though they felt unwell, so that when they reported sick they might well be accused of malingering. The situation was complicated not only by the multiplicity of other symptoms of which the soldiers complained — pains in the joints, sore throats, cough and breathlessness — but also by disturbing emotional signs such as weeping at the mildest rebuke. The disease had a prolonged course, often lasting several months, and there were several deaths. The morbidity of those who lived was a serious drain on the defensive resources of the island.

Bruce realised that these men had a specific disease entity, and it was here that he made his first great contribution to medicine by isolating the causative micro-organism at post mortem and later from the blood. He named the bacterium *Micrococcus melitensis* but in 1920 it was renamed, in his honour, *Brucella* and the disease in humans, which was by no means restricted to Malta, brucellosis. Subsequently further species were identified, one of which, *Brucella abortus*, causes abortion in cattle. *Brucella melitensis* typically infects goats and it was through drinking goat's milk that the troops were infected; once this ceased the disease incidence declined dramatically. This was a major discovery and Bruce's first paper on the subject[23] was published in the year before he took up his appointment at Netley. In 1889 he gained further substantial bacteriological knowledge on secondment for some months to Robert Koch's laboratory in Germany.

Bruce thus brought to the medical school, where the pathology syllabus had not changed in thirty years, experience in bacteriology which was urgently needed for investigating tropical disease. He managed to persuade Aitken to let him start a short course in the subject. Clearly he hoped to succeed to the chair and indeed when Aitken fell ill in April 1892 he was put in temporary charge of the pathology laboratory.

The appointment to the chair aroused considerable interest and there was much speculation as to who would replace Aitken. The post, involving training medical officers who were charged with looking after the health of troops guarding the British Empire, was an important one. Surgeon General Welch was described as the fittest man for the job. He is credited with being the first to recognise that thoracic aortic aneurysm was due to syphilis.[24] The *BMJ* pressed for his appointment:[25]

'For five years he discharged the duties of assistant professor (1871–1876) in this branch of medical science with conspicuous ability, proving himself not only in possession of the requisite knowledge but also of the not very common gift of being able to communicate that knowledge to others. In addition to this Dr Welch has the inestimable advantage of a perfect familiarity with the ways, habits, modes of life and disease to which the British soldier is liable in every climate in which he serves, this was an advantage the late Sir William Aitken never enjoyed, and the want of it hampered him in his work to the end, as it will any civilian who may be appointed to fill his place.'

Welch was in fact offered the chair but refused it, as acceptance would have meant a salary reduction of £150 a year. The *BMJ* commented:

'It will not surprise our readers to learn that upon the above handsome conditions the appointment has been declined — with or without thanks we cannot say and it is now believed that a civilian is to fill the vacant chair.'

The suggestion that a civilian was to be appointed annoyed army medical officers, who felt that they were being passed over. They received, perhaps surprisingly, considerable support from civilian members of the profession one of whom pointed out that there was 'no inducement for young men of professional distinction to enter a service which entails long continued residence in dangerous climates, when posts such as this, to which they are legitimately entitled to aspire in the lapse of years, are denied them.'[26]

In none of the correspondence concerning the chair is there any mention of Bruce, who was admirably qualified for it and was acting as *locum tenens*. The trouble was that in spite of his scientific achievements, his lucid teaching and his attempts to modernise the syllabus he was not, at this stage of his career, at all popular with those in authority. A large, burly figure — he had once considered becoming a professional boxer — he was also a man of uncertain temper. There had been an unfortunate incident on Portsmouth railway station when he was reported for using strong language to the railway officials.[27] He escaped being dismissed the service but the field marshal in command issued a severe reprimand, as did the director general of the Army Medical Service. Bruce was also considered to be too fond of the bottle and, according to Wright, to be a womaniser.[28] This latter statement may well have been an exaggeration, although it was not inconsistent with his devotion to his wife and workmate throughout his life.

No one being obviously suitable or available among army medical officers, the director general turned for advice to Sims Woodhead, the director of the combined laboratories of the Royal College of Physicians of London and the Royal College of Surgeons of England, where Wright on his return from Australia, was working. Wright himself described it as the greatest stroke of luck a man ever had that Sims Woodhead recommended him. He was offered the post, at a salary of £700 a year for five years in the first instance, but it was a renewable contract. This was a good income when one considers that an experienced general practitioner at this time was lucky to earn an average of £500 per annum and needed to sustain the 'paraphernalia of gentility'.[29] Originally the professor of pathology received £600 annually whereas the professors of medicine, surgery and hygiene each had £700, but at Florence Nightingale's insistence this was rectified and Aitken was placed on an equal footing with the others. Her opinion of Wright's appointment is not recorded.

In assessing the relative claims of Bruce and Wright to the chair it is appropriate to look at their scientific achievements by the year 1892, as opposed to their personal qualities. Both had eight publications to their credit. Bruce, at 37, had written four papers on Malta fever in which he had described the bacterium causing the disease; he was later to play a role in elucidating its mode of transmission via goat's milk to humans. By the standards of the time this was a major advance. Malta fever was attacking hundreds of servicemen each year and their average

length of time in hospital was 85 days.[30] Moreover it was a discovery
made under difficult conditions of garrison life, with primitive
equipment and while undertaking the routine duties of a medical
officer in charge of the health of a large number of soldiers in a foreign
climate. He had also written a penetrating analysis of an epidemic of
cholera in Malta in 1887.[31] A further paper described a method for
studying experimental infections in animals, and the other works were
review articles on natural history. He had very direct methods of
investigating biological problems experimentally. In Malta fever, for
instance, once he had isolated the bacillus he attempted to produce the
disease in animals. In this he was at first unsuccessful as he used mice,
guinea pigs and rabbits; but tenacity of purpose was one of his
outstanding qualities and finally he was successful in transmitting the
disease to monkeys.

    In contrast, Wright arrived at Netley in 1892, six years younger than
Bruce, with no experience of army life and with scientific achievements
that must be regarded as inferior. He published no scientific paper
until 1891, in spite of extensive visits to continental laboratories and
time spent in university appointments in Cambridge and Sydney. Most
of his research had been conducted on blood coagulation in the hope of
alleviating suffering from haemorrhagic diseases, notably haemophilia.
This was a continuation of work initiated by Wooldridge before his
untimely death, on the properties of fibrinogen and its conversion to
fibrin when forming a blood clot. Wright realised the importance of
calcium in the process of blood coagulation and attempted,
unsuccessfully, to stem the haemorrhage in haemophiliacs by giving
calcium chloride intravenously. In experimental animals he also
produced intravascular coagulation by injecting fibrinogen, produced
from extracts of the thymus gland or from testicles, and had
investigated the relationship between the carbon dioxide content of
the blood and coagulation. None of these experiments produced
results of immediate significance, but there were two papers which had
implications for the future. In one, written in 1891, he suggested that
removing calcium from the blood by adding a small quantity of
ammonium oxalate, and thus preventing it clotting when placed in a
glass bottle, could be of considerable use in blood transfusion. This
was of no immediate use as the various blood groups had not been
identified at this time and thus transfusion of incompatible blood was a
major hazard. Secondly, in the same year he wrote a paper
investigating the possibility of producing immunity to anthrax by
injecting fibrinogen. This was not a success but it indicated that
Wright's mind was turning to the subject of immunity, which was to

occupy him for the remainder of his life and to which he was to make outstanding contributions. Even so at this stage there was little to recommend him on scientific grounds in preference to Bruce.

The situation at Netley when Wright arrived in September 1892 was difficult. The two men were temperamentally unsuited to each other. Bruce was naturally resentful at being passed over. Both he and Wright were large moustached men of fierce appearance, but there the similarity ended. Bruce was, certainly at first acquaintance, of a somewhat sullen and taciturn disposition; he was fond of alcohol. In contrast Wright, a younger man and a virtual teetotaller, had been called an Irish windbag in Australia and did a lot of his thinking aloud. His knowledge of literature was immense, and throughout his life he agonised over problems in moral philosophy. Fortunately he was possessed of considerable resilience, and was not disconcerted by the lack of a warm welcome from the regular service officers.

His formal duties were not arduous. There were two courses a year, each of four months duration, attended by medically qualified men desirous of a commission in the Army Medical Service. He taught on three mornings a week, and could devote the remainder of his time to research. He realised at once that the curriculum needed revision. The men needed instruction in the prevention of infectious bacterial and parasitic diseases rather than in, or at least in addition to, the morbid anatomy of such conditions. The only instruction given on infection was by the professor of surgery. The pathology course had not altered significantly since 1862 when the booklet on *Organisation of the Practical Army Medical School* listed its main features as: 'Lectures and demonstrations on Morbid Anatomy, illustrated by specimens selected from the Museum, and aided by accessory methods of observation, such as carefully recorded Clinical Histories of Cases of the more important and severe diseases prevalent at Military Stations abroad'. Practical instruction was confined to 'opening of dead bodies' and specific emphasis was given to 'manual labour and dexterity' in carrying out this task. There was instruction in the use of the microscope and identification of parasites, but these were the only subjects relevant to diagnosis during life.[32]

Bruce had attempted to revise the course but not being in absolute authority had been frustrated in this aim. Wright's experience of bacteriology at the time of his appointment was negligible — his primary interests being in haematology and diabetes — but he was quick to realise its significance. He read much of the relevant literature before taking up his appointment, stimulated in part by his friend William Bulloch, pathologist and bacteriologist to the London

Hospital. It is not clear where the credit for the radical change in the pathology syllabus at Netley should be allocated, but certainly by the middle of the 1890s it would have been unrecognisable to those surgeons on probation who had attended the course in the first three decades of the school's existence. In 1896 morbid anatomy is not even mentioned. The first lecture was on 'Classification and life conditions of micro-organisms' and the rest of the 16 lectures were devoted to bacteriological or immunological aspects of disease, with the exception of the last one which was concerned with disorders of the blood. Many of the subjects discussed would be familiar to the medical student of today.[33] Mechanisms of inflammation and the nature of the inflammatory process, general immunity and immunisation, phagocytosis, venereal diseases and diagnosis from examination of the blood serum, all feature prominently. The lectures were supplemented by practical classes showing the value of bacteriology in diagnosis. Here Wright was fortunate in that the laboratory was embedded in the hospital with its large number of patients coming from remote parts of the Empire and suffering from tropical disease; it was better served in this respect than any hospital in London, Liverpool or elsewhere.

As a lecturer at this time, and for some years to come, Wright was inspiring and had the capacity of communicating his enthusiasm. The practical demonstrations with which he illustrated each lecture were often used to explain a new technique. One of Wright's great contributions to medical science was his ardent advocacy of the experimental method and of measurement. At first these techniques were principally concerned with investigation of the blood. His contribution was to introduce micromethods. At this time syringes were inefficient and drawing blood by venepuncture was seldom used. Wright devised a series of methods whereby, following a small finger prick, drops of blood could be drawn up into very fine bore glass tubes — capillary tubes. These he made himself by heating a wide-bore tube in a gas flame and drawing it out. He used these tubes for a variety of investigations. One of the simplest was to measure the clotting time of blood. To do this drops of blood were drawn up into a series of capillary tubes of equal bore and blown out at time intervals, usually of 30 seconds, until one was found to be blocked by clot. The time from drawing up the blood into the tube until it clotted was termed the *clotting time*. (This is not the same as the *bleeding time*, which is the time taken from wounding the skin to cessation of bleeding in the living subject and which depends on many other factors besides the clotting time.)

Figure 5
*'Oakhurst', the Wright's house in Netley, in 1895. Wright is standing in the
doorway. (Giles Romanes)*

During his first year at Netley Wright continued his research into
blood coagulation, but little of significance emerged. His work on
calcium did have some practical application in the apparently
unrelated field of infant feeding. Wright and his family lived at
Oakhurst, a house at Hamble not far from the hospital, and had an
adjacent meadow where they kept a cow. Jane Wright was not
inexperienced in the world of farming as she had an interest in the
estate at Coolcarrigan, Kilcock, County Kildare. Their newborn son
had great difficulty in digesting cow's milk due to its clotting as a result
of enzymic action of the gastric juices. Cow's milk contains much more
calcium than does human milk, and Wright discovered that if it was
treated with sodium citrate, which rendered the calcium inert, the milk
clots that were formed in the stomach were friable, less firm and thus
more easily digestible.[34] This method of treating cow's milk for infant
feeding was widely adopted; it was to prove of considerable use
following the birth of the Wrights' third and last child, Doris Helen

MacNaughton ('Dolly'), on 13 August 1894. Yet Wright soon realised that, intriguing as was his work on blood coagulation, it had little relevance to the needs of army surgeons on probation, and so he directed his energies towards bacteriology.

This was, of course, the field in which Bruce had a primary interest and one to which he had made an outstanding contribution. Difficulties between two such powerful but different personalities were inevitable. Wright was already turning towards methods of producing immunity to infectious diseases, as evidenced by his experiments carried out in London on Wooldridge's useless method for protection against anthrax by injection of tissue fibrinogen. Both men were aware of immunity against smallpox produced by vaccination, and of Pasteur's induction of immunity against anthrax by injection of attenuated living anthrax bacilli, and were anxious to extend this principle to other bacterial diseases. Typhoid was an obvious candidate and this is dealt with in Chapter 3. Cholera was the other main life-threatening alimentary disorder that was prevalent in India, in spite of attempts to purify the water supply. In that country a Ukrainian refugee, Waldemar Haffkine, claimed to have developed a vaccine against cholera that excited much interest in the European scientific community. In January 1893 Haffkine visited the Army Medical School at Netley to demonstrate his methods. Immediately following his visit Wright and Bruce published a joint paper[35] explaining the method and outlining some general principles of immunology. One of their opening paragraphs is worth quoting as it shows considerable insight, remarkable for that time, into the problems involved in producing immunity to infectious disease:

> 'Microbial infections are conveniently divided into septicaemias and intoxications. In the case of the former the bacteria multiply freely in the blood and produce their poisons there. In the case of the latter the micro-organisms do not proliferate in the blood, but the bacterial poisons become absorbed into the system from some point — generally a point on the inner or outer surface of the body — at which bacteria have effected a lodgement.'

The classic example of septicaemia that was engaging Wright at this time was typhoid. He was to demonstrate that injection of dead typhoid bacilli in humans could produce antibodies to the bacilli in the subject's serum and that these would protect against future infection with that organism. Diphtheria was the most frequently encountered infection of the second type where the infecting bacteria do not, or only very rarely, enter the bloodstream. Serious consequences of the disease are due to toxins produced by the diphtheria bacilli, *Corynebacterium diphtheriae*, which are absorbed from the areas of the tonsils and throat that are infected. At that time these could only be counteracted by injection of an anti-toxin that had been raised in the serum of an animal, usually a horse, following repeated injection of a toxin-producing diphtheria bacillus. While these two examples provided Wright with a rationale for prevention and treatment of some infections, they did not by any means provide the basis for dealing with all infections, as he was shortly to discover when studying cholera and, to his cost, Malta fever.

In cholera the infecting organism *Vibrio cholerae* is confined to the alimentary canal and rarely enters the bloodstream. Once the *Vibrio* is ingested, usually from a faecally contaminated water supply, it attaches itself to the cells of the intestinal epithelium where it multiplies and liberates its toxin, which damages the cells allowing a massive outpouring of water and salts. This results in profuse watery diarrhoea and consequent dehydration which is often fatal. Haffkine's vaccine consisted of killed cholera bacteria and was given by injection and thus, because it gave rise to antibodies in the blood rather than in the wall of the intestines, resulted in a very dubious degree of immunity. Yet the principle of injecting dead (or attenuated living) organisms in order to induce immunity to infectious disease stimulated Wright to employ it in a variety of bacterial diseases.

An obvious candidate for this method of producing immunity was Malta fever. There is no evidence of any joint publication on this by Wright and Bruce. Indeed they formally collaborated over only one other paper[36] and that on a method for staining white blood cells. Bruce's term as assistant professor of pathology was limited by regulation to five years and came to an end in 1894. According to Cantlie[37], Wright applied, with Bruce's consent, to retain him but this was not allowed. Bruce was posted to South Africa and was almost immediately seconded to Northern Zululand to investigate nagana, a disease that was destroying the cattle in that country. Together with his wife, within two months, he established that the disease was associated with the presence of a trypanosome in the blood and was transmitted by bites from the tsetse fly. By any standards this was a major discovery and was indeed the first occasion on which it was established that disease could be transmitted by suctorial insects. The parasitic protozoon was named *Trypanosoma brucei brucei*. Subsequently it was demonstrated that sleeping sickness in humans was caused by a similar organism and was also transmitted through the bite of a tsetse fly. This work led to Bruce's election as a Fellow of the Royal Society in 1899, though by that time he was in the besieged town of Ladysmith. He was succeeded at Netley by David Semple.

The departure of Bruce did not inhibit Wright from working on Malta fever. He was familiar with research by Gruber and Pfeiffer that had shown that when the serum of patients who had recovered from typhoid was mixed with a suspension of typhoid bacilli it caused them to clump together, that is, to agglutinate. This was due to the presence of specific antibodies or agglutinins in the patient's serum which acted only on typhoid bacilli and not on other organisms. Wright considered that this might be a phenomenon that could facilitate differentiation of the numerous bacterial causes of fever. Indeed he found that serum from patients suffering from Malta fever had antibodies against the organism causing the disease, *Brucella melitensis*, and against no other microbe. He saw that this provided a valuable method of diagnosing the disease, whose clinical features are by no means specific, and distinguishing it from other causes of fever and in particular from typhoid. He published this, the first laboratory investigation into the diagnosis of pyrexia of unknown origin, in collaboration with one of the Netley officers, Captain F Smith.[38] His method is still used today.

Wright went further. He postulated that the presence of such antibodies in the serum afforded protection against disease, and that if they could be produced in the healthy subject they would provide immunity when that subject was exposed to infection. This was the basis of the method used by Pasteur to protect sheep from anthrax, and was the principle Wright was himself to use in his work on typhoid. He decided that production of antibodies against *Brucella melitensis* by injecting dead organisms should protect against Malta fever. He was wrong. The reason for this is that immunity is not solely dependent on the presence of antibodies in the serum. In some diseases it is more dependent on cellular immunity, that is the ability of the cells in the blood and tissues to ingest and destroy organisms. Malta fever is one such disorder; tuberculosis is another. Yet Wright, after demonstrating that immunity was apparently induced in monkeys following injection of dead organisms, was so convinced that he inoculated himself with dead *Brucella melitensis* bacteria, producing antibodies in his serum and, believing he was now immune to the disease, followed this after a suitable interval with an injection of live organisms. To his dismay he developed a severe attack of Malta fever from which he did not fully recover for several months. He experienced the characteristically unpleasant symptoms of general listlessness and malaise associated with an undulant fever. He also suffered emotional disturbances and Colebrook[39] records that Wright, an outwardly unsentimental man,

Figure 6
Wright in his laboratory at Netley. (The Wellcome Library, London)

burst into tears while reading Kipling's *Captains courageous* (1897) during a railway journey and had to hide behind a newspaper to cover his embarrassment. Even today vaccine against brucellosis is far from fully effective in that any protection provided is very short-lived.

The importance of this work and subsequent studies on typhoid was twofold. Firstly, it demonstrated the value of the pathology laboratory in the diagnosis of disease in the living patient. This was an aspect of medicine that Wright preached for the rest of his days and was indeed to blossom to such effect that today few patients visiting a doctor or entering hospital can escape without having blood and other body fluids examined in the laboratory. Secondly, it stimulated Wright to develop methods which, although now mostly superseded, were to form the foundation of modern laboratory technology. All his life he was a great opponent of the 'Harley Street ethos'. He was critical of clinical acumen based on inspection, palpation, percussion and auscultation. He used to tease clinicians and medical students, demonstrating the fallibility of such methods by placing an object, usually a half-crown, under some blankets and inviting them to locate it. Frequently they failed. He was a firm advocate of measurement in the pathology laboratory and was one of the first medical men to propound medicine as a science rather than an art. At the time this was an unpopular view. Weatherall[40] relates the tale of Henry Dale, a future Nobel laureate, who in 1900 entered St Bartholomew's Hospital as a clinical student and was told by Samuel Gee 'that medicine was not a science but merely an empirical art, he must forget all the physiology he had learnt at Cambridge'. Unfortunately this attitude still persists in some quarters today.

While Wright was engaged in his studies on the serological diagnosis of Malta fever and on the prevention of typhoid by vaccination he was asked to serve on a commission of enquiry. During the rainy season of 1896 plague broke out in the city of Bombay; the total mortality from 23 September 1896 to 31 March 1897 was 33,161, which was an excess of 19,843 over the normal for this period. Most of those who died were plague victims.[41] The disease spread rapidly throughout the Bombay Presidency, into the Punjab, across to Calcutta and, to a lesser extent, to the Madras Presidency. Plague had from time to time ravaged the native population in various parts of the East. It had been carried from China to Hong Kong and it was there that, in the early 1890s, Alexandre Yersin had isolated the causative bacterium[42] and called it *Pasteurella pestis*. It was later to be named *Yersinia pestis*.

By 1898 the Government of India was so alarmed that, with the approval of the Secretary of State for India, it appointed a commission to enquire into the problem, under the chairmanship of T R Fraser, professor of materia medica in Edinburgh. The other members were Wright himself, J P Hewett, secretary to the Government of India in the Home Department, A E Cumine, a senior collector in the Bombay Presidency, Dr M A Ruffer, president of the Sanitary and Quarantine Council of Egypt, and C J Halifax as secretary of the commission. The appointment of Wright was slightly odd. Bruce would have been a more obvious choice, particularly in view of his fundamental work on the aetiology of Malta fever and nagana, but he was on active service in South Africa where war was imminent.

The commission arrived in Bombay on 26 November 1898 and stayed until 25 March 1899. They were charged with investigating (a) the origin of the different outbreaks of plague, (b) the manner in which the disease was communicated, (c) the effects of curative serum, and

(d) the effects of preventive inoculation. They failed to arrive at any worthwhile conclusion on any of these items and for this Wright, who by his own admission[43] wrote most of the report, must bear much responsibility. The commission travelled widely throughout the subcontinent and Wright, who was obsessed with the problem of typhoid fever, seems to have spent much of his time persuading the British troops to undergo vaccination against this disease rather than investigating plague. He recruited help for the bacteriological work on plague victims from C G Spencer and W G Liston, two army officers who had passed through his course at Netley. Two other old Netley students, H J Walton and S R Douglas, were given the task of testing the therapeutic effect of a serum (produced by Yersin) on those suffering from the disease in Bangalore; they found it to be of little value, though they were more favourably disposed towards a vaccine produced by Haffkine.

The commission's main concern was with the method of spread of the disease. Diagnosis was not a problem. The symptoms and signs had been well recognised in ancient Greece and in medieval times. Daniel Defoe had given a vivid but secondhand account of the 1665 epidemic in *The journal of the plague year* and significantly noted that animals, and especially rats, might be responsible for spreading the infection. The sufferers experience a sudden onset with chills, rigors, lethargy and headache but within a day the nature of their condition declares itself as the typical buboes make their appearance. These are painful lymph node swellings, forming characteristically in the groin but also in the armpit and neck. They may be up to four inches long, the skin over them being tense, reddened and very tender. Coma and high fever precede death, which may occur within two to four days of the buboes appearing.

Plague, like brucellosis, is a zoonosis, that is, an infectious disease of animals that can be transmitted to humans. It is an infection of rodents, notably the domestic rat, and is passed on to humans by the bites of the Oriental flea, *Xenopsylla cheopis*, which lives on the rat. The flea feeds on the blood of the rat, sucking organisms into its gut where they multiply. When an infected flea bites a human the organisms are regurgitated and enter the bloodstream. It was this cycle of events that members of the commission singularly failed to appreciate, in spite of finding dead rats infected with plague in the houses of those dying from the disease. Furthermore they received evidence, from a Major Charles of the IMS and a Dr Cook, that the disease had been introduced by rats conveyed in ships from plague-infested areas, notably those sailing from Hong Kong to Calcutta. These two gentlemen pointed out that 'diseased rats had escaped from ships and infected rats in the neighbourhood of the wharves, and in particular Fairlie Place, one of the first centres of plague in Calcutta.'[44] Furthermore, shortly after the commission returned from India, Simmond, working in Paris, in 1898 published experimental evidence that infected fleas from rats transferred themselves as parasites to humans.[45] They dismissed his work as 'so weak as to be hardly deserving of consideration'.[46]

The commission seemed obsessed by the thought that infection could be caused by contaminated clothing coming off ships and attached 'the greatest importance to the system of disinfecting clothing and bedding of the crews and lower classes of passengers.'[47] They also considered transmission from one human to another was significant. This is now known to occur, but only in about 2 per cent of cases when patients suffer from the rare form of pneumonic plague.

Although Wright claimed a major role in writing the main report, he and Ruffer added a minority memorandum lamenting the lack of notification in many instances of death due to plague. They were convinced that a policy that made no effective provision for the discovery of plague deaths was 'a policy foredoomed to failure'.[48] They advocated corpse inspection at the place of death and gave a series of external signs, such as the presence of buboes, which could be used in confirming the diagnosis. Unfortunately this was not an altogether sensible or practical plan as the native Indian population strongly objected to any interference with the body after death. Removal of plague-infected bodies had been the cause of riots in Garhshankars, with nine fatalities. Attempts to use troops to help in detection of cases and removal of bodies had, in one instance, resulted in murder of a magistrate and an army officer.

The overall results of the commission's work were so inconclusive that, after their full publication in 1902, the government of India decided to take further measures and accordingly once again approached the Secretary of State. On this occasion the Royal Society and the Lister Institute were consulted and a committee representing these two bodies, as well as the India Office, was convened and an annual grant of £5000 provided. The committee included David Bruce and Dr C J Martin, the latter being director of the Lister Institute and incidentally an old colleague of Wright's from his days in Sydney. Martin was dispatched to India: a commission was appointed there which included both Indian and European members; among the latter was W G Liston, who had previously worked with Wright. In 1908, following careful research they published their report[49] and three of their conclusions are worth quoting:

(a) Bubonic plague in humans is entirely dependent on the disease in the rat.

(b) The infection is conveyed from rat to rat and from rat to human solely by means of the rat flea.

(c) Insanitary conditions have no relation to the occurrence of plague, except insofar as they favour infestation by rats.

Thus they exposed the inadequacy of the previous commission's findings. The episode does not reflect well upon Wright. Why he was so dismissive of the role of suctorial insects in view of the evidence presented by some of the local medical profession and by Simmond must remain a mystery. Yet one cannot escape considering that his personal antagonism to Bruce, who had been the first to demonstrate that insects could transmit disease in the case of trypanosomiasis, may have influenced his thinking.

One reason why Wright may have welcomed his secondment to India in November 1898 was his increasingly difficult relationship with the army hierarchy. Throughout the last decade of the 19th century the *BMJ* contains regular reports concerning the Army Medical School. At the end of each course there was a prize-giving at which a distinguished guest, either a military or very occasionally a civilian figure, gave an address and distributed the prizes. After such ceremonies the entire party was entertained to a splendid luncheon in the officers' mess. The names of the more notable of those attending were listed in the medical press and always included the professors of surgery, medicine and hygiene; Wright's name is conspicuously absent, though he did receive mention in the speech given by the C-in-C Sir George White in 1899 in connection with anti-typhoid vaccine. Queen Victoria frequently visited the hospital — in 1898 she went there no less than three times — and the names of those presented to her are listed but again Wright is not mentioned. It seems there was a smouldering resentment against the solitary civilian professor. Wright had a thick skin and may not have been troubled too much by the cold-shouldering. The same was not true of his wife and no doubt the social ostracism added to the strained relationship that was developing between the couple.

Wright showed impatience with routine military duties that his students and technical staff had to perform. Colebrook[50] relates how on one occasion Wright 'strode out on to the parade ground and plucked' one of his technicians from the ranks of the platoon that was undergoing drill instruction. There were difficulties in obtaining adequate staff for a laboratory that was becoming increasingly involved not only with research but as a centre for production of vaccines and diphtheria anti-toxin. In 1896 Wright wrote to the War

Office on the need for a second assistant; the *BMJ*[51] commented: 'Of late the work carried on there in experiments and the manufacture of anti-toxin, in addition to the ordinary current work has taxed the professor and his single assistant'. The War Office[52] acceded to his request but only on condition that 'this officer will, however, be available for tours of orderly duty, in addition to his laboratory duties'. Surgeon Captain F Smith was appointed.[53] He had risen from the ranks, having been a staff sergeant in the Medical Staff Corps. In those days, when social class consciousness was at its zenith, no doubt he was considered to be a suitable candidate for the post attached to the troublesome half-Irish civilian. Anyhow it proved a happy choice: Smith collaborated with Wright on the seminal paper on laboratory diagnosis of fevers of unknown origin.

If Wright was not altogether accepted by his fellow professors, he was warmly received by the students. Considering that many of the surgeons on probation came from the lower reaches of the pass lists in the undergraduate medical schools, a surprising number of those attending Wright's courses, or acting as his assistants, went on to achieve distinction in medicine. S Lyle Cummins left the Army after some years to become the first professor of tuberculosis in Cardiff. S R Douglas, who joined Wright at St Mary's, and later became a Fellow of the Royal Society and the first director of bacteriology at the National Institute for Medical Research. L W Harrison performed pioneer work in the diagnosis and treatment of venereal disease; many clinics dealing with sexually transmitted disease are today named after him. W F Harvey, a histopathologist, was celebrated for his studies of tumours and founded the tumour registry at the Royal College of Physicians in Edinburgh. George Lamb became director of the Pasteur Institute of India at Kasauli. W B Leishman, later to be director general of the Army Medical Services and a Fellow of the Royal Society, was renowned not only for his work on the parasitic disease that bears his name, but also for his conduct of anti-typhoid inoculation trials and for the haematological stain named after him. Glen Liston, who performed essential work for the second plague commission, became after the First World War a notable bacteriologist in Edinburgh. Leonard Rogers, an authority on tropical medicine and another Fellow of the Royal Society, was distinguished for revolutionising the treatment of amoebic dysentery and for his studies on kala-azar and cholera. David Semple, the co-author with Wright of the paper on the serological diagnosis of Malta fever, was subsequently another director of the Pasteur Institute in India, a member of the Medical Research Council of India and eventually director general of public health services in Egypt.

These men remained loyal to Wright all their lives. They are a testimony to the effectiveness of his teaching and his ability to communicate his enthusiasm for his subject. But by 1900 his relations with the army were becoming increasingly strained. There had been talk of closing the school at Netley, and now there was a strong feeling that it should move to London to be in closer proximity to the undergraduate medical schools. It was not this that finally made Wright seek fresh fields, however, but the stubborn antagonism the Army authorities exhibited towards his work on the prevention of typhoid fever; yet it was this that was to bring him to the attention of a wider public.

Notes

1   Benson AC, ed. *Letters of Queen Victoria* vol 3 p113. London: John Murray, 1908.
2   Rundle A. *History of the Royal Victoria Hospital, Netley.* Draft chapters, CMAC RAMC 1091 (Box 222).
3   Smith FB. *Florence Nightingale: reputation and power* p68. London: Croom Helm, 1982.
4   Secretary of State for War, 1845–6, 1852–5, 1859–60; responsible for F Nightingale going to the Crimea.
5   RAMC 1139(S4)2.
6   Rundle, unpublished CMAC RAMC 1091.
7   Smith FB. *Florence Nightingale: reputation and power* p76. London: Croom Helm, 1982.
8   RAMC 1139(S4) 13.
9   Cantlie N. *A history of the Army Medical Department* vol 2 p231. Edinburgh: Churchill Livingstone, 1974.
10 *BMJ* 1864; **i**: 496.
11 Ibid p533.
12   *BMJ* 1864; **ii**: 62.
13 *Medical Times and Gazette* 16 May 1863.
14 *Medical Times and Gazette* 6 February 1864.
15 *BMJ* 1869; **i**: 29.
16 *BMJ* 1881; **i**: 88.
17 *BMJ* 1886; **ii**: 827.
18 Ibid.
19 *BMJ* 1887; **ii**: 136.
20   *BMJ* 1888; **ii**: 823.
21 Ibid.
22 Coroners' post-mortem examinations provided a considerable part of his income. In 1897, during Wright's time, the War Office ruled that 'Army medical officers are not entitled, as they have been hitherto, to receive fees for attending coroner's inquests or making post-mortem examinations on the bodies of patients dying in military hospitals.'
23 Bruce D. *Practitioner* 1867; **39**: 161.
24 Cantlie N. *A history of the Army Medical Department* vol 2 p206. Edinburgh: Churchill Livingstone, 1974.
25 *BMJ* 1892; **ii**: 89.
26 Campbell EK. *BMJ* 1892; **ii**: 334.
27 Harris F. *J RAMC* 1955; **101**: 80.
28 Colebrook Diaries CMAC.
29 Digby A. *Making a medical living* pp141, 142. Cambridge: Cambridge University Press, 1994.
30 Vassalo DJ. *J RAMC* 1992; **138**: 140.
31 *Trand Epidemiol Soc* 1888–9; **8**: 1.
32 *Organisation of the Practical Army Medical School: including subjects to be taught by the professors* p25. HMSO, 1862.

33 *Regulations for the guidance of officers and surgeons on probation attending the Army Medical School at Netley* p39 *et seq.* HMSO, 1898.

34 Wright AE. *Lancet*; **ii:** 194.

35 Wright AE, Bruce D. *BMJ* 1893; **i:** 227.

36 Wright AE, Bruce D. Ibid p400.

37 Cantlie N. *A history of the Army Medical Department* vol 2 p231. Edinburgh: Churchill Livingstone, 1974.

38 *Lancet* 1897; **i:** 656.

39 Colebrook L. *Almroth Wright: provocative doctor and thinker* p29. London: Heinemann, 1954.

40 Weatherall DJ, Ledingham JGG, Warrell DA, eds. *Oxford textbook of medicine* 3rd edn p7. Oxford: Oxford University Press, 1996.

41 Indian Plague Commission 1898–1899.

42 A Gram-negative rod with striking bipolar staining.

43 Colebrook Diaries CMAC PP/COL.0.(.).

44 Indian Plague Commission 1901 (Cd 810) p40. In *Parliamentary Papers* **LXXII**: 268.

45 Simmond P-L. La propagation de la peste. *Ann l'Inst Pasteur* 1898; **12**: 625–687.

46 Indian Plague Commission 1901 (Cd 810) p77. In *Parliamentary Papers* **LXXII**: 268.

47 Ibid p613.

48 Indian Plague Commission 1902 vol 72 Appendix p495.

49 Second Indian Plague Commission. *The etiology and epidemiology of plague: a summary of the work of the Plague Commission* p93. Superintendent of Government Printing, India: Calcutta, 1908.

50 Colebrook L. *Almroth Wright: provocative doctor and thinker* p45. London: Heinemann, 1954.

51 *BMJ* 1896; **ii**: 692.

52 *BMJ* 1896; **ii**: 1172.

53 *BMJ* 1896; **ii**: 1355.

Chapter 3

The Fight against Typhoid

One of the great mysteries of medicine until the 19th century concerned the causes of epidemics. These were attributed variously to the wrath of the Lord, cosmic forces and most popularly, following the writings of Hippocrates, Galen and others, to changes in the air which was contaminated by 'miasmas'. The nature of these miasmas, thought to be noxious exhalations from putrescent organic matter, was obscure. Even the microscope, invented by Leeuwenhoek in the 17th century, and its revelations of organisms invisible to the naked eye were not universally acknowledged by the conservative scientific establishment. Linnaeus (1707–78), the founder of modern botany, did not believe in microscopic observations and refused to acknowledge the existence of spermatozoa.[1] The possibility that such minute organisms could cause disease was not considered by the majority of the medical profession until the second half of the 19th century. There were a few notable exceptions: one was Benjamin Marten[2], who in 1720 published a book on phthisis (tuberculosis) in which he postulated that it was caused by invisible organisms inhaled from the breath of a consumptive patient.

Since earliest times it had been known that one of the major consequences of poor hygiene such as that experienced in war, overcrowding in mental asylums, social deprivation and famine was an epidemic of fever accompanied by disturbance of bowel function. Such disorders were frequently diagnosed simply as 'fever', and little consideration was given to the possibility that there were separate disease entities that could give rise to this one nonspecific sign. That this was indeed the case became apparent with the increasing number of post-mortem examinations and the consequent development of the science of morbid anatomy. In his book on fevers published in 1829 the Parisian physician Louis[3] noted that ulceration of the small intestinal mucosa was found in some patients dying of fever and not in others. He is credited with coining the word 'typhoid' for ulcerated cases and distinguishing this from typhus where no ulceration was present. The subject was one of great interest to thinking members of the profession, and it is evidence of the increasingly widespread acknowledgment of this that the specific differential diagnosis of fever was referred to by George Eliot in *Middlemarch* (1871–2). Robert Perry[4] in Glasgow in 1836 had confirmed the distinction made by Louis on the basis of his own observations of 4,000 patients and 300 post-mortem examinations.

William Jenner[5], who published in 1850 a volume entitled *On identity or non-identity of typhoid and typhus fevers*, is usually acknowledged in Britain as distinguishing between the two diseases. His views were based on his experience at the London Fever Hospital. He emphasised the intestinal lesions in typhoid and the serious and fatal complications of intestinal haemorrhage and perforation. Jenner was a major figure in Victorian medicine, being physician to the Royal Household—he attended Prince Albert in 1861 when he died of typhoid, and the Prince of Wales in 1871 when he also contracted the disease—and President of the Royal College of Physicians for six years. Credit in Britain for distinguishing between the two diseases should, however, go to William Budd. In 1840 Budd submitted an essay for the Thackeray prize to the Provincial Surgeons Association entitled *The causes of continued fevers of Great Britain and Ireland*, in which he demonstrated that typhus and typhoid were two distinct diseases. One of the adjudicators, Sir John Forbes, thought the essay to be 'the most able'[6] of those submitted but that it was too revolutionary in its conclusions to be accepted for first prize. Unfortunately, the essay was never published. Budd[7] also made the most fundamental contribution to the study of the origin and spread of the disease and has strong claims to be considered the father of epidemiology. While in general practice in Devon, he demonstrated the infectious nature of typhoid by showing how it was spread from the village of North Tawton to the surrounding villages of Marchard, Chaffcombe, Loosebear and Bow by patients who had contracted or were incubating the disease. Other nearby villages that were not so visited but were equally insanitary remained unaffected. From 1841 until his death in 1880 he was consulting physician to the Royal Infirmary in Bristol, a city which in 1842, according to the Health of Towns Commission appointed by the government, was 'the third most unhealthy town in England'. Only Liverpool and Manchester were judged worse.

From an early date Budd had realised the role played by the water supply in spreading both typhoid and cholera. Independently of Snow[8], he arrived at the conclusion that cholera could be spread by water. He became one of the first directors of the Bristol Waterworks

Company. He was confirmed in his opinions by experience in his own practice in Bristol[9] where, in 1847, he dealt with an outbreak of typhoid in Richmond Terrace in Clifton. This involved only 13 of the 34 houses in the terrace; all of these drew their water from a single well, which was known to be contaminated by sewage, whereas the remainder of the houses had a separate uncontaminated water supply. The observations of Budd and Snow led to progressive improvements in the supply and quality of domestic water, and a consequent decline in the incidence of disease.

Yet the decline in typhoid was much less than that of cholera. The reason for this is that the typhoid bacillus can persist for a considerable time in the faeces of patients who have recovered from the disease, such people becoming 'carriers' and a source of infection for those who have not had the disease. From 1865 onwards cholera was very rare in Britain, but typhoid persisted with 54,000 cases annually in the decade 1871–80. A city the size of Edinburgh, for instance, would be expected to have had 1,000 cases a year.[10] In the British Empire and especially in India, where the equivalent of a battalion of British (but not Indian) troops was rendered useless by the disease every year, it assumed considerable importance.

In the Boer War (1899–1902[11]), where 557,653 men were deployed with an average operational strength of 209,404, there were 59,750 cases of 'enteric fever' (as typhoid was then called) with 8227 deaths more than the deaths due to enemy action. (The figures given for incidence and death vary somewhat according to the source consulted but the general trend is the same.) Nor was this a purely British or South African problem. In the Franco-Prussian War (1870–71) the German Army had 73,393 cases and 6965 deaths; in French operations in Tunisia in the 1870s there were from a total strength of 20,000 men 4200 cases with 1039 deaths; and in the Spanish-American conflict, of the 107,973 men in the American Army, 20,738 contracted the disease with 1580 fatalities. Clearly this was a major military problem and any attempt to deal with it was to be welcomed.

Diagnosis remained imprecise; thus, differentiation between typhoid and the related paratyphoid fevers was not yet established. Nevertheless, all were enteric fevers whose spread, infectivity and clinical features were similar. Statistics illustrated the extent of the problem but gave no idea of the suffering endured by those who contracted the disease, which was no respecter of class. No one was more conscious of this than Budd, as shown by his description of the social dilemma in the homes of those afflicted[12]:

'The real amount of suffering involved in this is, however, but feebly represented by these bald figures. No one can know what they really imply who has not had experience of this fever in his own home. The dreary and painful night watches the great length of the period over which the anxiety is extended the long suspense between hope and fear, and the large number of cases in which hope is disappointed and the worst fear is at last realised, make up a sum of distress that is scarcely found in the history of any other acute disorder. Even in the highest class of society, the introduction of this fever into the household is an event that generally long stands prominently out in the record of family afflictions. But if this is true of the mansions of the rich, who have every means of alleviation which wealth can command, how much more true must it be of the cottages of the poor, who have scant provision for the necessaries of life and none for its great emergencies . . .

As the disease is, by far, the most fatal to persons in middle life, the father and mother, or both, are often the first to succumb, and the young survivors being left without support, their home is broken up and their destitution becomes complete.

How often have I seen in past days, in the single, narrow chamber of the day-labourer's cottage, the father in the coffin, the mother in the sick bed in muttering delirium, and nothing to relieve the desolation of the children but the devotion of some poor neighbour, who in many cases paid the penalty of her kindness in becoming herself victim of the same disorder?'

Budd's work on the spread and nature of typhoid is remarkable because it took place several years before the discovery in 1880 of the typhoid bacillus by Eberth,[13] who found the organism in spleen and mesenteric lymph nodes at post-mortem examination on 12 fatal cases. In 1884, Gaffky[14] managed to grow the bacillus in pure culture using the methods developed by Koch. This organism, which is the cause of typhoid, belongs to the group of bacteria known as *Salmonella* and its correct name is *Salmonella typhi*. These are small motile rods, 3 μm long and 0.1 μm diameter, possessing flagellae, thread-like appendages attached to the surface of the bacillus, the beating action of which allows it to swim in a liquid medium. They belong to a taxonomic group of bacteria known as 'Gram-negative bacteria' because they fail to take up a particular stain devised by Christian Gram. The response of bacteria to treatment with this stain depends on the complex structure of their walls and they are accordingly classified into two major groups: those that take up the stain, Gram-positive, and those that fail to do so, Gram-negative. Morphologically *S. typhi* are indistinguishable from many other Gram-negative bacilli, the best known of which is *Escherichia coli*, but they are readily identified by their biochemical reactions—they do not ferment lactose and do produce acid from glucose—but more especially by their unique protein or antigenic structure, which can be recognised by serological means. Patients are infected by eating food or drinking water containing the bacillus which, when it reaches the small intestine, lodges in the small masses of lymphatic tissue known as Peyer's patches. Here it multiplies and enters the bloodstream. The incubation period from ingesting the organism to onset of symptoms is 10 to 14 days. The symptoms, apart from fever, are very variable — hence the difficulty in specific diagnosis experienced by 19th-century physicians before the advent of laboratory investigation.

The onset is often insidious with headache accompanied by increasing lassitude. The patient takes to his bed, but muscular and joint pains make rest difficult. Sleep is intermittent and unrefreshing. Some may suffer profuse nose bleeds. At first there is constipation with abdominal distension and pain but in the later stages watery green or bloody diarrhoea. By the second week marked giddiness, accompanied by intense ringing in the ears, makes any attempt to reach the water closet unsuccessful resulting in soiling of bed linen and the floor. The temperature increases remorselessly over the first seven days, accompanied by ungovernable bouts of shivering, and remains at 104°F or higher for the next two to three weeks. Initially there is little to distinguish the disease on clinical grounds from other fevers, but between seven and ten days after onset a rash of rose-red spots each two or three millimetres in diameter, lasting two to three days, appears on the abdominal wall and at this time the attendant physician may feel an enlarged spleen. (These are manifestations of the organism entering the bloodstream and represent an important difference from that other scourge of overcrowding and insanitary conditions, cholera, where the organism remains confined to the alimentary canal.) From an early stage there is complete loss of appetite and consequent rapid wasting of the face and limbs. The skin is hot and dry. The lips are crusted with scabs, the mouth remains open revealing a furred black tongue and there is a faecal odour to the breath. Mental apathy is profound and accompanied by confusion with incoherent rambling speech. Towards the end of the third week early signs of recovery may be seen, with abatement of the fever, but all too often there ensue the fatal complications of intestinal perforation and haemorrhage. The ashen face, the tremulous wasted hands plucking at the bedclothes and the muttering delirium herald impending death. In Victorian times the physician was powerless to avert this inevitable outcome. When an army in the field was affected, as in the Boer War, the suffering and distress of the sick soldiers was extreme. Transported across rough country, often in open horse-drawn wagons, or lying closely packed in hospital tents with primitive sanitary facilities and little or no nursing care it is unsurprising that a fatal outcome was all too frequent. The complete inability of the physician to provide any help when it was most needed caused Wright extreme 'pain in the mind' and stimulated him to devote his energies to preventing the disease.

In the 19th century mortality was high, up to 20 per cent in many epidemics. Those that survived it were known to be unlikely to suffer a second attack; as with smallpox, following an attack of the disease they had developed immunity. Yet it was not appreciated until the early part of the 20th century that a small proportion of survivors continued to excrete typhoid bacilli in their faeces. In these folk the organisms remained lodged in the gall bladder, where they can live for many years and pass into the intestine and thus the faeces. Unless there is efficient treatment of sewage, faeces from such carriers may contaminate the water supply and form the starting point of an epidemic. When carriers become food handlers they represent an especial danger and several celebrated epidemics have been traced to such a source. The most notorious is that due to Mary Mallon[15] in the USA. She was employed as a cook in 1906 and spread typhoid among at least seven different households where she worked, moving on from each place as soon as the disease struck. She was run to earth by Major George Soper of the US Army Sanitary Corps and eventually, as she continued to excrete bacilli, was confined to an isolation hospital in New York for over 20 years until her death. Other similar reports were published in Britain, where the Ledinghams[16] in 1908 found three faecal carriers in a mental asylum where there were recurrent outbreaks of the disease. Another well-reported incident occurred in Strasbourg[17] where the owner of a bakery was discovered to be a carrier and the source of an epidemic. The danger and frequency of the carrier state were well illustrated also in 1908 in the army in India,[18] where it was shown that convalescent cases excreted the organism, often intermittently for a very long time after clinical recovery. Such carriers were sometimes employed on cookhouse duties. Nursing orderlies in enteric wards were often seconded for six months from their units and, when they returned, they were found in some instances to excrete the organism whether or not they had suffered from clinical disease.

At this point it is relevant to cite the main sources of infection. Contamination of water by faecal material due to inadequate sewage treatment has already been mentioned but milk and other foods may be infected due to contact with faeces via the hands of carriers or from flies that have previously settled on faeces. In 1904 Newman[19] reported that 150 epidemics had been traced to a polluted milk supply. Shellfish were also a potent source of infection; they feed by filtering the water in river beds and, if this contains untreated sewage, the organisms therein lodge in their gills.

By the last decade of the 19th century it was apparent that prevention of typhoid and other infectious diseases was likely to be more productive in their control than attempts at treatment of patients. Although incidence in the civil population declined in the last three decades of the century, though not nearly as dramatically as did cholera, in all armies it remained depressingly high[20] due to fouling of the ground with faeces and urine and the infestation of camp areas with myriads of flies. In British Army units stationed in India, Africa and other tropical areas the situation was acute. Yet in civilian hospitals little by way of research was taking place and it was only in the Army Medical School at Netley that the problem was being addressed.

In January 1893 Wright received a visit at Netley from Waldemar Haffkine, a refugee from Odessa who had worked with Metchnikoff at the Pasteur Institute in Paris and who had gone to India to study cholera, the other main epidemic problem in that country. Pasteur had demonstrated that immunity to a disease, in particular anthrax, could be induced by injecting organisms which had become attenuated, that is had lost their virulence and when injected into a susceptible subject did not give rise to the disease, or only to a minor form of it.

Attenuation may be achieved in a variety of ways. Passage of the organism through animals can be effective or, as Pasteur did with anthrax, the organism can be grown at higher than the optimum temperature and without exposure to air, that is anaerobically. Haffkine claimed that the heat-killed bacterium responsible for cholera, *Vibrio cholerae*, was capable, when injected subcutaneously, of inducing immunity to the disease. In fact his claims were exaggerated (as mentioned in Chapter 2) and even today vaccines against this disease are effective for only a very limited period.

This was not the first attempt to protect humans from disease by inducing immunity, Jenner's smallpox vaccine being the classic example. The experimental approach, albeit primitive, was used by D E Salmon and Theobald Smith[21] in 1886. They published an article entitled 'On a new method of producing immunity from contagious diseases'. They used the hog cholera bacillus and performed their experiments on pigeons. The bacillus was cultured in a liquid medium and then killed by heating for two hours at 58–60°C. Inoculation with these killed bacilli enabled pigeons to withstand multiple doses of the living organisms whereas pigeons not so treated died within 24 hours. They concluded, incorrectly, that the immunity produced was due to 'chemical products' generated by the organisms rather than by the dead organisms themselves.

Ten years later a series of independent observations by Pfeiffer and Kolle[22] in Germany, by Widal in France and by Gruber in Austria as well as by Wright, pointed the way to vaccination in typhoid. All had observed that when serum taken from patients who had recovered from typhoid fever was mixed with living typhoid bacilli the bacteria lost motility and clumped together or agglutinated, a reaction usually associated with the name of Widal. The reaction is specific, that is, serum from patients who have had typhoid will only agglutinate typhoid bacilli and not other bacteria — a phenomenon that is used for diagnostic purposes. Similar reactions had been observed with sera from patients who had had Malta fever (brucellosis) and cholera. Indeed one of the first well-documented reports of the agglutination reaction employed the cholera *Vibrio*; it was published by an Englishman named Durham in 1894 while he was in receipt of a studentship in Gruber's department in Vienna. Together[23] they proposed that bacteria that caused specific fevers could be identified by bringing them into contact with serum from a patient or animal who had undergone an attack of that fever. Unfortunately Wright, and others at this time, considered this phenomenon to represent a general rule for diagnosis and, even more seriously, to point to a general method for treatment of infection. That matters were not so simple soon became evident; but Wright persisted in this belief for many years even after he had conducted the potentially disastrous experiment, described in Chapter 2, of inoculating himself in 1898 with *Brucella*, the organism responsible for Malta fever. The opinion with reference to treatment was stimulated by Pfeiffer's observation that organisms, and in particular the cholera *Vibrio*, not only agglutinated but became lysed when mixed with the appropriate anti-serum.

As soon as Wright learned of Pfeiffer's experiment he determined to attack the problem of typhoid. His first experiments injecting dead typhoid bacilli into humans were conducted in 1896 in connection with an investigation into what he called serous haemorrhage[24], a term he used to describe urticarial oedema, that is leakage of serum into the tissues. But the paper which is usually quoted as being the first to record active immunisation against typhoid in humans was published in the *British Medical Journal* by Wright and Semple[25] on 30 January 1897. In contrast to some of Wright's later papers it is a model of clarity and was original in the concepts and practice it recorded. The authors started by acknowledging their debt to Haffkine who had suggested 'that the method of vaccination which has proved so effectual in combating cholera epidemics in India (sic) might, *mutatis mutandis*, be also applied to the prophylaxis of typhoid fever'. They also noted that a reprint of Wright's 1896 communication to the *Lancet* had been sent to Pfeiffer — an important point when a dispute arose as to who had first originated the idea of anti-typhoid inoculation.

Next they laid down the aims of vaccination, that is, to achieve immunity equal to or greater than that accruing to a patient who undergoes and recovers from an attack of the disease and, moreover, to achieve such immunity without any risk to life or health. They enumerated three ways in which this might be accomplished: firstly, inoculating the subject with organisms that cause the disease; secondly, inoculating organisms that have lost their virulence either naturally, as in smallpox, or artificially as with attenuation in, for instance, anthrax; thirdly, with measured quantities of dead organisms. It was the third method that Wright and Semple used in a study that would enable them to claim priority in being the first to do so in humans. They drew attention to its advantages: that there was no danger of causing the disease, that vaccines could be handled and distributed through the post with no risk of disseminating the disease, and finally that dead vaccines were less likely to undergo diminution in strength than live vaccines. Furthermore they were able to measure the number of dead organisms given, that is to measure the dose accurately.

Their first experiments were performed on themselves and on 16 medical officers undergoing training at the Army Medical School at Netley. It was at once apparent that the consequences of inoculation with the vaccine were not pleasant and often of an alarming nature. This was of considerable importance when it came to persuading volunteers to undergo the procedure for their own good! These first injections were given in the flank. Within two to three hours tenderness developed at this site, which in many instances extended upwards to the axilla and downwards to the groin accompanied by the 'red lines of inflamed lymphatics'. Some of this may well have been due to inadequate sterilisation procedures but fortunately in all these cases the symptoms subsided within 24 to 48 hours.

More alarming were constitutional changes which occurred at the same time and manifested themselves as 'faintness and collapse' together with vomiting and loss of appetite. In their paper they played down these features and stated that by the next day eight of the first eleven patients had returned to their normal condition of health; but they also noted that the remainder 'looked somewhat shaken in health for some three weeks after'. They were able to assess the effect of their procedures by mixing living typhoid bacilli with varying dilutions of serum taken from those who had undergone vaccination. Sera in dilutions varying from 1 in 10 to 1 in 200 were mixed with living typhoid bacilli. They observed that at dilutions of up to 100 times the bacteria clumped together (ie they agglutinated), lost their motility and sank to the bottom of the tube in which the experiment had been conducted. The organisms themselves shrank and were 'definitely devitalised' (ie dead). These effects were not seen immediately after the injections but were apparent a few days later and were strongest in two to four weeks. Wright's certainty that this represented protection against the disease was borne out by the daring procedure of injecting one of his volunteers with live bacilli after he had received three vaccinations with dead bacilli spaced at fortnightly intervals. They found that the subject developed no ill effects and certainly did not contract the disease. There was, however, uncertainty as to the duration of immunity that vaccination produced.

Wright enthusiastically concluded that he had discovered a method of inducing immunity, and at once looked around for a suitable group of people on whom he could test his hypothesis. In writing of his dilemma with regard to duration of induced immunity he stated, very significantly in view of the controversy that was to engulf the whole subject later, 'we depend entirely upon statistics of the incidence of the disease'. Wright and Semple concluded their paper with the suggestion that it would be expedient to vaccinate young soldiers going abroad to areas where typhoid was endemic, and to vaccinate nurses attending typhoid patients and those living in the vicinity of a typhoid epidemic.

Wright's first paper was published on 19 September 1896, and Pfeiffer and Kolle's paper describing inoculation with dead typhoid bacilli on the following 12 November. Wright always claimed priority, but this did not go unchallenged in Germany where in 1907 Friederberger[26] vigorously defended his old chief Pfeiffer, whom he considered to have deserved that honour. Pfeiffer mentioned to some German colleagues that Wright had stolen the credit for typhoid inoculation and word of this reached Wright. When the two men encountered each other at a scientific meeting Wright tackled him about this accusation. Pfeiffer[27] is reported to have replied 'but people said I had stolen it from you so what else could I do?' It seems fairer to conclude that both were working on the subject and that credit should be shared.[28]

It was unfortunate, but also inevitable given his temperament and his intense faith in his vaccine, that Wright should approach the task of proving the worth of his product in a blunderbuss fashion. Yet criticism, of which there was a great deal in the next few years, must be viewed in the light of knowledge available at the turn of the century. Today any new drug or medical procedure is subject to severe scrutiny before it is tested on patients. Even when a drug is passed for possible clinical use it has to undergo carefully controlled trials. In the late 19th century statistical sampling techniques were primitive and tests of significance were limited. In view of the devastation wrought by typhoid, it is not surprising that Wright went ahead without further ado and tried out his vaccine in what he considered appropriate circumstances.

In 1897 an outbreak of typhoid occurred among patients and staff at the Barming Lunatic Asylum in Maidstone. Wright at once offered his services. Before inoculations were undertaken 12 cases of the disease had occurred among the staff of approximately 200. A single inoculation was offered to all; 84 accepted and 116 refused. There were no further cases in the inoculated group but four of the uninoculated staff developed the disease. These results encouraged Wright to proceed with his customary evangelical vigour.

Another opportunity presented itself in the following year. In India, during the rainy season of 1896 there was an outbreak of plague among the native population involving large areas of the subcontinent. As related in Chapter 2 the Governor General, with the approval of the Secretary of State for India, appointed a commission of inquiry with Wright as a member. The commission landed in Bombay on 26 November 1898. Although plague was the immediate problem, typhoid among the British troops was no less of a concern. Official statistics in the annual reports from the Army Medical Department were startling, and the position was deteriorating. Thus in 1889 there were 1093 admissions and 283 deaths due to typhoid, but by 1898 there were 2375 admissions and 657 deaths[29]; these figures were for the British Army and not the Indian Army. The seriousness of the problem can be appreciated when it is realised that the majority of deaths were in men aged between 19 to 30 years. The persistence and indeed increase in typhoid among British troops was particularly alarming as improvements in water supply had resulted in dramatic decreases in incidence of those other water-borne diseases, cholera and dysentery. The Army Medical Department Reports show that the mortality per 1000 from dysentery fell from 2.62 in the decade 1860–69 to 0.88 in 1890–99, and mortality from cholera from 8.86 in 1860–69 to 1.25 in 1890–99. During this time the mean overall mortality from typhoid rose from 2.88 in 1860–69 to 7.81 in 1890–99. The Principal Medical Officer, Surgeon-General Taylor, wrote in the Army Medical Report for 1898:

'The liability of troops on service to enteric fever even when encamped on what appears to be virgin soil is a fact in regard to which almost all observers are unanimous and a considerable part of the increase in both the admissions and mortality rates for 1898 can be accounted for by field services.'

In army camps there were open latrines and officers and men commonly urinated on the ground where, as Harrison[30] showed, under the dry and dusty conditions of India the typhoid bacillus could survive for several days. Flies and insect life of all descriptions were plentiful and had ready access both to latrines and to food prepared for the men. Conditions were thus ideal for a soldier who was a carrier of the bacillus to transmit the disease to his fellows. Wright saw his visit to India as a glorious opportunity to try out his vaccine and thus revolutionise the situation.

The Plague Commission travelled widely throughout India, and a series of military stations lay on their route. Whenever possible Wright,[31,32] would ask the commanding officer if he could address the troops in order to convince them of the efficacy of his vaccine and ask them to volunteer to receive it. In this he was very successful. There were considerable technical difficulties to overcome, however. As Wright described it, it was 'necessary to manufacture vaccine en route during the intervals which occurred during the sittings of the Plague Commission in Calcutta and Agra respectively' using local laboratories. The energy of the man was truly astonishing when one considers that the commission worked very hard and Wright, according to his own account, wrote most of its report. He standardised the vaccine on guinea pigs 'which were carried about from place to place for the purpose of keeping them continuously under observation'. The bottles in which it was kept had to be repeatedly opened and the vaccine resterilised at 60°C, a procedure which 'was far from ideal' both in respect of sterilising the vaccine and maintaining its potency.[33,34] In going ahead with these inoculations Wright omitted to seek the official sanction of the Government of India or of the Commander in Chief, merely asking permission from the local battalion or station commanders, who all seem to have assented to his requests. Volunteers were apparently readily forthcoming. The inoculations frequently gave rise to unpleasant local and systemic symptoms but were never fatal and, when suffering from these, the men had the opportunity of being relieved of duty for a few days. This may well have been a factor in their readiness to volunteer.

The attitude of the authorities to the whole process of immunisation was ambivalent. In 1897, the Government of India had actually proposed to the Secretary of State for War that anti-typhoid inoculation be given on a voluntary basis to officers and men about to embark for the sub-continent. Furthermore they requested that Wright should be seconded to the Government of India for that purpose. Permission for this was at that time refused, the reason for the decision being given as 'the diversity of opinion held by the leading medical authorities'. It can be inferred that Bruce, the most scientifically distinguished officer in the RAMC, was consulted and that he was implacably opposed to any proposal originating from Wright. Yet in a letter dated 24 January 1898, it was stated that Lord Lansdowne, who was Secretary of State for War, objected[35] only on grounds of public expense and not to voluntary 'operations at private cost'. It was this condition that provided Wright with his opportunity to test the vaccine. He experienced no problem in funding the manufacture of vaccine and, as has been described, went ahead with enthusiasm and with the connivance of local commanders. On news of this reaching the Commander in Chief and the Government of India, however, orders were at once issued to stop the inoculations[36] and they were then abandoned. By that time over 2000 men had been given the vaccine. Wright himself gives a figure of 2835, not all of whom were inoculated by him personally.

He was greatly encouraged by the results. It would appear that only five or six of those inoculated developed typhoid and in them it was a mild form; in two instances it seemed that the disease was actually incubating at the time of the inoculation. Unfortunately, record-keeping was abysmally poor, only one dose of vaccine was administered and no attempt was made to examine the serum of those who had been inoculated to ascertain whether they had developed antibodies. The controls were those who refused the vaccine, and follow-up observation was dependent on the conscientiousness of the regimental medical officers who sent in their returns to Wright when he was back at Netley. By the standards of today the entire process was a prime example of how not to conduct a clinical trial of a new procedure. Yet it must be realised that a situation of this type had never previously been encountered.

By 25 May 1899 the Government of India had reversed its attitude[37], expressing to the Secretary of State their alarm at the increased incidence of typhoid among British troops. His attention was drawn to the fact that in 1890 the hospital admission rate for the disease among these men had been 18.5 per 1000 whereas in 1897 it was 32.4, and the corresponding death rate had risen from 4.91 to 9.01. The Indian Government was of the opinion 'that every practicable means should be tried to guard against the ravages made by this disease'. They believed that the anti-typhoid inoculations had afforded 'satisfactory proof that the inoculation, when properly carried out, affords an immunity equal to or greater than that obtained by a person who has undergone an attack of the disease; further the operation is one which does not cause any risk to health'. They recommended resuming the inoculations for an extended trial. The letter was accompanied by a strongly worded communication in similar vein from the principal medical officer to Her Majesty's Forces in India. As a result, in August 1899 the Secretary of State approved resumption of inoculation at public expense. Additionally he would 'be glad to be furnished with returns, as soon as there are sufficient data available, showing the comparative prevalence and intensity of the disease among inoculated and uninoculated soldiers.'

Wright reported the results of the inoculations he had undertaken at the end of 1898 and beginning of 1899. As the date of his publication in the *Lancet* was 20 January 1900, the length of follow-up was unacceptably short; but he claimed that incidence of the disease among the 2835 inoculated was 0.95 per cent, and among the 8460 uninoculated it was 2.50 per cent. No statistical evaluation in the modern sense was applied to these results, though they pointed in a hopeful direction. Yet by the time of Wright's paper a dramatic turn in international events had caused the protection of troops from typhoid to be a matter of the utmost urgency.

★   ★   ★   ★   ★

The Cape was a self-governing British colony but unlike Natal it had a minority of British settlers, the majority being formed by the Cape Dutch who had their own political party, the Afrikaner Bond. Cecil Rhodes had achieved the notable political feat of gaining their support in developing South Africa as a partnership. The Orange Free State was Boer in population but disposed towards the concept of a federal South Africa dominated by the British. This was in sharp contrast to the other Boer state, the Transvaal, under Paul Kruger, which was vehemently opposed to federation under the British and had even made overtures to Germany in the hope of enlisting assistance in opposition to such a move. Considerable tension developed between the Boers and the British, which was heightened by the failure of the Jameson raid across the Transvaal to Johannesburg in January 1896. All goodwill between the two nations was now sacrificed, and enmity was further exacerbated by public support given to the Boers by the German Kaiser. Large quantities of arms were imported into the Transvaal, and war became inevitable in spite of attempts to come to a peaceful settlement at the Bloemfontein conference in May 1899. On

10 October 1899 the Boers issued an ultimatum calling on the British to withdraw their troops from the frontier of the Transvaal and to cease sending reinforcements to the region. This was rejected, and a state of war existed.

From the start of hostilities the attitude of the British military establishment to the medical consequences of a campaign was characterised by indifference. Recruits to the army from all walks of life came forward, unaware of dangers other than enemy bullets on the field of battle; the British government did not make any effort to disabuse them. In the opening stages of the war there was a series of setbacks accompanied by heavy casualties, the result of inappropriate equipment and poor generalship. Bad news reaching England concerning the lack of military success was soon compounded by fearful reports of large numbers of both soldiers and civilians incapacitated by illness, especially in besieged centres such as Ladysmith, where Bruce and his wife were among those incarcerated, and Mafeking. In Ladysmith alone there were 2000 cases of enteric and dysentery in a hospital built for 300 patients. Bruce himself went down with typhoid. It is not recorded whether he had been inoculated but his experiences during the siege may well have added to his prejudices. Certainly conditions in the town were bad. Lady Bruce in a letter to her brother recorded that her husband was in charge of the hospital where there were 1000 patients with typhoid. Sir George White[38] who commanded the garrison wrote on 4 January 1900, 56 days before it was relieved: 'My force here is reduced terribly in efficiency by disease, and there is more enteric and dysentery every day. I have before me a sick report of one month ago. The total sick and wounded then was 436, today the total is 1578. A month ago, 1st December, there were 29 cases of enteric fever; today there are 506 besides 285 not yet diagnosed.' Ironically, Wright was writing in the *Lancet*[39] at the same time concerning the results of inoculation at Ladysmith, which he considered encouraging. There were 10,529 uninoculated men, 1 in 7 of whom went down with typhoid. This was in contrast to the 1705 inoculated men, of whom only 1 in 48 contracted the disease. Inoculation was not popular with the troops because of the unpleasant side-effects. Some anti-typhoid vaccine sent to South Africa was dumped overboard in Southampton Water and returned by the coastguards to Wright at Netley.[40]

The situation was even more serious when Roberts led his troops into Bloemfontein. Enteric fever broke out among the soldiers, and the sick were soon 'dying at the rate of fifty per day'. Dr Arthur Conan Doyle found himself dealing with these circumstances and in a letter to the *BMJ* published on 7 July 1900, he recounted his experiences: 'The outbreak of enteric among troops in South Africa was a calamity the magnitude of which had not been foreseen and which even now is not fully appreciated'. He found in one month ten to twelve thousand men 'down with the most debilitating and lingering of continued fevers'. He praised the work of the devoted medical orderly, 'not a picturesque figure', and a member of a group that was to come under severe criticism from other quarters. Theirs was a dangerous occupation; 34 doctors, nurses and orderlies attending the sick in Bloemfontein — 50 per cent — contracted the disease and two died. Most significantly, Conan Doyle advised strongly in favour of anti-typhoid inoculation and he considered that the gravest error was committed in not making it compulsory for all military personnel. He conceded that his evidence for this opinion was largely anecdotal, but he pointed out that he had no deaths among those who had been inoculated and that in that group the disease ran a modified course.

By July 1900 a combination of the news from South Africa and the reports of the special correspondent to *The Times* were causing widespread disquiet. The *Times* reporter was Burdett-Coutts[41], MP for Westminster, who sent back a series of dispatches entitled 'Our wars and our wounded'. His first reports were cautiously worded. Thus on 23 March 1900 he wrote: 'The intrinsic merit of the performance of the Royal Army Medical Corps in this campaign is likely to conceal from view some grave underlying dangers which nothing but good fortune has averted.' The fact that the number of men struck down by disease was at least three times as great as that of the wounded appeared to have escaped the notice of the authorities. Wryly, Burdett-Coutts commented that the mere mention in the House of Commons of the Army Medical Services was sufficient to empty the benches.

By 11 April he was reporting that 'it is obvious that for many years the department of healing has not advanced *pari passu* with the department of maiming.' On 13 and 14 April he recorded the curmudgeonly attitude of both the Army Medical Department and the Red Cross Society towards generous civilian help for treatment of the sick and wounded. The accommodation and standard of care offered by voluntary hospitals, such as the Portland set up in South Africa by civilians, was recognised as superior to anything the RAMC could provide. Yet it was the dispatch dated 29 May, though not published until 27 June, that caused the greatest stir. News had reached him that a dinner had been held in London at the Reform Club on 28 April to celebrate the work of the RAMC. One of the speakers had said, 'It would not be possible to have anything more complete or better arranged than the medical service in this war.' This incensed Burdett-Coutts. His report began:

'A long time has elapsed since the dispatch of the last preceding letter.[42] During that period the growing scenes of neglect and inhumanity, of suffering and death, which have been the lot of the British soldier in the closing chapter of this war have made up a picture which it is impossible any longer to conceal from the eyes of the British public.'

The dispatch recorded in detail the horrors experienced by the wounded and sick; men in the worst stages of typhoid with only a blanket and a thin waterproof sheet between them and hard ground; no medicine or milk; three doctors to deal with 350 seriously ill patients; a few untrained private soldiers to act as medical orderlies; no ambulances, only ox wagons used to transport the wounded a journey of 40 miles; and other similar scandals. This dispatch was signed by Burdett-Coutts rather than appearing, as all the others had done, under the anonymous heading of 'From our own correspondent'.

These reports, combined with unrest in the House of Commons and the urging of Lord Roberts, led the government to appoint a commission to 'consider and report upon the care and treatment of the sick and wounded during the South African Campaign'. The composition of the commission was subject to some comment in the House of Commons. The anti-war Radical MP Henry Labouchere raised the matter by saying that Lord Roberts had asked for some men of 'sound common sense' in addition to the two doctors proposed by the Prime Minister, Mr Balfour. He was strongly supported by Burdett-Coutts, by the Liberal leader Campbell-Bannerman and by several other members. Balfour responded with bad grace saying 'that it is not a matter of easy negotiation, nor is it to be rapidly carried through'. Despite these dampening comments, the commission was appointed and commenced work with commendable alacrity, holding its first meeting on 23 July and taking evidence at Netley from Wright on 4 August, as well as from invalided officers and from men due to sail for South Africa.

Sir Robert Romer chaired the commission. He was at this time a Lord Justice of Appeal but he had studied mathematics at Cambridge, being senior wrangler in 1863 and professor of mathematics at Queen's College, Cork in 1865. He had the rare distinction, for a lawyer, of being elected a Fellow of the Royal Society in 1899 by virtue of his mathematical abilities. He was known to be genial as well as quick-witted and lucid. Of greater significance, however, was his close relationship to Wright's friend Lord Moulton, also a mathematician; they sat together on the Appeal Court. The other member selected for his 'sound common sense' was a Glasgow merchant, Sir David Richmond, who had been Lord Provost of that city and was personally known to Balfour. He described himself as 'not being very strong' and it would seem that he was appointed to fill that place which is set aside on every Royal Commission for the man not likely to cause trouble. The President of the Royal College of Physicians of London, Sir William Selby Church, who was noted for his precision and clear judgment and for an unusual lack of interest in private practice, was one of the medical members. The other was Daniel John Cunningham, a Fellow of the Royal Society, who at that time was professor of anatomy at Trinity College, Dublin. Later he was to take the chair in Edinburgh, as was his son after him, and became known to all medical students in the 20th century for his textbook of anatomy.

The commissioners took evidence not only from RAMC officers of all grades and from civilian medical personnel but also from the sick and wounded. They believed that private soldiers were very slow to complain 'more from a feeling of loyalty for their cloth than from a fear of being punished for complaining to their superiors'. This was not a universally accepted view. In a letter to the *Spectator*[43] T W Edmonds, secretary to the Durban Government Hospital, thought 'that complaints would not come from Tommy Atkins. He would be a marked man in his regiment if it got out.'

The commission[44] found that the magnitude of the war took the authorities by surprise: 'The RAMC was wholly insufficient in staff and equipment for such a war, and it is not so constituted as to have means provided by which its staff could be very materially enlarged, or its deficiencies promptly made good.' In retrospect it can be seen that the authorities entirely neglected the two factors which could have kept a fit army in the field: strict attention to sanitation and preventive inoculation. There were cogent reasons for neglect of inoculation; it was new and had not been subjected to a rigorous controlled trial, indeed the circumstances of the war provided an ideal setting for such a trial and it was tragic that this opportunity was not taken.

With regard to the lack of sanitary facilities, in the initial stages of the war at least, the army was guilty of gross negligence. In his evidence to the commission Sir James Clark RAMC, commanding the Edinburgh and East Scotland Hospital, stated that:

'The sanitary officer was condemned by Lord Wolseley as a useless encumbrance in time of war. If there had been a sanitary department with the present army, with a

Table 3.1
Morbidity and mortality for Cape Colony, Orange Free State and Transvaal

Injuries				Disease			
Officers		Men		Officers		Men	
Died	Invalided	Died	Invalided	Died	Invalided	Died	Invalided
31	112	261	2,203	65	483	2,623	12,914

Table 3.2
Morbidity and mortality for Natal

Injuries				Disease			
Officers		Men		Officers		Men	
Died	Invalided	Died	Invalided	Died	Invalided	Died	Invalided
58	174	658	3,497	97	652	4,464	19,588

thoroughly competent sanitary officer at its head, a large amount of the sickness which has done far more to waste our forces than the bullets of the enemy might have been avoided.'

The truth of this is all too evident from the statistics quoted to the commission by Major Bedford, staff officer to the principal medical officer of the army. The return of deaths and invaliding of officers and men from the commencement of the war to the end of July 1900 for Cape Colony, Orange Free State and Transvaal were as shown in Table 3.1, and figures for the Natal army were even more alarming (Table 3.2).

The conditions endured by injured or sick men were frightful. Burdett-Coutts in *The Times* on 14 April 1900 complained, 'Many of the wounded were sent back to Kimberley in bullock wagons, and we can well imagine the excruciating suffering caused by such a method of conveyance.' The hospitals were mainly under canvas, the major part consisting of bell-tents suitable for accommodating half-a-dozen fit and active men. Conditions when such tents were used as hospital wards can be understood from evidence given to the commission by W S Le Grand, a sergeant in the 36th Company, Imperial Yeomanry:

'There were seven to eight men to a tent with only one orderly to do everything (change sheets, wash men who had evacuated in bed, give medicines, empty pans at a special latrine, scrub floors etc). For every ward or tent only one pan was allowed and I have seen men writhing in agony waiting for the said pan (and I have experienced it myself), though I imagine a wire to Cape Town would have brought up a hundred.'

Urine utensils were too small. The St John Ambulance men 'were the most uncouth, rough, dirty, slovenly hobbledehoy lot I ever came across.' According to a Private Harold Meades, a ward orderly had as many as 80 to 90 patients to look after and at times one doctor appeared to be doing the work of the entire hospital. Civilian doctors were much preferred by all ranks and there was a general opinion that the RAMC officers were incompetent. The report drew attention to this distrust among the army of the skill and professional competence of doctors in the RAMC and considered this was due among other things to difficulty in recruiting men of good standing. Those doctors who did join the army were encouraged to be too military in their habits. Thus it was found that all patients in the wards of a military hospital who were able to do so had to stand to attention when officers entered the ward.

The medical orderlies were criticised for brutality, and the commission recommended that 'Strict enquiry should be made in various military hospitals in South Africa and proper steps taken to stamp out, where it exists, pilfering by orderlies of the stimulants, comforts or property of patients, and the receipt of bribes by orderlies from patients.' Perhaps here lies the origin of the jibe common among combatant troops that RAMC stood for Rob All My Comrades!

The report of the commission concluded with various suggestions for remedying defects in the care of sick and wounded soldiers, and in particular with providing for adequate postgraduate training for RAMC officers to enable them to keep abreast of recent advances. They drew attention to the need for a reserve of medical officers to ensure sufficient numbers in a 'Great War'. Most significantly they recommended employing in the higher posts of the service 'men selected for their merits rather than by seniority'. This last point had been raised by Burdett-Coutts but was not one favoured by the medical establishment. The *BMJ* in an editorial had commented that 'it is difficult to see what better system could be adopted than seniority tempered by selection. Promotion purely by merit would engender suspicions of favouritism and make army service so distasteful and uncertain that few would care to enter it.'[45] The employment of more female nurses, improvement in the quality of ambulance vehicles and, most importantly, recruitment of qualified sanitary officers were emphasised as necessary. Yet it is difficult to avoid the view that the report was ultimately a whitewash. The commissioners acknowledged that there were evils and oversights: 'But in concluding our Report, we desire to say that in our judgment, reviewing the campaign as a whole, it has not been one where it can properly be said that the medical and hospital arrangements have broken down. There has been nothing in the nature of a scandal with regard to the care of the sick and wounded, no general or widespread neglect of patients, or indifference to their suffering.' No one reading the evidence provided to the commission by soldiers who had taken part in the war and been fortunate enough to survive could endorse these conclusions. The most notable feature of the entire document was, however, the lack of any reference to inoculation as a possible preventive measure against the ravages of typhoid fever that played such a major role in interfering with efficient prosecution of military operations.

The condition and administration of the Army Medical Services became a matter of national interest as a consequence of debate in Parliament and the report of the Royal Commission in 1901. In November the Secretary of State for War, St John Brodrick, removed these matters from the direct control of the adjutant and quartermaster-general and set up an advisory board for the Army Medical Services. Its chairman was Surgeon-General Taylor who by this time was director general of the Army Medical Services[46] and therefore had a seat on the War Office Council and Army Board with direct access to the Secretary of State. He was, as has already been mentioned, only too well aware from his experiences in India of the ravages of typhoid on an army in the field. The vice-chairman was Keogh, and he would shortly succeed Taylor. There were two RAMC members: Major W G Macpherson, an expert in sanitation, and Bruce who was listed as an expert in tropical diseases. These were joined by five civilians who were all well-established members of the medical profession, but they did not include Wright.

One of the first matters referred to the Board in February 1902 concerned enteric fever, and in particular the large number of cases occurring in South Africa. The Board considered that boiling of water was the first essential step in preventing the disease and experiments in various methods were undertaken. The Permanent Executive Committee of the War Office on 6 April 1902 authorised a trial[47] of an unwieldy system whereby water sterilisers, which were conceived by a Dr Leigh Canney but might well have been designed by Mr Heath Robinson himself, should be supplied to each battalion together with eight storage carts. The quartermaster-general's department was alarmed at this development, and a Colonel P H N Lake pointed out that at least 200 water carts would be needed for an army corps and that a large number of additional horse-drawn vehicles would be required for forage, oil for burners and to carry the sterilisers. Because of these reservations a limited trial was authorised. This never took place. On 22 April it was postponed on orders from the

Secretary of State and on 29 July 1902 he explained, in response to a question in the House of Commons from Sir Michael Foster[48], that cessation of hostilities had prevented the experiment being carried out. A suggestion from Keogh that a trial should take place at the next large manoeuvres was noted.

Meanwhile the Advisory Board[49] had been giving its attention to the question of preventive inoculation. It reported on 25 September 1902 to the Secretary of State[50] in a manner calculated to dampen enthusiasm for the procedure. They expressed the opinion that it was undesirable that therapeutic agents of any kind which could be obtained from 'ordinary commercial sources' should be manufactured by the Army Medical School. Furthermore, they considered it undesirable that officers of the RAMC while attending courses at the Army Medical School should have instruction in production of vaccines. They did state that in expressing this opinion they were not averse to research by professors at the school having as their research objective discovery of new sera. Their worry was that if RAMC officers were encouraged to produce their own vaccines, inevitably under conditions that were far from ideal, the results might well be lethal. They concluded this part of their report with the firm recommendations:

(a) that it was inexpedient that preparation of therapeutic agents should be undertaken at the Army Medical School, and

(b) that the preparation of sera, anti-diphtheritic or otherwise, at present carried on at Netley should be discontinued.

Nothing could have been more calculated to infuriate Wright, who had developed the production of anti-sera at Netley and, it seems, financed his research on the proceeds. But he had not been altogether tactful in presenting the case for inoculation — it was characteristic of Wright throughout his life that he should consider a remark acceptable on the grounds that it was true. When he had completed his evidence the chairman asked him if he had anything further to say and he is reported to have replied 'No, sir. I have given you the facts — I can't give you the brains'.

If the first part of the report angered Wright the second section, which dealt with preparation and application of anti-typhoid 'fluid' together with the results of inoculations against enteric fever in the army, was to drive him to resign from Netley. The board was aware that there was a difference of opinion in the medical profession as to the efficacy of anti-typhoid inoculation. It must also have known of the considerable personal antagonism existing between Wright and Bruce. It was thus most unfortunate that they decided to delegate assessment of the

Figure 7
David Bruce, a photograph taken when he was a Major-general and Commandant of the Royal Army Medical College. (Journal of the Royal Army Medical Corps)

statistics to Bruce alone and to base their conclusions on views expressed in an appendix[51] he wrote to their report. His 12-page analysis examined selected published reports. The conclusions he reached, viewed at this distance, were entirely reasonable given the evidence available. He drew attention to certain obvious discrepancies. Thus the outbreak at the Maidstone Asylum had been reported in the *Lancet* on no less than three occasions — by Wright in March 1898, in 1900 in an article entitled 'Preventive inoculation against typhoid' by A G R Foulerton, and in another article by Wright in 1902. The figures given in all these publications were different. Bruce then detailed the reports from the British garrison in India and those available from South Africa. In the latter there appeared to be 'an enormous incidence among the inoculated'. He also noted fallacies liable to occur in diagnosis when dealing with soldiers in the field at war.

Bruce summarised his findings by stating that the statistics available to him 'were not sufficiently extensive to permit any conclusions being drawn as to the utility of Wright's anti-typhoid inoculation'. He did, however, recognise the importance of the subject and suggested that further trials should be conducted 'under strict supervision'. He proposed inoculation of 50 per cent of each regiment or unit proceeding to a station where the disease was endemic, and added the rider that inoculations should be performed by a skilled medical officer at least three months before embarkation. Until such a trial had been conducted he considered that inoculation of troops on transport ships should be discontinued. The advisory board on receiving Bruce's paper went further and recommended that all preparation and distribution of the vaccine be discontinued. In arriving at this decision they stated that they were influenced by Wright's own observation that in certain individuals following inoculation a 'negative phase' occurred for a short period during which such men were more susceptible to infection by the typhoid bacillus than uninoculated subjects. Wright considered that this phenomenon was related to men being given an unduly large dose of vaccine. This observation appears to have been mistaken: it was not confirmed by Leishman's subsequent extensive investigations into the matter.[52] The board referred to the 'admission' by Wright that inoculation of troops shortly before entering a zone where enteric was rife would render individuals who experienced this negative phase more prone to the disease and 'increase peril to life'. If it was considered desirable to resume inoculation they recommended that Wright should prepare a detailed scheme 'showing exactly on what lines, and with what precautions, he would propose that the system should be carried out'.

This report was issued on 25 September. Wright was incensed, although there was a clear indication that the board would look favourably on a carefully designed experimental trial of the type suggested in Bruce's appendix. Wright brushed any such suggestion aside and at once applied for the combined post of pathologist and bacteriologist at St Mary's Hospital. In this he was successful, accepting the job on 24 October. Yet he offered to continue to teach RAMC officers at the Army Medical School, which was being transferred to London. The Medical Advisory Board considered this proposal on 28 November but resolved, not surprisingly, that 'such an appointment [at St Mary's] was incompatible with due performance of his duties as professor in the Medical Staff College'. The Secretary of State, Brodrick, and the Army Council felt that they had to accept the recommendations of the advisory board.[53] Wright was not content to let the matter of inoculation rest and, once freed from the constraints of the army authorities, he fired off a letter to the War Office placing his services at the disposal of the Secretary of

State for carrying out anti-typhoid inoculation in the army. Brodrick forwarded the letter to the advisory board which on 9 April 1903 after due consideration, and in the absence of Bruce who was in Uganda investigating sleeping sickness, referred the Secretary of State to their report of 25 September 1902 in which they suggested that Wright should submit a detailed scheme for testing the vaccine.

Here was something of an impasse but the Civil Service came to the rescue when on 25 April 1903 the permanent under-secretary, G F Wilson,[54] suggested at Wright's instigation that the Royal Society be asked, semi-officially, to appoint a committee to consider the question. On 2 May the Secretary of State replied, 'Certainly at once. Inform Professor Wright', and a week later a letter was sent to the Royal Society. They stalled, asking for all relevant reports and papers; these were sent by the Medical Advisory Board on 28 May. On 2 June the Royal Society[55] declined to undertake the task saying 'it was not a matter for experimental investigation but of published statistics'. They recommended that the Royal College of Physicians be consulted. It appears that this was a political hot potato which the Royal Society refused to handle; and their suggestion of the College of Physicians as an alternative was singularly inappropriate because many physicians at that time were peculiarly averse to numerical analysis of any sort. But questions were being asked in the House and the political pressure to do something was intense. Today, when a medical practitioner may pass an entire professional lifetime in Britain without encountering a single patient with typhoid fever, this may be difficult to understand but at the beginning of the 20th century enteric was a major problem in the Empire and to a certain extent at home.

On 19 June G F Wilson wrote to the Registrar of the College of Physicians asking their opinion[56], stating:

'Mr Brodrick recognises the great importance of the subject to the Army and indeed to the Empire, but he feels that public opinion would not sustain the adoption of any compulsory measure of inoculation against typhoid in the services unless overwhelming proof were afforded of its practical safety and high prophylactic value, and he is fully aware of the difficulties of ensuring that inoculation urged by authority should in practice be a voluntary act on the part of the private soldier.'

The College of Physicians acted with uncharacteristic briskness. On 2 July 1903 it appointed a committee of respected Fellows: Tooth[57], Rose Bradford[58], Simpson[59] and Caiger[60] with Samuel Gee[61] as chairman. They held a meeting on 9 July at which they heard evidence from Wright. Most of the relevant publications were in their hands, with the crucial exception of those relating to the meetings of the Army Medical Advisory Board. They asked for these but the director general refused to hand them over, and it was only by appealing directly to the Secretary of State that they were obtained. Two further meetings were held and on 27 July they issued their report[62], which was succinct and unequivocal in its conclusions:

'After careful scrutiny of the statistics from both official and private sources which have been made available, we are of the opinion that not only is a lessened susceptibility to the disease brought about as a result of these inoculations, but that case mortality is largely reduced.

We are further of the opinion that with due care the process of inoculation is devoid of direct danger, but that under special circumstances there may possibly be some temporary increase of susceptibility to infection immediately following inoculation; and it is, therefore, desirable that the preparation of the vaccine and the inoculations should be carried out under skilled supervision.'

Here was a direct rebuttal of the views expressed by the Medical Advisory Board. On receiving the report, on 5 January 1904, via the council of the Royal Army Medical College to whom it was initially sent, it proposed yet another committee. On 14 January the Director-General of the Army Medical Services, Surgeon-General W Taylor, wrote to the Secretary of State, now Arnold-Forster, recommending that this new committee should be made up of eight medical scientists with Bruce as chairman.[63] There were only two RAMC officers, the other being Leishman. The remainder were civilians and included William Bulloch, bacteriologist to the London Hospital, Professor A Macfadyen from the Lister Institute, F F Caiger, the medical superintendent of the South Western Fever Hospital, James Galloway, a physician at the Charing Cross Hospital, W H Bower, a medical officer of health, and Wright. Arnold-Forster replied[64] on 16 February approving formation of a mixed committee of civilian and military experts 'but in view of what has taken place I think Col Bruce ought not to be chairman of the committee, I imagine he will not wish to be'. The advisory board replied on 10 March[65]:

'With regard to the proposed committee on anti-typhoid inoculation the Board notes the objection by the Secretary of State to Col Bruce FRS as chairman. In reference to this decision the Board observes with satisfaction that the objection does not seem to have occurred to any of the gentlemen provisionally invited to serve. In deference, however, to the opinion expressed by Mr Arnold-Forster the Board recommends that at the first meeting of the Anti-Typhoid Committee the chair should be taken by Surgeon-General Keogh, and that selection of a permanent chairman should be left to the decision of the committee.'

The committee met on 11 May 1904 and elected as chairman Dr C J Martin, Director of the Lister Institute, who had been added to the committee. Both he and Dr R Blow of the Local Government Board had been coopted at the suggestion of Bruce. It worked speedily, holding six meetings, and issued an interim report[66] on 9 July 1904 having reviewed all relevant documents. Their conclusion was that: 'The records which are available up to date furnish proof that the practice of anti-typhoid inoculations in the army has resulted in a substantial reduction in the incidence and death rate from enteric fever among the inoculated.' In stating this they were strongly influenced by experimental evidence that it was possible to produce resistance to typhoid in animals by inoculation, and that antibodies to the typhoid bacillus developed in humans following inoculation. They recommended 'that the practice of voluntary inoculation against enteric fever in the army be resumed'. They also recommended that further research should be conducted to determine the optimum dose of vaccine, whether the best results were obtained by one or two inoculations, and the duration of protection. Animal experiments conducted with a view to improving the quality of the vaccine and serological studies on patients suffering from, or convalescent from, typhoid were also suggested. They realised that this would be time-consuming and pointed out that active cooperation and the supervision of experts who had made a special study of this type of work would be needed. Until such a programme was set up they suggested that inoculation under careful supervision, and at least one month prior to embarkation, should be offered on a voluntary basis to each regiment proceeding from home to India. If this was implemented they considered that a junior officer should go with each regiment and remain with it for three years to collect statistics, and that the headquarters of the Army Medical Department should collect the statistics relating to those inoculated in units not going to India.

This interim report was signed on 9 July 1904 by Martin and six members of the committee, but not by Bruce who had gone to Malta for four weeks in connection with a Royal Society Committee appointed to carry out investigations into Mediterranean fever. Bulloch and Wright also did not sign, issuing a minority report which, while agreeing with the main recommendations, considered that a 'quasi-permanent organisation' was required in order that the vaccine and details of the inoculations could be modified in the light of research. This appeared unreasonable because the main body of the committee had gone a long way to meeting Wright's demands. A further meeting was held on 12 October[67] at which it was hoped to resolve any difference of opinion. By this time Bruce had returned and considerable argument ensued, with the result that Bulloch and Wright resigned. Before they did so, however, one important appointment had been agreed. Leishman, who had succeeded Wright as professor of pathology at the Army Medical School, was elected to preside over future research into the vaccine. This was a most fortunate appointment. Leishman possessed an excellent intellect, had done first-class research and was a man of tact and integrity. He appears to have steered a smooth course between Bruce, who was the premier scientific figure in the army, and Wright who had proposed him for the task of investigating the vaccine.[68]

All now should have been well but, at the suggestion of Bruce, Lt Col R J Simpson, who had been staff officer to the principal medical officer of the South African Field Force, submitted the statistics relating to typhoid fever in the Boer War to Karl Pearson.[69] Yet before Pearson could record his findings, and indeed before the interim report had been issued, *The Times* on 27 October published a leading article, which the *BMJ*[70] described as attempting to prejudice public opinion in favour of anti-typhoid inoculation. Furthermore the article questioned the scientific competence of the members of the Army Medical Advisory Board. In this the *BMJ* saw, probably correctly, the hand of Wright himself and commented: 'To us the really curious thing is that *The Times* should have allowed itself to be used as a resonant mask for the publication of a private grievance.' At this time Pearson was Goldsmid professor of applied mathematics and mechanics at University College, London, and was later to take the Galton chair of eugenics; his primary interest was the application of statistics to biological problems. His pupils included Major Greenwood, who himself recruited Bradford Hill to the subject; thus Pearson can also be regarded as one of the fathers of modern epidemiology. In many ways he resembled Wright; both had demonic energy, both were fluent in several foreign languages, both had studied law and both were influential lecturers. They also shared an interest in ethics and philosophy. Pearson was actually called to the Bar by the Inner Temple in 1882, and his wide interests may be gauged from the fact that in that year he published *The Trinity: a nineteenth century passion play*. Again like Wright, he was to become an atheist. Although an inspirational teacher and research worker, he was intolerant and hostile to those who did not share his views. An insight into the nature of his character can be gained from part of a letter he wrote to Galton[71] in 1897, after an acrimonious argument following which he resigned from a committee of the Royal Society: 'I always succeed in creating hostility without getting others to see my views.'

When presented by Simpson with the miscellaneous and jumbled data, Pearson would perhaps have been wise merely to indicate that it was unsuitable for any meaningful statistical analysis and that a properly controlled trial was needed. Instead he published an article in the *BMJ*[72] on 5 November 1904 in which he compared firstly the association of inoculation and freedom from typhoid, and secondly the association of inoculation and recovery from typhoid, using a coefficient of correlation method. He considered that, in general, beneficial results of inoculation could in many instances be due to chance. It must be realised that in reporting his findings many variables were not taken into consideration. Thus there was considerable variation in individual doses of vaccine; some soldiers had two doses of vaccine, others only one; the actual strength of the vaccine varied greatly not only between but also within regiments. Pearson did, however, point out the need for further investigation: 'If further experimental inoculations were made, which seems fairly justifiable by the Ladysmith if not by the other returns, the greatest care ought to be taken to get homogeneous material, that is, men of like caution, subjected to the same environment . . . It would seem to be possible to call for volunteers, but while keeping a register of all men who volunteered, only to inoculate every second volunteer'. This was a perfectly reasonable proposal and no one should have taken exception to it. It is indeed possible that Wright would not have done so, but Pearson added a further paragraph criticising the vaccine itself in which he stated: 'I should say that the data indicate that a more effective serum or a more effective method of administration must be found before inoculation ought to become a routine practice in the army.' There ensued a polemical correspondence in the *BMJ* that lasted throughout November and December of that year.

Wright lost no time in replying and the *BMJ* of 12 November carried a long letter from him. He accused the Army Medical Advisory Board of partiality in taking action on Bruce's report which he contended was 'vitiated by palpable bias'. He claimed that he was never informed that Bruce was to review his work and that he was never given an opportunity to reply to Bruce's criticisms. He also took issue with the *BMJ* for suggesting that he was aggrieved at the appointment of Leishman to preside over the research when it was he, Wright, who had proposed him for the task.

They continued to trade insults on a weekly basis until 31 December. Their heated correspondence was to some extent futile, as each refused to see the other's point of view. Wright had no knowledge of statistical method and Pearson seems to have been ignorant of difficulties likely to be encountered in a field situation among army troops. Thus the precise number of men inoculated was difficult to determine due to continual transfer of personnel within and between regiments. In South Africa whether a man was inoculated or not depended often on his own statement. Some soldiers claimed to have been inoculated when they had not been in order to avoid the unpleasant side-effects associated with the procedure. In some instances there was confusion in a soldier's mind between smallpox vaccination and anti-typhoid inoculation. Statistical returns dependent on the soldier's word were thus unreliable. The diagnosis of typhoid itself presented some difficulty. Paratyphoid A and B are less serious diseases but their symptoms are similar to those of typhoid, and this was not fully appreciated at the time. The anti-typhoid vaccine was initially prepared from the typhoid bacillus alone, and it was not until 1915 that a triple vaccine against all three conditions was introduced.

Pearson did his case no good by refusing an invitation to appear before the War Office Anti-typhoid Committee[73] and 'thrash out every doubtful point' because he felt he would be treated as a hostile witness. Yet in his letter of 17 December[74] he gave one memorable recommendation, which most unfortunately was to be ignored for over forty years:

> 'I hold that there is a crying need for a more exact treatment of statistics in medical science. I am fully aware that the medical curriculum is already overcrowded but this does not hinder individual medical men from pursuing a special training in statistics, nor non-statistical medical men consulting statisticians. In this manner not only will a corps of expert medical statisticians be created (which is immensely needed not alone for medical research and the public health and registration services), but a more friendly relation will be established between the medical man and the professional statistician.'

Medical men at this time were suspicious of mathematics in general and statistics in particular. This was in depressing contrast to lawyers where a mathematical education, as in the cases of Lords Romer and Moulton, both Cambridge wranglers, was no bar to appointment to the judiciary. Unfortunately this sceptical attitude towards the higher levels of numeracy persisted even after the Second World War due to the attitude of senior members of the profession, and many schools denied boys and girls in sixth forms the opportunity to study higher mathematics if they took biology. Yet statistical method represents one of the most powerful weapons available for the study of disease and ignorance of the subject is to blame for delaying important advances in public health. The scepticism greeting initial results into the links between cigarette smoking and lung cancer, and cigarette smoking and ischaemic heart disease, provide more recent examples.

It was most unfortunate that in assessing the results of anti-typhoid inoculation the clash of personalities among those chiefly charged with the task was against calm reasoning or the formulation of a meaningful trial. There were faults on all sides. Firstly, preparation of the vaccine was not standardised. This was not achieved with any measure of success until Leishman's careful work in the later part of the first decade of the 20th century, which he summarised in his Harben lectures in 1910. He determined the optimum temperature for killing typhoid bacilli while maintaining their maximum antigenicity, that is their power to induce immunity by production of antibodies to the organism. Problems with regard to purity, preservation and storage were also addressed. Furthermore, although this was not fully understood at the time, all strains of *Salmonella typhi*, the typhoid bacillus, are not equally effective in vaccine production. Use of an inefficient vaccine made from what is termed a rough strain, or one lacking a constituent known as the Vi antigen, has little effect in preventing the disease; such an inadequate vaccine is considered to have been responsible for failure to protect the Italian army in the Western Desert in the 1939–45 war when they experienced a serious outbreak of typhoid. This may have played an important role in their defeat.[75] It was pure luck that Wright chose a suitable strain.

Secondly, the question of dosage was of great significance. Not only was the quantity in each inoculation not constant but there seems to have been only half-hearted efforts to standardise the numbers of dead organisms per millilitre of fluid. In addition there was no systematic follow-up of the results of single inoculation as compared with two inoculations spaced at an interval of a fortnight. At this time it would have been possible to ascertain which procedure gave rise to the better production of antibodies since the Widal reaction, which measures the level of antibodies to typhoid bacilli in the serum, was available and in use at Netley. A relatively short and simple experiment would have revealed that two inoculations were very much more effective than a single dose, and often general systematic disturbance was less likely to occur following the second injection.

Thirdly, sampling of those to be inoculated was carried out in a manner totally unsuited to producing data suitable for significant statistical analysis.

These defects were not entirely due to Wright and the regimental doctors. Public opinion was uneducated and powerless to impose a more scientific curriculum on an unwilling and sceptical medical profession. As for the army, those in authority were not noted for their intellectual capacity in planning a military operation on the field of battle let alone for expressing anxiety for such peripheral concerns as the health, comfort and welfare of the private soldier. This last defect, though not the first, was particularly true of the Commander-in-Chief, Wolseley, appointed in 1895 on the death of the Duke of Cambridge. He had risen from a poor Irish Protestant background and was known to have gained, from extensive active service, a profound respect for the fighting qualities of the British soldier. After the Crimea and wars in China and Burma he was keenly aware that the army with its system of purchase of commissions was in need of change. He was an ardent supporter of the Cardwell reforms, and the author of an influential small work *The soldier's pocket book*, outlining methods of preparing for war in time of peace. Something of an iconoclast, he did not endear himself to the establishment, particularly as he was largely instrumental in enforcing reorganisation and training of the army along modern lines. (He was the model for Gilbert's 'modern Major-General'.) Disraeli, while admiring many of his qualities, described him to Queen Victoria as an egoist and a braggart. It was thus especially unfortunate that he did not pay adequate attention to hygiene. He it was who described the sanitation officer as an unnecessary encumbrance to an army on the march.

It is not surprising that inoculation was not encouraged in an environment where the regimental medical officer was not always accorded respect. On the other hand some of the reluctance on the part of commanding officers can be attributed to their concern about the acute discomfort that followed the procedure. On 4 September 1899, for example[76], 108 NCOs and men of the 2nd Battalion the Gloucestershire Regiment left the Jersey station for India. Before embarkation their commanding officer Lt Col Roberts addressed them on the advantages of inoculation and called for volunteers: 51 men came forward. After about seven hours each man experienced severe pyrexia, up to 101°F, which subsided within 24 hours. In some men local symptoms were severe and the affected men were unable to perform duties for four days. A Captain Porter RAMC suggested[77] that all men receiving inoculation should be excused duty for four days. Clearly many commanding officers were reluctant to sanction this.

Nor were matters improved by the hostility to anti-typhoid inoculation expressed by some prominent members of the medical profession. J W Washbourn, a physician to Guy's Hospital and to the London Fever Hospital, wrote to the *BMJ*[78] that, although it was probably premature to pass an opinion, so far as he could judge 'it did not have a marked effect in mitigating the attacks'. A physician in fashionable Cadogan Place, Dr Maclagan, went further stating that it did not confer immunity at all.[79] The ignorance of the general public was such that a chairman of magistrates could declare in 1901 that typhoid was not an infectious disease.[80] There were a few more enlightened views. Celtic commonsense was injected into the argument by Colonel Henry Cayley[81], who was in charge of the Scottish National Red Cross Hospital in South Africa. He found that typhoid was less frequent and less severe in inoculated men and nursing staff, but pointed out the urgent need for research into the variable quality of the vaccine, whether one or two inoculations were needed and the optimum dose of vaccine.

The appointment of Leishman to superintend research into anti-typhoid inoculation unfortunately did not lead to rapid results. In part this was because Leishman was fully occupied with his duties as the newly appointed professor of pathology at the Army Medical School and heavily involved in the transfer of the school from Netley to London. The initial experiment of inoculating only one half of those volunteering in a regiment embarking for an overseas posting was also doomed because the regiment selected was sent not to India but to Bermuda where there was very little typhoid anyway. Yet Leishman did, through careful animal experimentation, improve the quality of the vaccine, notably by standardising the temperature at which the inoculate was sterilised. He attributed variable results regarding the comparative incidence of typhoid in the inoculated and non-inoculated soldiers as being often and indeed largely due to variation in the quality of the vaccine and the dose administered.

If Britain was slow to embrace anti-typhoid inoculation, other countries were not. The devastation caused by the disease in the Boer War had not gone unnoticed in the United States, or in Germany where similar impairments of military operations in the Franco-Prussian War had not been forgotten. In both countries Wright was held in high regard. In the United States Army, voluntary inoculation was introduced in the early part of the century and by 1911 it was compulsory, three doses being given at intervals of one week immediately on entry into the service.

The Prussian Government appointed a committee of bacterio-logists[82] to consider the question with regard to immunising the German Army. It included such world-renowned figures as Koch, Kolle, Dönitz, Kirchner and Gaffky, the last-named being director of the Institute for Infectious Diseases in Berlin. In their report in 1905 they considered the experience in the British Army accumulated from 'the energy of English army doctors put forth in response to the continually reiterated stimulus coming to them from A E Wright'. They expressed their appreciation of the 'admirable tenacity' characterising his work. In contrast, they were scathing in their comments on the attitude of the British Army Medical Advisory Board. They pointed out that 'in view of the opposition which anti-typhoid inoculation had encountered in certain quarters in England it is quite certain that anything which could have been alleged against anti-typhoid inoculation in this respect would certainly have been alleged.' They also noted that in England:

> 'the care of anti-typhoid inoculation is delegated to a committee which as present constituted includes members of the hostile Medical Advisory Board. The policy of this committee appears to be to sit down and await the results of inoculation which were carried out in a single regiment last autumn. And the irony of fate has appointed that the particular regiment should be now be quartered in a station which is practically never visited by typhoid fever.'

The *Lancet* described this as a policy lineally descended from that which abolished all anti-typhoid inoculation, and suspended collection of all further returns with respect to the incidence of typhoid fever in the many thousands who had been inoculated. Somewhat surprisingly, in view of the report of their committee, the German Army adopted a limited inoculation policy, but with characteristic thoroughness instituted screening of recruits to detect and exclude typhoid carriers. Thus by 1911 any recruit who had been in contact with typhoid during the 12 months prior to his joining the army had his faeces and urine examined for the typhoid bacillus on three occasions at intervals of one week. If more than 12 months had elapsed since his exposure a Widal's test was carried out. Anyone excreting typhoid bacilli was invalided out of the service. The folly of this limited approach became apparent in 1915 when there was a small epidemic of typhoid in the German Army on the Western Front; this was quickly brought under control when compulsory inoculation was introduced.

By 1906 Haldane, who was now Secretary of State for War, was convinced of the efficiency of inoculation mainly because of its success in India. Yet he received conflicting opinions from the army medical authorities. He decided to back Wright. Dr John Freeman, who was lodging with Wright in his house in Park Crescent at the time, arrived home one day with Wright to find a letter from Haldane stating that it was necessary to 'build up Wright' and to do this he was proposing to put his name forward for a knighthood. After some hesitation Wright

accepted. His standing was further enhanced by his election as a
Fellow of the Royal Society; his name had been proposed by Burdon-
Sanderson and others three years previously, mentioning his work on
anti-typhoid inoculation. Meanwhile Leishman had continued his
careful researches, aided by RAMC officers who were trained by him
and attached to regiments proceeding overseas. He published the
results for the years since 1905[83] and demonstrated that the incidence
of typhoid fever was only a fifth of that in inoculated subjects, and that
the incidence of death in inoculated subjects who did contract the
disease was only a tenth of that in the uninoculated subjects.

In 1911 a commission appointed by the French Government
recommended anti-typhoid inoculation of all persons exposed to risk of
infection.[84] In spite of this the French medical establishment, in the shape
of the Académie de Médicine, failed to endorse the commission's
conclusions. Nevertheless the Minister of War made arrangements to
vaccinate all troops in Morocco, Algiers and the French colonies.

Yet in Britain the authorities still hesitated. In 1912, following
Leishman's painstaking research the Anti-typhoid Committee,
appointed by the Army Council some eight years before on 16
March 1904, issued their final report.[85] They found a substantial
difference between inoculated soldiers, among whom the incidence of
typhoid was 0.539 per cent, and uninoculated soldiers where the
incidence was 3.0 per cent. They concluded that the difference could
be due only to inoculation and not to other factors, stating that 'Every
measure which may be considered practicable should be employed to
extend the practice of anti-typhoid inoculation in the army. In the
opinion of the Committee its universal application is desirable.' The
report was signed by seven members of the committee. Significantly,
there was a note at the end of the document stating that 'Col Sir David
Bruce was abroad when this report was signed.' Possibly this was the
result of some cunning on the part of the chairman because Bruce as
late as 1910, in his presidential address to the United Services Medical
Society, had said 'Anti-typhoid inoculation was in vogue during the
last South African war but it proved useless.'[86]

Following this report it might be thought that inoculation would
become compulsory in the armed services. Not so. It was introduced
on a voluntary basis only; indeed this was the position in August 1914
at the onset of the Great War. The situation alarmed Wright, who went
at once to see Kitchener and offered him the services of the laboratories
at St Mary's to produce vaccine enough to inoculate the expeditionary
force. As a direct result of Wright's pleading the War Office issued a
communiqué to all RAMC officers, reported in the *Lancet*[87] of

15 August 1914, commenting that improved sanitary facilities on their own would not safeguard against an outbreak of typhoid in northern France. Attention was drawn to the possibility firstly, of some men incubating the disease when they joined the expeditionary force, secondly of some recruits being carriers and thirdly that there would be contacts with local inhabitants who might well be suffering from or incubating the disease. The War Office recognised the value of inoculation and encouraged all medical officers to seize 'every opportunity' to offer it to all men under their charge. It was still only to be given to volunteers, but in a very short time it became virtually compulsory when Kitchener ruled that no one was to be drafted overseas who had not been inoculated. This ruling was no doubt the result of a strongly worded letter to both the *BMJ* and the *Lancet* on 22 August from Leishman[88], regretting that officially inoculation was still voluntary in the British Army. In this letter he drew attention to the situation in India, where 93 per cent of the British garrison at this time were inoculated and where the death rate from typhoid had fallen from up to 600 per year to less than 20 in 1913. In the American Army, where inoculation was compulsory, there were only three cases and no deaths. Leishman had a reserve of 170,000 doses of vaccine, and more was available from the Lister Institute and from Wright at St Mary's. (By 1915 St Mary's had distributed the 'stupendous figure of 3,880,000 doses of anti-typhoid vaccine' to the British, Belgian and Serbian armies.[89]) Leishman received support from the Presidents of the Edinburgh Royal Colleges of Physicians and Surgeons[90] who offered the services of their Fellows for performing the inoculations if the RAMC officers were too occupied with other duties.

All this should have been enough to convince the medical profession, but on 28 September *The Times* published a lengthy letter from Wright putting the case for compulsory inoculation. It was, unusually for him, a letter which could be understood by any layman, but the argument was weakened by his additional advocacy of simultaneous inoculation against septic infection using 'an anti-sepsis vaccine ie a mixed staphylococcus and streptococcus vaccine' that was unproven and actually useless. This was acknowledged even by Colebrook, who thought that in promoting this anti-sepsis vaccine Wright was going 'rather beyond the facts', there being no convincing evidence of its efficacy.

The consequence of all this activity on the part of Wright and his associates was that, in contrast to the Boer War and the Franco-Prussian War, typhoid was not a problem during 1914–18 on the Western Front, where by the end of 1915 almost 100 per cent of the

British Expeditionary Force had been inoculated. Comparison of the statistics with those of the Boer War clearly illustrate the point. In an expeditionary force whose mean strength was two million there were only 20,139 cases in the four years and only 1,191 deaths, most of these in men who had evaded inoculation. In the Boer War, in which the mean strength of the army was 208,226 men, there were 57,684 cases and 9,022 deaths. It has been suggested[91] that this dramatic decrease was in the main due to better sanitation and water sterilisation, but conditions in the trenches on the Western Front were appalling. Men often spent days sheltering in shell-holes filled with faeces and urine contaminated water, which they drank. In the autumn and summer flies were everywhere and thus conditions were ideal for an outbreak of typhoid. Yet none occurred, and for this credit must be given to Wright's persistent promotion of anti-typhoid inoculation, which was a considerable factor in achieving a successful outcome to the conflict. This was certainly the view of such distinguished and knowledgeable men as Osler and Cushing. Colebrook estimated that without anti-typhoid inoculation there would have been 967,500 cases of typhoid and 125,000 deaths.[92] Perhaps Sir Arthur Hurst, in his book *Medical diseases of war* published in 1940[93], can be allowed the final verdict. He wrote:

'There is no doubt that the almost universal inoculation practised in the last war (1914–18) is the explanation of the very small numbers of cases which occurred. The official returns showed that the admission rate for typhoid fever amongst the troops in France who had not been inoculated was 15 times as great as amongst those who had been inoculated and the death rate was 70 times as high.'

Throughout the war years the extraordinary and diverting activities of the British Union for the Abolition of Vivisection (BUAV) provided consistent opposition to all forms of vaccination because they considered vaccines had been developed as a result of work involving animal experimentation. The BUAV was led by an eccentric medical practitioner, Dr Walter Hadwen, who edited their journal *The Abolitionist*. Hadwen had been a brilliant medical student, qualifying in 1877, but he does not seem to have believed in any of the advances in medicine that took place after that date. In particular he did not agree with the germ theory of disease, which he described as 'one of the strongest and most ruinous delusions that have ever oppressed or afflicted the human race'. In this he was supported by Florence Nightingale. In the issue of *The Abolitionist* of 1 June 1914 Hadwen wrote 'To talk of wholesale typhoid inoculation is to revert to the

superstitious folly of Edward Jenner and his cowpox filth of a century
ago.' Hadwen encouraged his disciples to penetrate camps where
recruits were drafted and persuade them to refuse inoculation. He also
instituted a vigorous poster campaign. In all this the BUAV were
supported in the House of Commons by H G Chancellor, who asked
questions in support of those soldiers who refused inoculation and
were thus not drafted overseas. It is fortunate that that all these efforts
were of no avail.

With hindsight it is easy to criticise Wright and his fellow-enthusiasts
for not conducting a statistically reliable controlled trial. But at that
time no such trial had been carried out. To have satisfied the purists
Cockburn[94] considered the following rules should have been observed:

(a) The men to be inoculated and the men to serve as controls should be chosen so
    that when considered as groups they are alike in every respect.
(b) The groups must be subject to the same risk of exposure.
(c) The two groups must be observed with the same thoroughness over the same
    period.
(d) The clinical diagnosis of disease in the two groups must if possible be confirmed
    by objective means such as isolation of the infecting organism.
(e) Neither the observers nor the subjects should know until the end of the
    investigation whether a particular person belongs to the test or control group.

Clearly these criteria were not satisfied in any of the prewar trials of
anti-typhoid vaccine. Yet fortunately in 1915 Greenwood[95], a disciple
of Pearson and statistician to the Lister Institute, was able to issue a
favourable report and this carried considerable weight with both the lay
and scientific establishments. It would be a foolhardy person today
who would venture into an area where typhoid was endemic without
anti-typhoid inoculation.

Wright and Bruce never reconciled their differences. Wright
maintained that Bruce was the only man he had ever hated.
Embarrassing encounters between the two were mercifully few. One
occurred when they were presented together for honorary degrees at
the Queen's University, Belfast. Bruce at first refused to go up to the
dais with Wright but the latter turned to him and muttered, 'Don't be
an ass — I don't like it any more than you do'. An awkward situation
was averted and they went up to receive their degrees together.[96]

Notes

1 Quoted by Bulloch W. *The history of bacteriology*. London: Oxford University Press, 1938.
2 Marten B. *A new theory of consumption: more especially of a phthisis or consumption of the lungs*.
  London: Knaplock, Bell, Hooke and King, 1720.
3 Louis, P Ch A. *Recherches pathologiques et thérapeutiques sur la maladie typhoide*. Paris, 1829.

4 Perry R. *Edin Med and Surg J* 1836; **45**: 64.

5 Jenner W. *Medical Times* 1849–51; **2023** (collection of 20 papers in all).

6 Goodall EW. *William Budd*. Bristol: Arrowsmith, 1936.

7 Budd W. On intestinal fever: its mode of propagation. *Lancet* 1856; **ii**; 694.

8 John Snow (1834–1903) introduced ether to Britain. He deduced that cholera was spread by water and in the epidemic in Soho in 1848 recommended removal of the handle of the Broad Street pump, used as a source of water by the local inhabitants.

9 Budd W. Intestinal fever, essentially contagious. *Lancet* 1859; **ii**: 4, 28, 55, 80.

10 Patrick A. *The enteric fevers 1800–1920*. Edinburgh: Royal College of Physicians Publications no 2, 1955.

11 Macpherson WG, Herringham WP, Elliott TR, Balfour A, eds. *History of the Great War: medical services*. Vol 1. *Diseases of the war*, p11. HMSO, 1922.

12 Budd W. *Typhoid fever: its nature, mode of spreading and prevention*. London: Longman, 1873.

13 Eberth CJ. *Virchow Archiv* 1880; **81**, 58.

14 Gaffky G. Mitth a d Kaiserl. *Gesundheitsante* 1884; **2**: 372.

15 Wills C. *Plagues: their origin, history and future* pp135–41. London: Oxford University Press, 1996.

16 Ledingham A and JCG. *BMJ* 1908; **i**: 15.

17 Patrick A. *The enteric fevers 1800–1920* p30. Edinburgh: Royal College of Physicians Publications no 2, 1955.

18 Semple D, Greig EDW. Sci Mem Med Sanit Dep India no 32, 1908.

19 Newman G. *Practitioner* 1904; **7** (2): 55.

20 Vaughan VC. *Med News NY* 1899; **7** (4): 604.

21 Salmon DE, Smith T. On a new method of producing immunity from contagious diseases. *Proc Biol Soc* 1886; **3**: 29.

22 Pfeiffer R, Kolle W. *Dtsch med Wschr* 1896; **2** (2): 735.

23 Gruber M, Durham HE. *Münch med Wehnschr* 1896: 285.

24 Wright AE. *Lancet* 1896; **ii**: 807.

25 Wright AE, Semple D. *BMJ* 1897; **i**: 256.

26 Friederberger E. *Centralblatt für Bakteriologie Paristenkunde und Infections Krankheit* 1907; **4** (4): 560.

27 Colebrook papers PP/COL/C 11.

28 Groschel DHM, Hornick RB. *Rev Infectious Dis* 1981; **3**: 1251.

29 Leishman WB. *J Roy Inst Public Health* 1910; **1** (8), 387.

30 Harrison WS. *J RAMC* 1904; **3**: 42.

31 *BMJ* 1899; **i**: 232.

32 *BMJ* 1899; **i**: 572.

33 Wright AE, Leishman WB. *BMJ* 1900; **i**: 122.

34 Notes from India. *Lancet* 1899; **i**: 929, 934.

35 Notes from India. *Lancet* 1899; **ii**: 182.

36 Notes from India. *Lancet* 1899; **i**: 929.

37 Notes from India. *Lancet* 1899; **ii**: 182.

38 Sharp G. *The siege of Ladysmith*. London: Purnell, 1976.

39 Wright AE. *Lancet* 1900; **ii**: 95.

40 Colebrook L. Obituary of AE Wright. *Lancet* 1947; **i**: 654.

41 Born in 1852 in the USA as William Lehman Ashmead Bartlett of American parents but English grandparents, he had been educated in England and was awarded the first scholarship at Keble College, Oxford. In 1881 he married the extremely wealthy Baroness Burdett-Coutts, a lady 37 years his senior, and by royal licence assumed her name. The marriage caused considerable gossip at the time but Lady St Helier, a friend of Wright's, records in her memoirs that it was a happy union.

42 Two of his earlier and highly critical reports had not been published 'owing to pressure on our space', according to the editor of *The Times*.

43 *Spectator* 11 Auguust 1900.

44 Reports from commissioners, inspectors and others. *Care and treatment of the sick and wounded during the South African campaign* vol 29. HMSO, 1901.

45 *BMJ* 1900; **i**: 1044.
46 *Lancet* 1901; **ii**: 1429.
47 Permanent Executive Committee of the War Office, 6 April 1902. PRO/WO 163, 581.
48 Foster was Liberal Unionist MP for London University. He had been professor of physiology at Cambridge and at University College, London; he was secretary of the Royal Society.
49 The board had appointed a subcommittee to report on (i) preparation of all sera and (ii) preparation and application of anti-typhoid fluid. The subcommittee's findings were adopted as the board's report.
50 Report of Advisory Board for Army Medical Services to the secretary of state, 25 September 1902, published in *J RAMC* 1905; **5**: 242.
51 Ibid, appendix.
52 Harben lectures. *J Roy Inst of Pub Health* 1910; **1** (8): 385.
53 PRO/WO 163. Proceedings of the Permanent Executive Committee of the War Office for 1902, 28 November.
54 PRO/WO 243/1, 25 April 1903.
55 PRO/WO 243/1, 2 June 1903.
56 Committee minute book, Royal College of Physicians, 2 July 1903.
57 Howard Tooth, a neurologist on the staff of St Bartholomew's Hospital and the National Hospital for the Paralysed and Epileptic. He had been a physician to the Portland Hospital in South Africa.
58 John Rose Bradford FRS, Fellow of University College, London, physician at UCH and the National Hospital for the Paralysed and Epileptic.
59 William J Ritchie Simpson, professor of hygiene, King's College, London.
60 Frederick Ford Caiger, medical superintendent of the London Fever Hospital.
61 Samuel Jones Gee, physician to St Bartholomew's Hospital and to the Prince of Wales.
62 Royal College of Physicians minute book 27 July 1903.
63 PRO/WO 243/3 pp11, 12.
64 Ibid 16 February 1904.
65 Ibid 10 March 1904.
66 Interim report of the Anti-typhoid Inoculation Committee. HMSO: Cd 2698, 9 July 1904.
67 Final report of the Anti-typhoid Committee. HMSO, 1912.
68 *BMJ* 1904; **ii**: 1344.
69 *BMJ* 1904; **ii**: 1243.
70 *BMJ* 1904; **ii**: 1259.
71 Pearson ES. *Karl Pearson*. Cambridge: Cambridge University Press, 1938.
72 *BMJ* 1904; **ii**: 1243.
73 *BMJ* 1904; **ii**: 1614.
74 *BMJ* 1904; **ii**: 1667.
75 *The conquest of plague* p54. Oxford University Press, 1950.
76 *BMJ* 1899; **ii**: 747.
77 *BMJ* 1900; **ii**: 883.
78 *BMJ* 1900; **i**: 1455.
79 *BMJ* 1900; **i**: 1455.
80 *Lancet* 1901; **ii**: 1134.
81 *BMJ* 1901; **i**: 84.
82 *Lancet* 1905; **i**: 1453.
83 *J Roy Inst Public Health* 1910; **1** (8) 385.
84 *J RAMC* 1912; **18**: 600.
85 Final report of the Anti-typhoid Committee. HMSO, 1912.
86 Quoted by Cockburn WC. *J RAMC* 1955; **101**: 171.
87 *Lancet* 1914; **ii**: 465.
88 *BMJ* 1914; **ii**: 369.
89 *St Mary's Hospital Gazette* 1914 (February): 22.
90 *Lancet* 1914; **ii**: 718.
91 Cockburn WC. *J RAMC* 1955; **101**: 171.

92 Colebrook L. *Almroth Wright, provocative doctor and thinker* p42. London: William Heinemann, 1954.

93 Hurst A. *Medical diseases of war*. 2nd edn. London: Edward Arnold, 1940.

94 Cockburn WC. *J RAMC* 1955; **101**: 171.

95 Greenwood M, Yule GU. *Proc Roy Soc Med* 1915; 8 113.

96 Colebrook L. *Almroth Wright, provocative doctor and thinker* p36. London: William Heinemann, 1954. In this reference Bruce appears as X. Colebrook asserts that Wright was grateful to Bruce as he was the only person who inspired him to hate.

Chapter 4

A New Department at St Mary's, Praed Street

Wright's appointment at St Mary's, as with his appointment at Netley, was surrounded by controversy. In 1902 pathologists were not regarded with favour by the all-powerful consultant physicians, who still relied largely on clinical intuition in arriving at a diagnosis. There were very few full-time professional pathologists in England at that time. Such pathology as was carried out consisted almost solely of post-mortem examinations. In the London teaching hospitals these were performed by young doctors who were appointed as museum curators or demonstrators. They received a small stipend, usually £100 a year, and were expected to supervise the mounting and cataloguing of museum specimens in addition to their duties in carrying out necropsies on patients dying in the hospital. These men were aspiring physicians who hoped to be elected as such, when a vacancy occurred, to the staff. Often they maintained a private practice 'on the side'. True, chairs of pathology had been established at University College, London in 1828 and at King's College, London in 1831, but these were all held by physicians whose main interest was, and whose main income came from, private consulting medical practice.[1] Again their primary pathological concern was with morbid anatomy. Even by the end of the 19th century there was little interest in laboratory investigation of the living patient, and few facilities available for such studies. Most tests on blood and urine were of an extremely simple nature and were carried out in small side rooms, ill-equipped and badly lit, leading off the wards.

St Mary's seems to have been no exception. The hospital was a more recent foundation than St Bartholomew's, Guy's, St Thomas's or the London, dating with its small medical school from the middle of the 19th century. When the medical school opened there were fewer than 20 students.[2] A pathologist is not mentioned in the first list of 22 paid lecturers, though a Mr Hornidge is listed as a pathologist on the staff of the hospital. In 1856 a junior house surgeon, C J Mellor, was appointed unpaid curator of the pathological museum.

Towards the end of the century pathology assumed greater importance in the medical curriculum. In 1886, a laboratory for teaching students was established but this seems to have been used mainly for cutting histological sections. By 1890, although many physicians still did not believe in the germ theory of disease, it was obvious to the medical school authorities that the science of bacteriology was becoming of increasing importance; and Leonard Rogers was appointed demonstrator in that subject. At the time he was a senior student (he did not pass the conjoint examination until 1891); later, he was to achieve world-wide fame as an authority on tropical medicine. In 1896 H G Plimmer, a man of considerable independent means, took up the post of bacteriologist with a stipend of £100 a year. In 1899 he was given the position of pathologist and might well have remained there for the rest of his professional life; by 1902, however, he had become interested in cancer research and resigned his post in order to pursue his studies elsewhere.[3] He had two assistants, Drs Paine and Maguire, who resigned at the same time. It was a sign of the increasing specialisation in medicine that Maguire gave as his reason: 'Pathology is now so much a specialised subject, that it is impossible to teach it thoroughly unless one can give a certain time each day to the laboratory, and this I cannot do'.[4] It would appear that a considerable amount of the teaching and routine work of the department had fallen on the shoulders of Dr F J Poynton, a St Mary's man, who following these resignations was given the combined posts of medical registrar and pathologist. His research interests centred on juvenile rheumatism, a common disease at that time, and together with Paine he claimed that the cause was infection by a bacterium which they named *Diplococcus rheumaticus*. They had isolated this organism post-mortem from the heart valves of patients who had died from the disease. (Though this work excited considerable interest at the time, it was later shown to be flawed because the organism was a post-mortem contaminant and was identified as *Streptococcus faecalis*, a common inhabitant of the large bowel.) In view of his work at the hospital and medical school Poynton considered he would be appointed to any permanent post in pathology that was established.

On 10 October 1902 a subcommittee of the board of management of the hospital met to consider future arrangements for the pathological department. They recommended that three separate posts should be created: a pathologist with the title of lecturer, at a salary of £250 per annum, together with a bacteriologist at a salary of £150 per annum, and an assistant pathologist and curator of the museum at a salary of £100 per annum. These appointments they required to be filled as a matter of urgency and they suggested in their report that 'It may be advisable to notify the vacancies in the hospital and medical school before proceeding to advertisement; the subcommittee being of the opinion that capable men for the posts will probably be forthcoming from among those connected with the hospital'.[5] They also recognised the need for facilities for pathological chemistry, a subject that was in its infancy but was assuming increasing importance in the study of such common conditions as diabetes mellitus and uraemia.

Events moved swiftly and by 23 October the medical school committee had reached a decision. They had advertised in the medical press and received applications for the post of pathologist from J Broadbent—who had strong family connections with the hospital and later became a distinguished physician on the staff—and Drs Theodore Fisher, Freyburger and F J Poynton. Only two applications were forthcoming for the post of bacteriologist, from D J Morgan and P Shekwance. The minutes add that a special application had been received for the combined post of bacteriologist and pathologist from Almroth Wright. The committee unanimously recommended to the board that such a position be offered to Wright.[6] The reasons for this deviation from their previous recommendation that the two posts should be separate was 'that it will be invaluable to the hospital to obtain the services of so skilled a pathologist, and to the best interests of the medical school, to add to its teaching staff so eminent a scientific investigator and so able a teacher'. Financial expediency may also have been a reason: Wright was appointed at an initial salary of £300 per annum, which thus represented a saving of £100 (approximately £5000 in today's terms) on what the board had been proposing to spend. The medical school was deeply in debt. The hospital board of management had set up a committee in 1901 to investigate the financial affairs of the school and found that these had been conducted in a 'most unbusiness like manner'; indeed, there was a liability of £6000 in respect of student fees. The dean, Dr H A Caley, was desperate to conserve every penny. The situation was largely saved by the generosity of Henry Harben, a member of the board, who gave £3000 out of his own pocket towards paying off the debt and was to give even more at a later date.[7] Wright himslf was making a considerable financial sacrifice, his salary having been £700 at Netley; but he accepted the post in a letter written from 83 Victoria Street and dated 27 October.[8] His salary was later increased to £400, and he was also able to supplement his income from private practice.

The committee must have greeted Wright's application with relief and the speed with which they acted can be gleaned from the aggrieved response of Poynton to the news of Wright's appointment. He is recorded as saying:

'I left the hospital when Sir Almroth Wright was elected pathologist thereby excluding me from that post . . . it is of interest, perhaps, that after having served two years as Editor of the *Gazette*, two years as medical tutor and two years as medical registrar and pathologist, that the envelope of my testimonials was not opened at my last application.'

He subsequently had a distinguished career as a consultant at Great Ormond Street Hospital.

The accommodation given to Wright on his arrival was primitive 'one small room in the old medical school'. A further room was given to William Wilcox for chemical pathology. There was a lack of the most basic equipment and Wright at once put in for a grant to remedy this defect. As a result of the enquiry into the finances of the medical school, which had revealed the irregular and unsatisfactory methods of accounting, the board had extricated the school from its difficulties and brought it under its direct control and subject to 'the laws of the hospital'. A new medical school committee was constituted,[9] consisting of 12 members including Mr Harben and General Shaw Stewart with the dean as chairman. They met on 14 November 1902, and one of the first items on the agenda was a request for apparatus from the pathological and bacteriological department. The list of items requested gives some idea of the run-down state of the laboratory: a microscope with appliances (£50), pulsometer pump (£5), Doudrey's incubator (£9.10s.), autoclave no.4 (£18), steam steriliser 20″×48″ (approximately £6), microtome (Cambridge rocker improved model, £9.10s.). The board gave a grant of up to £100.

Yet this did nothing to improve the accommodation, and on 17 December Wright represented to the board that certain structural improvements were urgently required. Alarmed at this, the board proceeded to investigate the matter 'on the spot'; fortunately they were convinced of the necessity for the alterations. An estimate of £99 for the work was received from Higgs and Hill, and the board recommended that it be put in hand.[10] Even this estimate fell short of what was required and on 28 January 1903 a further £12 12s. was needed for rearranging and extending electrical fittings. At this meeting the medical school committee noted that 'special votes of money may be necessary for new arrangements in the pathological and physiological departments.'[11] The estimated total expenditure for the medical school, including salaries, establishment charges etc was £3950. 9s. 2d. Of this sum the estimate for pathology, excluding salaries, was a modest £105. Furthermore the committee minuted that £33. 5s. had been spent in the first quarter and, as they warned the department about this, it seemed that more money was unlikely to be found. Wright brought his own financial position to the notice of the medical school committee on 6 November 1903 in the form of a letter in which he stated that in coming to St Mary's he had made a financial sacrifice of £600 per annum—Wright's arithmetic was never his best subject—and that he had been promised that his salary would be increased to £500 after a year. He added, 'I think you will know also that I am doing all I can to conduct the pathological department and carry on pathological teaching in such a manner as to advance the interests of the school and to bring credit to the hospital'.[12] Curiously, when this was brought to the finance committee early in 1904 Wright withdrew his request. No reason was given but the likely explanation was that by that time he had built up a very considerable private practice.

For a hospital experiencing severe financial difficulties the sudden advent of what amounted to a new department, headed by a thrusting and enthusiastic man who was determined to promote teaching and research, presented problems. Wright's terms of appointment included responsibility not only for bacteriology, in which he was intensely interested, but also for post-mortem examinations for whose performance he had little enthusiasm but which were assuming increasing importance in official circles. Thus on 10 February 1903 the board of management received a letter from the Central Hospital Council for London recommending that post-mortem examinations be performed on all patients dying in constituent hospitals unless relatives expressed an objection. A month later improvements to the post-mortem room were started, incurring unexpected expense.[13]

Matters were further complicated on 16 March, when the board of management discussed a communication from London County Council indicating that it was desirable that post-mortem examinations should be entrusted to specially skilled pathologists.[14] Wright did not wish to take on this work and there was difficulty and procrastination in implementing the recommendations; but in May 1903 Dr Broadbent was appointed to carry out post-mortem examinations. His remuneration was not such a problem because many of the examinations were undertaken at the behest of the coroner, and a fee was paid for each of these. Broadbent continued as assistant pathologist until 29 May 1905, when he resigned on being appointed to the hospital staff as a physician. He was succeeded on 13 July that year by Bernard Spilsbury, who subsequently became the foremost forensic pathologist in the country. Prior to this, on 9 March, the medical school committee had recommended that Wright be relieved of the duty of making post-mortem examinations.[15] Spilsbury stayed at St Mary's until 1919 when he left to take up an appointment at St Thomas's following a dispute with the medical committee and Wilfred Harris, one of the physicians, over his status.[16]

Throughout his early years at St Mary's the parsimonious attitude of the board to financial provision for pathology caused Wright intense irritation. The rules regarding the use of electric light in the laboratory provide an example of this. All electricity was cut off from the laboratory at 6 pm; this represented a real hardship for Wright who, being engaged in private practice in the mornings, had to conduct most of his research later in the day. The limit of 6 pm was extended by one hour in 1904 but it was decreed that if any lecturer wanted 'to use electric current beyond 7 pm' he must apply to the school secretary before 4.30 on that day! Wright was angered by this and as a result of a letter he wrote to the committee the limit was extended to 9 pm on 3 June 1904.[17] Even small items of equipment had to be submitted to the Medical School Committee before they could be purchased. For instance, on 14 October 1904 Wright applied for a grant of £8. 10s. in order to purchase an electric centrifuge, but he had to return to the committee when the cost was revised to £10.

Such a system was unsatisfactory and on 12 May 1905 Wright asked the medical school for a complete review of the practice whereby ordinary supplies, by which he meant consumables, were obtained.[18] These supplies were subject to great delay, and a further irritation was that he did not have freedom of choice in selecting suppliers. The position was a difficult one as the pathology department was performing all the investigations for the hospital, and these were increasing year by year, yet it was under the jurisdiction of, and formally financed by, the medical school. Maintenance costs were inevitably rising as more consumables were needed for the increasing number of investigations demanded by the hospital. An agreement was reached on 2 March 1906 that costs of maintenance of the department should be charged to the hospital.[19]

By this time Wright, who had been appointed to the medical school committee in December 1904, had become a figure to be reckoned with. He had been elected a Fellow of the Royal Society in May 1906 as a result of his work on typhoid,[20] and he had been knighted in the birthday honours that year. Furthermore his teaching was receiving wide recognition. He was invited in the autumn of 1906 to give a Harvey Lecture in New York and also the Herter Lectures at Johns Hopkins University, Baltimore — the only occasion on which he visited the United States. The medical school committee recommended that the course of lectures he was to give in advanced pathology should be recognised by the Board of Advanced Studies of the University of London.[21] These lectures, whose main subject was 'The principles of therapeutic inoculations', were started on 16 January 1907 and were given every week in the library of the medical school for two terms. The fee for attendance was two guineas (£2. 2s.), the money going to the medical school.

During the period up to 1908 the department was drawing financial support from two other sources. The first was private practice. At the time of Wright's arrival at St Mary's his reputation was considerable among influential figures in government and society, mainly because of his championing of typhoid inoculation. His acquaintances included national figures from political and artistic circles such as Haldane, Balfour, Gilbert Murray and Granville Barker, as well as friends from the world of science. These men recommended Wright as a physician to their relations and friends, enabling him to build up an extensive consulting general medical practice. To do him justice he detested the Harley Street ethos but the practice, which he conducted in the mornings, did supply much-needed cash. He was popular with patients, many of whom came repeatedly simply to talk to him. Freeman relates how one wealthy American woman, with whom he chatted mainly about philosophy, insisted on a proper account to cover all her visits. Wright sent an invoice: 'To professional treatment two guineas: to comforting words twenty guineas: Total twenty-two guineas.'[22] He diverted some of the money from private practice to the laboratory to be used for research purposes. More often he persuaded his wealthy acquaintances and patients to donate money to the department—by 1908 they had contributed £17,000, a very considerable sum for those days.[23]

Secondly, the department was actively engaged in production of vaccines, and the sale of these was to generate a substantial income. On 11 December 1905 the board of management of the hospital had recommended that a department of therapeutic inoculation be established and that 'Dr Wright be invited to accept the office of director for a period of five years'.[24] The duty of the director was to investigate and treat suitable hospital patients sent to him by the honorary medical and surgical staff. Such patients were to be under the joint control of the director and member of staff concerned. They also proposed two other important recommendations: firstly, that Wright should be accorded the full privileges as a member of the honorary staff, thus putting him on a par with the physicians and surgeons, and secondly, that he should have the right to treat, in the hospital, patients

other than those sent by members of the hospital staff. On 22 February
1906 the board agreed that these patients should pay fees to the
department and at the same meeting Wright was formally elected to
the staff. These fees provided only a small proportion of the running
costs; precise figures have not survived. A greater amount came from
the sale of vaccines to medical practitioners. Yet the keeping of
accounts and other minutiae of administration became exceedingly
tedious, and was not a task suited to a man of Wright's temperament.
At this time specific therapy for disease was virtually nonexistent and
vaccines appeared to have enormous potential for the treatment of
infections. It is thus not surprising that the pharmaceutical houses were
interested in acquiring them. Wright was able to negotiate an
agreement with Parke Davis, who undertook to distribute vaccines
produced at St Mary's and to pay the department an appropriate sum
from the profits. It was this money that paid for 'all the routine and
capital expenditure of the department' for the next 38 years. The sums
involved must have been considerable: they paid for the staff salaries
and maintenance expenses and also enabled Wright to put aside some
money so that he could undertake 'certain compassionate
expenditure'.[25]

The hospital board of management and the medical school
committee no doubt welcomed this arrangement, although they took
some time to ratify it. The apportionment of expenses between the
hospital and the school was a constant source of difficulty. The major
part of the hospital was financed through payments made from King
Edward's Fund but none of this money was to be used for the medical
school. Clearly, at times it was difficult to earmark where the funds
were going, particularly in the case of a pathology department which,
in addition to teaching and research, was carrying out routine
investigations on hospital patients. On 31 May 1906 the
discretionary fund committee of the board had proposed that a fund
be established into which subscriptions should be paid on the
understanding that 'they may be applied in whole or in part at the
discretion of the hospital authorities for the purposes of the hospital or
of the medical school'. This proposal was not supported, the board
giving as its reason that: 'the establishment of such a fund at the
present time would be likely to be interpreted by the general public,
including the great majority of the subscribers to the hospital, as an
admission that in the past the medical school had been secretly
subsidised by the board from hospital funds contributed for the relief
of the poor'. Instead members of the board were asked to use their
personal influence to induce members of the public to give a special

Figure 8
*Some of the staff of the inoculation department circa 1908. Wright is in the centre with Leonard Noon on
his left. Stewart Douglas is on the other side of Wright (only half in the picture). The two figures at the
back are John Freeman and Leonard Colebrook. Note the formal dress; Noon wears a black coat and pin-
stripe trousers. (The Wellcome Library, London)*

contribution for the purposes of the medical school.[26] They added:
'Furtherance of medical progress is an object which probably does not
appeal to the majority and the intimate bearing on the efficiency of the
hospital of the upkeep of the medical school is not perceived by all.'
Plainly this was a delicate area. On 29 November 1906 a letter was
received from King Edward's Fund asking for a written certificate to
the effect that no payments had been made to the medical school out of
general funds subscribed for the relief of the sick poor. This was
necessary before any payment could be made to the hospital for the
next year.[27]

Accommodation for the increasing workload of Wright's department
was urgently needed. The Clarence Wing of the hospital in Praed
Street was not occupied. The foundation stone of this memorial to
Albert Victor, Duke of Clarence, had been laid by the Prince of Wales
on 17 December 1892, but the response of the public to the request for
money for the building had been unenthusiastic and it was not
completed until 1904. Even then lack of funds prevented it from being
occupied, and on 13 December 1906 the board not only formally
approved the sale of vaccines but also agreed that 'the treatment work
of the inoculation department be temporarily transferred to the
maternity section of the Clarence Memorial Wing.' The department

was to pay rent for the rooms used.[28] By this time the patients visiting Wright in his laboratory had become so numerous that they often blocked the stairways and passages; he needed both out-patient facilities and beds for in-patients. Yet the move did not take place immediately because Wright wanted to be absolutely sure of his financial backing and that sufficient money would be forthcoming from his vaccine sales.

The formal agreement with Parke Davis, it seems, was signed at, or shortly after, a board meeting held on 20 February 1908 but the Clarence Wing was not yet occupied. By the end of the year the board was anxious to start receiving rent, and at their meeting on 26 November they forcefully drew attention to the fact 'that it is now more than twelve months since Sir A E Wright's proposal for the opening of the Clarence Wing . . . and that nothing has yet come of it . . . It was resolved that Sir A E Wright be informed that unless funds are forthcoming by 21 January 1909 which will enable the board, on the basis laid down in their resolution of 29 October last, to order that 31 beds be equipped and opened for patients for treatment by inoculation, the board will be compelled to resort to the question of devoting these beds to another purpose.' [29]

This ultimatum provided ammunition for Wright to persuade his friend the leader of the Conservative party and former Prime Minister, Mr A J Balfour, to call a meeting, and this Balfour did at the House of Commons taking the chair himself.[30] The group that met constituted themselves 'The House Committee of the Inoculation Department' and consisted of the Rt Hon Lord Farquhar,[31] the Rt Hon Rupert Guinness[32], Rt Hon Sir Fletcher Moulton[33], Sir John Dickson Poynder, Sir Almroth Wright, Mr J Bonn[34], Mr L E Ralli[35] and Mr H A Harben[36]. In addition to agreeing that they should be the house committee they agreed unanimously that:

(a) All matters relating to the general administration of the laboratories, fixing of salaries and of the tenure of scientific staff and wages of subordinate staff, etc, should be settled by the house committee.

(b) That the committee should be called together when deemed necessary by Sir Almroth Wright, and that two members with Sir Almroth should form a quorum.

Mr Harben reported these resolutions to the Board on 7 January 1909 and Lord Justice Fletcher Moulton and Mr Harben were deputed to draw up an agreement, which was formally ratified on 18 March. Then, on 27 May, it was reported that the wards would be ready for occupancy by 15 June. The department actually moved in on 1 July, and the hospital received the first payment for maintenance on that day. Wright had established a self-financing empire within, but largely independent of, the hospital. He had power to appoint and dismiss staff at will and to fix their salaries. It was a situation inconceivable today, but it was to last until the advent of the National Health Service in 1948.

The arrangements with Parke Davis were mainly cordial though there were occasional squalls. In 1912 they attempted the sale of vaccines in the United States of America and correspondence was opened between Wright and Rupert Blue, the Surgeon General in Washington. The vaccines sent to the United States were found to be contaminated and the licence to sell them was refused. This matter was never satisfactorily resolved. The agreement with Parke Davis included a clause which gave them exclusive control over vaccines produced at St Mary's in return for a guarantee that the company would not market any vaccines of their own in competition with products from the inoculation department. Yet in 1913 Parke Davis were found to be selling Phylacogens vaccine, a product of their own whose function was never clearly established. Wright claimed this was a breach of the agreement and it seemed at one point as if legal action would follow. The matter was resolved through the good offices of Max Bonn, by then a member of the house committee. Parke Davis claimed that Phylacogens vaccine was an anti-toxin and thus did not come under the agreement — a very weak argument. Even so Bonn advised against any legal action as it would damage relationships between the two parties — something to be avoided at all costs, as the sale of Wright's vaccines was considerable and rising year by year. Matters seem to have been amicably settled. Although no detailed accounts have survived the minutes of the house committee indicate that income regularly exceeded expenditure and the committee were able to set aside considerable sums for investment. Thus in 1919 they invested £5000 out of income in gilt-edged securities — the inoculation department was a registered charity and could not, as such, invest in the equity market. Indeed after the Great War income continued to increase and the department remained on friendly terms with Parke Davis; so much so that in February 1923 the company asked Wright to undertake the testing and bottling of all their sera, much of which had previously been carried out at Cambridge.[37]

Staffing the department was not a problem. To medical students Wright was an inspiring personality. Here was someone who was approaching clinical medicine from a scientific viewpoint. Aged 41 on arrival at St Mary's, a nonsmoker and a virtual teetotaller, he displayed a fanatical devotion to his subject. His assistants always referred to him as the Old Man. Wright's striking appearance was to alter little in the years to come. A large man, over six feet tall, moustached with massive hands and feet, he appeared at first sight a clumsy giant. One contemporary wrote that 'His mere appearance, highly suggestive of Tenniel's illustration of the Lion in *Alice Through the Looking Glass*, a kindly, dishevelled, but formidable creature was fascinating'.[38] His impressively bushy eyebrows — they flicked up and down when he was amused — added to the leonine picture; John Freeman, a close friend, said 'He could almost speak with those eyebrows'.[39] He always wore a starched wing-collar shirt but did not sport a bow tie; and his suits, though of good quality, invariably had a crumpled appearance. As with many big men his movements were slow, but any impression of clumsiness was an illusion as he performed the most intricate of laboratory techniques and manipulations with great precision. Years of working at the bench had given him rounded shoulders. That the effect of this man on the medical students was considerable can be gauged from the impression he made on Freeman:

'His personality seemed like a draught of wine to the young men of that day: his freedom of thought, freedom of manner and freedom of language, while distasteful to the more orthodox elders, was a heady but stimulating brew for us youngsters'.

Such a man was unlikely to appeal to the many grand but largely ineffectual consultant physicians who populated the Harley Street area. Wright hated pomposity and Freeman quoted him as saying 'Dignity is a mysterious gesture of the body designed to hide deficiencies of the mind.' At his first public lecture at St Mary's he said 'Unless physicians soon learn to do something, they will be reduced to a position little better than that of head nurse.'[40] Two physicians walked out. But such radical statements were welcomed by junior members of the profession, and it is no surprise that he found it easy to recruit staff of high quality.

At Netley, Wright had ready-made assistants in the medical officers under instruction, while mundane tasks such as cleaning the laboratory and its equipment were carried out under strict supervision by private soldiers. He was fortunate on arrival at St Mary's that an able first assistant was available in Captain Stewart Rankin Douglas. Educated at Haileybury and St Bartholomew's Hospital, Douglas had been one of the surgeons on probation at Netley in 1897. It was there that he first met Wright. The two had met again the following year when

Figure 9
Leonard Noon in the laboratory at St Mary's in 1910. He is smoking, something that is strictly prohibited in a bacteriology laboratory today. At this time he had advanced pulmonary tuberculosis, and he died in 1911. (The Wellcome Library, London)

Douglas had assisted the Plague Commission and impressed Wright with his ability. Unfortunately Douglas experienced much ill-health. He suffered from recurrent bouts of malaria while in India, and was further debilitated by a severe attack of amoebic dysentery while in China at the time of the Boxer rebellion. He developed a liver abscess from which he nearly died, and in 1901 he had been forced to retire from the Indian Army. His health after this was never good but he always remained cheerful and good-tempered. Temperamentally he and Wright were quite different. Douglas enjoyed fine wines and cigars, loved the outdoor life, was a keen fly fisherman and bird watcher, and possessed a Rabelaisian sense of humour.[41] Yet the two men worked amicably together for many years until Douglas left in 1920 to become director of the Medical Research Council's department of bacteriology at Hampstead. There is little doubt that Wright's success in building up a new department owed much to

Figure 10
A laboratory tea party before the First World War. Wright is listening to Douglas and Fleming while Freeman looks on. (The Wellcome Library, London)

Douglas, who exhibited great technical skill and was a gifted administrator. His initial salary was derisory, being £100 per annum, but he had private means — a small pension, and no doubt he earned money in private practice.

The remainder of the staff were recruited almost entirely from students at St Mary's. Among the earliest to join was John Freeman who was to stay in the department for the rest of his working life, as did some others. He came to St Mary's from Charterhouse and Oxford, but characteristically interrupted his medical studies to enlist as a lance-corporal in the Oxfordshire Light Infantry during the Boer War. After qualification and until his marriage in 1907 he lived with Wright, firstly at 7 Seymour Place and later at 6 Park Crescent. He developed an interest in allergic disorders and wrote an important work on hay fever. Through his influence an old school friend, Leonard Noon, came to work in the laboratory. Noon was a crack shot, and shooting was to form the main outside interest of the laboratory staff, both Freeman and Fleming being keen supporters of the hospital team. Noon's main research interest was in allergic disorders, but he was to die prematurely of tuberculosis in 1913; Colebrook was of the opinion that he was the brightest of all the young members of the laboratory. Alexander Fleming joined the department in 1906 and he was followed in 1908 by Leonard Colebrook, who was to achieve renown in the conquest of puerperal fever and in the treatment of burns. Others who followed included Parry Morgan and Carmalt Jones, both of whom

Figure 11
Wright emerging from the sea in Dorset during one of the laboratory week-end outings. He considered this the best photograph ever taken of him! (Alexander Fleming Laboratory Museum, St Mary's Hospital, London)

were later to distinguish themselves in bacteriological research. Self-financing research scientists from abroad were frequent short-term visitors and included such distinguished names as Metchnikoff and Ehrlich. Salaries for the more permanent laboratory members were far from generous and seldom more than £100 a year. In 1907 some of the ancillary workers were even more poorly rewarded. Thus the charlady, the only female on the staff, had £16 a year, the pathology lab boy £18; in contrast the post-mortem porter received £78 plus tips and the pathology porter £73.

Wright generated an excellent team spirit among his staff. One of these, Colebrook, had a cottage named 'Golter Gap' at Kimmeridge near Swanage on the Dorset coast, and occasionally they would all go down there with Wright for the weekend.[42] Their time was spent walking, swimming and climbing the cliffs. Wright did swim but had little interest in any other form of physical exercise and occupied himself with a study of the local flora. At other times he would revisit his old friends in the Netley area. In 1913, together with Colebrook, he spent some time at Hamble with his friend Keble Chatterton[43], a journalist and author, sailing in the vicinity of Southampton Water.[44]

Wright always maintained that his laboratory was a republic. Of course it was nothing of the sort and there was never doubt as to who was in charge. He was described as a benign despot. Yet he never expected anyone to undertake a task he would not do himself. He was a prodigious worker. Freeman described how, on the evening after he had been appointed as a demonstrator he found Wright in the laboratory 'in semidarkness the only light coming from two smoky yellow flares from Bunsen burners with the air cut off from their base. He was swearing heartily as he tried to perform some delicate manoeuvre with a capillary glass tube and mercury.'[45] Freeman immediately went out and bought some gas mantles, placed these over the Bunsen burners and soon had the laboratory well lit, whereupon Wright said, 'Now we can work all night.' And he probably did. His enthusiasm and undaunted pertinacity were infectious and his staff often stayed far into the night. Carmalt Jones never heard him give an order, and later wrote: 'A chief, who without orders given, kept a team of young men out of their beds till past midnight several times a week, and for years on end, had some remarkable qualities.'[46] It was an unwritten rule that the work of the day must be done that day and by medical staff, not by the technicians. It is the nature and significance of that work that is considered in the next chapter.

Notes

1 Foster WD. *Pathology as a profession in Great Britain* p4. London: Royal College of Pathologists, 1981.
2 Cope Z. *The history of St Mary's Hospital Medical School* p23. London: Heinemann, 1954.
3 MS/AD/3 28 January 1902 p375.
4 Ibid 15 October 1902 p382.
5 Ibid 9 October p378.
6 Ibid 23 October 1902 p390.
7 Cope Z. *The history of St Mary's Hospital Medical School* p56. London: Heinemann, 1954.
8 BOM 27 October 1902.
9 MS/AD/3 14 November 1902.
10 Ibid 17 December 1902.
11 BOM 23 January 1903.
12 MS/AD 6 November 1903.
13 BOM 10 February 1903.
14 Ibid 16 March 1903
15 Ibid 9 March 1905.
16 Brown K. Personal communication.
17 MS/AD 3 June 1904.
18 Ibid 12 May 1905.
19 Ibid 2 March 1906.

20 His proposers included CJ Martin, EH Starling, Victor Horsley and Sherrington but not Bruce.

21 MS/AD 18 July 1906.

22 Freeman J. *St Mary's Hospital Gazette* 1952: 98.

23 Wright AE. *A short history of the inoculation department.* Privately printed.

24 BOM 11 December 1905 pp601–3.

25 Wright AE. *A short history of the inoculation department.* Privately printed.

26 BOM 31 May 1906.

27 Ibid 29 November 1906.

28 Ibid 13 December 1906.

29 Ibid 26 November 1908.

30 Ibid. Report by Mr HA Harben to BOM 7 January 1909.

31 Master of the Household of Edward VII, later Earl of St Marylebone; President of the London Municipal Society.

32 MP and member of the London County Council.

33 Lord Justice of Appeal, and member of the Senate of London University.

34 Merchant banker who became treasurer of the inoculation department.

35 Governor of the London Hospital, and senior partner in Ralli Bros.

36 Deputy chairman, Prudential Assurance Company, and chairman of St Mary's Hospital Management Board.

37 Details of the various relationships of the inoculation department with other bodies are to be found in the recently discovered minutes of the house committee, now in the archives of St Mary's Hospital. Uncatalogued WF 1.

38 Greenwood M. [Obituary of AE Wright] *Lancet* 1947; i: 656.

39 Freeman J. *St Mary's Hospital Gazette* 1952: 54.

40 Freeman J. *BMJ* 1947; i: 659.

41 Wright had a similar sense of humour. He used to shock his women friends by asking them if they had heard what the Irish guardsman said to his girlfriend in the park: 'Your pants are coming down.' 'Is that a fact?' replied the girl. 'No, it's a prophecy!'

42 Brown K. *St Mary's Hospital Gazette* 1994; **100**: 512.

43 Lt-Com Edward Keble Chatterton RNVR (1878–1944), journalist on the *Daily Mail* and author of numerous works on seafaring.

44 CMAC PP/COL Colebrook diaries, 1 September 1913.

45 Freeman J. *St Mary's Hospital Gazette* 1952: 94.

46 Carmalt-Jones DW. *Lancet* 1947; i: 930.

Chapter 5

The Birth of Vaccine Therapy

It is a truism that human beings live in an environment containing micro-organisms capable of causing serious disease. Protection against infection arising from such hostile bacteria and parasites is, to some extent, provided by natural barriers such as the skin and the mucous membranes lining the gut and respiratory tract. (Wright achieved some notoriety in the early years of the century when he gave a lecture on the dangers of washing to a lay audience. Vigorous scrubbing of the skin often resulted in small abrasions that provided the portal of entry for organisms, giving rise to boils on the neck and other favoured sites for aggressive ablution.) Yet these surface barriers on their own provide insufficient protection and are easily breached. That we do not constantly fall victim to infection is due to other defence mechanisms that have developed during the course of evolution; the study of these constitutes the science of immunology. Infection occurs when the body is assailed by overwhelming numbers of pathogenic micro-organisms or when the body's defences are weakened or when both conditions are present. Even today the fact that some organisms are pathogenic to humans and not to animals, and vice versa, remains largely an enigma. At the end of the 19th century, with the discovery that bacteria played a major role in the causation of some human diseases, interest became focused on systems whereby invasion of the body by bacteria could be prevented or counteracted. Two rival schools of thought, known respectively as the cellular and the humoral theories of immunity, arose concerning resistance to infection.

The cellular theory was based on the experimental observations of Metchnikoff, a Russian emigré zoologist.[1] In 1883, when he was studying the microscopic appearances of living cells, he noticed that in the transparent starfish there were motile cells which had the ability to ingest foreign particles. He introduced a rose thorn under the skin of a starfish and saw that it became surrounded and engulfed by cells. In the following years he and others were able to demonstrate that fungal spores and bacteria introduced into a wide variety of animals, ranging from the flea to the rabbit, caused the capillary blood vessels to dilate at

105

the point where the organisms settled. The white cells of the blood then migrated through the capillary walls into the surrounding tissues and engulfed the foreign bacteria or spores, a process that was termed phagocytosis. Furthermore Metchnikoff was able to identify two types of cell that possessed this property. The first was the most plentiful white cell found in the peripheral blood, the neutrophil polymorpho-nuclear leucocyte — often referred to simply as neutrophils or polymorphs. This is a short-lived cell with a multilobed nucleus and numerous granules in its cytoplasm. The granules are now known to contain a complex system of enzymes capable of digesting some microbes, especially the pus-forming (pyogenic) bacteria. These leucocytes are motile and can ingest bacteria into their cytoplasm, thus enabling them to be attacked by the enzymes in the granules. This process of phagocytosis is complex and its basic mechanisms were only elucidated in the second half of the 20th century.

Metchnikoff also observed that the property of phagocytosis was possessed by certain cells present in the tissues. These he termed macrophages — in contrast to the neutrophil polymorphonuclear leucocytes that he had called microphages, though the latter term is no longer used. Macrophages are found in all parts of the body but are particularly frequent in the lung, liver, spleen and lymph nodes. They have a single rounded nucleus and plentiful cytoplasm, no granules of the type seen in the neutrophils and, unlike the latter, are long-lived. They are however motile and capable of ingesting and attacking micro-organisms. They are most effective against bacteria, viruses and parasites that live and grow in host cells. Metchnikoff proposed that these two cell types, constituting two of the essential constituents of the inflammatory reaction, played the major role in defence of the body against infecting organisms (see Figure 15, page 112). It is not surprising that at the end of the 19th century his views encountered vigorous opposition. At this time inflammation was thought by many to be an abnormal and harmful condition rather than a defence mechanism; indeed cellular uptake of organisms was regarded by many as a method of spreading disease.

The 'humoral theory' (so called because it involved the bodily humours or fluids) was based on the observation that those who had suffered from certain diseases and recovered became immune to a second attack from that disease. Such was the case in smallpox and, to a lesser extent, in typhoid fever. It was noted that blood serum taken from patients who had, for example, recovered from typhoid fever was capable of killing typhoid bacilli *in vitro*, that is in a test tube; similarly serum taken from those inoculated against typhoid, as described in

Chapter 3, also had this property. Serum from those who had not had the disease or had not been inoculated had little or no effect. These observations suggested that pathogenic organisms were killed by chemical means in the blood and phagocytes merely digested dead bacteria. There was some experimental evidence to substantiate this theory; several investigators were able to demonstrate the bactericidal properties of cell-free serum.

But killing bacteria was only one aspect of the problem. In two prevalent and potentially fatal disorders, diphtheria and tetanus, the bacteria responsible for the diseases did not enter the bloodstream and the disease manifestations were due to toxins produced by the bacteria and absorbed into the body. Behring, working in Robert Koch's laboratory in Berlin, was able to show that fluid taken from the pleural cavity of a guinea pig dying from diphtheria did not contain bacteria but that, if injected into another guinea pig, the fluid was toxic and gave rise to symptoms of the disease. If repeated small doses of the fluid were given, the animal became immune due to production by the guinea pig of its own anti-toxin. He also demonstrated that serum from immune guinea pigs was capable of neutralising diphtheria toxin *in vitro*.[2] Another of Koch's associates, Kitasato, had isolated the bacterium that caused tetanus and shown that it too produced its lethal effect by production of a toxin. Together with Behring[3] he immunised rabbits against tetanus and found, after an interval of a week, that a small quantity of cell-free serum from such a rabbit would protect another animal, in this case a mouse, against tetanus. It would also cure a mouse already infected with tetanus, and would neutralise the tetanus toxin *in vivo*. Shortly after these observations had been made, production of both diphtheria anti-toxin and tetanus anti-toxin was started in Germany and brought into clinical use.

For a very short time it was thought by some investigators that most infectious diseases were of this toxic type and that protection, and even cure, could be effected by anti-toxin antibodies. It was very soon apparent that this form of anti-toxic immunity, valuable though it was, was of practical application only in diphtheria and tetanus. It was not applicable to any other diseases, either then or now. In other infections direct killing of the infecting organisms was needed because it was the microbes themselves in the body that produced the disease. It had been shown by Nuttall[4] that cell-free serum of normal animals had a mild but active bactericidal effect on micro-organisms. Buchner[5] found that this was abolished if the serum was heated to $56°C$ and he named the factor responsible *alexine*. Shortly afterwards the German chemist

Ehrlich rechristened it *complement*, the name by which it is now universally known.

Ehrlich, a German chemist demonstrated that substances other than those of bacterial origin, including proteins of all types and even some polysaccharides, could induce production of antibodies. Such substances were known as antigens. He found that small injections of ricin, a poisonous extract of castor oil, could result in an animal forming anti-ricin antibodies. The serum from such an animal was capable of neutralising the poisonous effects of ricin if given to another animal. It soon became apparent that the outstanding characteristic of an antibody was its exquisite specificity. Thus, for example, an antibody against diphtheria toxin was useless against tetanus toxin or indeed any other toxin. The process whereby antibody reacted with toxins or bacteria was thought to be analogous to the chemical reaction of a strong acid with a strong base. It was on these grounds that Ehrlich[6] developed a chemical theory of immune mechanisms — the side-chain theory. He postulated that cells capable of forming antibodies had specific side-chains on their surface membranes that acted as receptors for antigens. The antigen had to possess the correct spatial configuration to fit the receptor, analogous to a key fitting a lock. He further proposed that when the antigen bound to the side-chain an antibody was formed and liberated into the serum.[7] A new receptor was formed in its place and the process repeated. This lock-and-key hypothesis was thought to explain the specificity that is so characteristic of antigen–antibody reactions (Figure 12).

In 1895 two further observations had strengthened the hand of those who believed that cell-free serum factors were all-important. Firstly a Frenchman, Bordet[8], ironically working in the same institute as Metchnikoff, demonstrated that bactericidal and bacteriolytic action depended upon two serum factors, namely heat-stable specific antibody and thermolabile complement. Secondly, those who favoured the humoral theory received support from the experimental work of Pfeiffer [9], another member of Koch's institute. He immunised guinea pigs against the *Vibrio cholerae*, the bacterium causing cholera. He then injected the living *Vibrio* into the peritoneal cavity of these immunised animals and found that in a few minutes the bacteria became immobile; this was followed by their degeneration and dissolution. All this was before any phagocytic cells had appeared. He concluded that the killing of infecting organisms was independent of cells and was entirely due to bactericidal substances in the serum. Metchnikoff countered this, without any sound experimental evidence, by suggesting that escaped 'ferments' (enzymes) from neutrophil

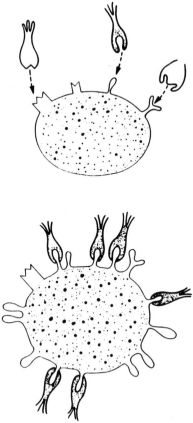

Figure 12
A diagrammatic representation of Ehrlich's side-chain theory of antibody production. He postulated that the antibody-forming cell carried a series of receptors in the form of projections or side-chains on its surface. Foreign antigens with the correct spatial configuration attached themselves to the appropriate receptor and the whole became detached and liberated into the serum as an antibody. A new receptor then formed on the cell surface and the process was repeated. (Adapted from Ehrlich P. Proc Roy Soc *1900;* **66***: 424. The Royal Society, London)*

polymorphonuclear leucocytes were responsible for killing the bacteria.

It was unfortunate that the conflict between the humoral and cellular theories of immunity was complicated by a strong element of xenophobia among the main contenders. Metchnikoff, although by birth a Russian, had settled in Paris under the aegis of Pasteur. The main protagonists of the humoral theory were German, centred for the most part in Koch's institute in Berlin. The Franco-Prussian war had ended in 1871 but the bitter memory of this defeat was uppermost in the minds of many Frenchmen. Pasteur himself was deeply resentful of German influence in scientific matters; he had returned an honorary degree received from Bonn University, describing the certificate as 'odious' and the nation as barbaric.[10] He quarrelled openly with

Robert Koch, and the latter is reported as resorting to character assassination in support of the humoral theory.[11]

Wright, and the British in general, adopted a fairly neutral stance. True, Lister did favour the French viewpoint, having studied with Pasteur; but Wright had studied in Germany and was also friendly with those working in Paris. He had a photograph of Metchnikoff in his laboratory and remained a friend of Ehrlich until the latter's death. Yet it is significant that Leishman, working with Wright at Netley in 1900, wrote in a study of the action of serum on bacteria that: 'A striking feature has been the extremely feeble power that these fluid constituents (ie blood serum) possess for destruction of the common *Staphylococcus pyogenes*, the spirillum of cholera, the micrococcus of Malta fever, the bacilli of anthrax and plague in comparison with that displayed for typhoid'.[12] He found that, even when producing conditions similar to those in the body as regards temperature and using normal fresh blood serum, the results of killing organisms by serum alone 'proved almost completely negative'. He contrasted this with the power of polymorphonuclear leucocytes to ingest and kill bacteria and devised a system whereby this could be measured in normal subjects and those with infections. His method was to incubate bacteria, cultured from a patient with an infection (eg staphylococci from an abscess), with the patient's polymorphonuclear leucocytes and then to count the number of bacteria phagocytosed within a given time by, say, 100 cells and thus obtain an average for the number of bacteria ingested by a single cell. This was then compared with the result from a control experiment, set up under identical conditions, using cells from a normal subject. By dividing the first average by the second average, he obtained a figure that he termed the phagocytic index. He claimed to demonstrate that the phagocytic power of the leucocytes was enhanced in infections.

It was thus appropriate that Wright's first major paper after arrival at St Mary's, written in collaboration with Douglas, should be concerned with reconciling the cellular and humoral theories.[13] Wright and Douglas began their paper with the statement: 'It is still a matter of uncertainty whether the blood fluids perform any role in connection with phagocytosis.' In an earlier paper[14] Wright and Windsor, another colleague at Netley, had noted the failure of serum on its own to kill certain organisms such as staphylococci, responsible for many skin infections, and the organisms causing Malta fever and plague — all diseases of topical importance at the time. What was required was a method whereby the bactericidal effects of serum and cells could be tested both separately and together; and here it is appropriate to mention a few points regarding their technique.

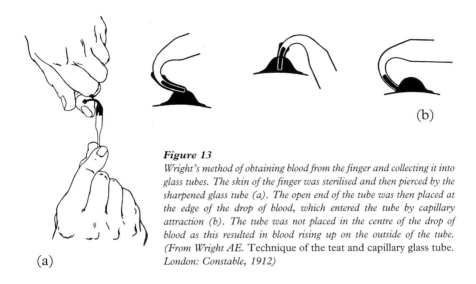

(b)

(a)

Figure 13
Wright's method of obtaining blood from the finger and collecting it into glass tubes. The skin of the finger was sterilised and then pierced by the sharpened glass tube (a). The open end of the tube was then placed at the edge of the drop of blood, which entered the tube by capillary attraction (b). The tube was not placed in the centre of the drop of blood as this resulted in blood rising up on the outside of the tube. (From Wright AE. Technique of the teat and capillary glass tube. *London: Constable, 1912)*

Wright and his associates differed from many of their continental contemporaries in that they worked with human serum and cells. It is difficult today to visualise the paucity of technical methods and apparatus that existed in hospital laboratories at the beginning of the 20th century. Syringes were primitive, made of poorly calibrated thick glass tubes and with ill-fitting metal plungers such that they frequently distributed their favours in both directions when required to perform an injection. Venepuncture was rare and the plungers provided an inefficient method of drawing blood up into the syringe. Yet in order to test the bactericidal power of various blood constituents it was necessary to obtain reliable measured samples from humans. Wright not only devised such methods, but also developed tests using only minute quantities of blood and serum. He did this by employing very simple materials — rubber teats, sealing wax, plasticine and capillary glass tubing; in 1912 he was to publish the cumulative results of many years research into such methodology in his classic text *Technique of the teat and capillary glass tube.* The many methods, or laboratory tricks as he called them, owed much to the manipulative skills of Stewart Douglas, and in later years to Alexander Fleming. Wright often quoted Ludwig's dictum '*die Methode ist alles*', which he loosely translated as 'the whole of science lies in technique'.[15]

Before considering their paper it is worth examining some of the methods used at that time for collecting blood. In describing 'drawing off blood in an aseptic manner', Wright[16] advocated sterilising the finger 'either by flaming it with alcohol or passing it repeatedly through

Figure 14

A collection of Wright's blood tubes in which blood has clotted, the clots having retracted and separated from the clear yellow serum. Some empty tubes and some capillary tubes, one with attached rubber teat, can be seen on the right of the picture. (Alexander Fleming Laboratory Museum, St Mary's Hospital, London)

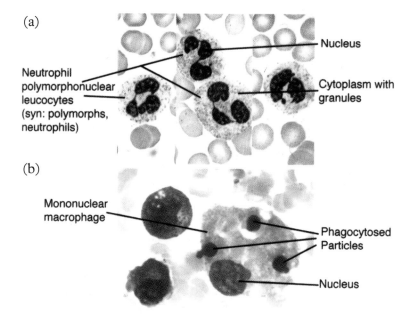

Figure 15

(a) Neutrophil polymorphonuclear leucocytes in the peripheral blood. These are capable of ingesting, ie phagocytosing, bacteria. (b) Macrophages, which can also ingest bacteria and foreign particles into their cytoplasm. The two smaller cells on the left of the picture are lymphocytes. (Professor K Gatter's specimen, John Radcliffe Hospital, Oxford)

the flame of a Bunsen burner' — not a course of action likely, one would imagine, to encourage colleagues or patients to volunteer for the procedure. It says much for Wright's personality that he was never short of either. The finger was pricked with the sharp end of a capillary tube that itself led into a small container called a blood capsule (Figure 13). Wright had devised these capsules and made them himself using a blowpipe flame and wide-bore glass tubing. Blood passed into the capsule by capillarity and when sufficient had been obtained the ends of the tube were sealed in a flame, taking care not to heat the blood. When the blood clotted, the clot retracted and separated from the serum. When serum was required the capsule was broken open at the point where the straight limb runs out from the capsule, by means of a glass-cutting knife which Wright himself had devised. Serum could then be drawn off using one of his capillary pipettes. If uncoagulated blood was required, he mixed four volumes of blood with one volume of 5% sodium citrate to remove the calcium. He also devised a series of calibrated pipettes made of capillary glass tubing, enabling him to use extremely small, but measured, quantities of serum or bacterial cultures in his immunological investigations.

To answer the question whether serum modified bacteria so that they became more susceptible to phagocytosis, Wright and Douglas conducted a series of carefully planned experiments employing a modified form of Leishman's phagocytic index to measure their results. They mixed together in capillary tubes, under varying conditions, measured volumes of suspensions of staphylococci, serum or plasma, and the white cells of the blood. The mixtures were then incubated at 37°C and the contents of the capillary tubes were gently blown out on to glass slides, spread into a film, appropriately stained and the numbers of bacteria counted in 50 or 100 white cells. The average number of organisms in a white cell was then calculated. Their procedure differed from Leishman's in that their experiments were conducted in capillary tubes, thus enabling them to use very small quantities of reagents. Also rather than using serum derived from clotted blood they often employed plasma taken from blood that had been citrated, to remove calcium, and thus did not clot. The citrated blood could be centrifuged in a tube, resulting in separation of the red blood cells, which settled at the bottom of the tube, from the supernatant consisting of clear cell-free plasma. In between these was the buffy coat composed of the white cells. Their paper took the form of answering a series of questions.

Firstly, did substitution of another medium other than serum or plasma exert an influence on phagocytosis? They found that phagocytosis of staphylococci, the bacteria they used in all their experiments, was enhanced by the presence of serum or plasma, there being no difference between the two, but that substitution of either by normal saline failed to do so.

Secondly, they asked did preheating serum to 60°C have an effect on phagocytosis? Unheated serum greatly enhanced phagocytosis, but this effect was completely nullified if the serum was preheated to 60°C before mixing with the staphylococci and white cells. They did not consider that heating the serum produced inhibiting elements, as the same effect was obtained if saline was substituted for serum. Rather they concluded that heat destroyed the substances in the serum that enhanced phagocytosis.

Thirdly, they asked: 'Do the blood fluids cooperate in phagocytosis by exerting a direct stimulating effect upon the phagocytes, or by effecting a modification in the bacteria?' To answer this they compared the effect of serum inactivated by heating before it came into contact with either bacteria or white blood cells with that of serum incubated after it had come into contact with bacteria but before it had come into contact with the white corpuscles. They found that when unheated serum was incubated at 37°C for 15 minutes with the staphylococci and then heated for 15 minutes to 60°C, cooled and then the white cells added to the mixture, there was no inhibition of phagocytosis. On the other hand if the serum had been heated to 60°C, cooled and then mixed with the staphylococci and white cells very little phagocytosis of the bacteria took place.

Wright and Douglas satisfied themselves that they had 'conclusive proof that the body fluids modify bacteria in a manner which renders them a ready prey to phagocytes'. They named this property an *opsonic* phenomenon, from the Greek opson (I cater for; I prepare victuals for). The serum factors that produced this effect were called *opsonins*. (It was not until the second half of the 20th century that it was established that opsonins formed part of a complex system of proteins, including some components of complement as well as some types of antibody.) They also claimed that opsonins were specific for each species of microbe. Thus the opsonic power of the serum in infection by one species of bacterium was increased in infection by that organism but was unaffected in regard to any other species of microbe. They established a method which they considered measured the opsonic power of the serum. Employing the micromethods referred to above, a known volume of the patient's serum was measured into a capillary pipette and this was mixed with an equal volume of a suspension of a culture of the infecting organism and a similar volume of white blood cells, that is neutrophil polymorphonuclear leucocytes taken from a normal subject. This mixture was incubated for a short time at 37°C. The white cells were then spread out on a glass slide, stained, examined under the high power of the microscope and the number of bacteria ingested in each of 100 white cells counted. The average number of bacteria in the white cells was then calculated. Coincident with this, an identical procedure was undertaken substituting serum from a normal subject for that of the patient. The *opsonic index* was calculated by dividing the average number of bacteria in the white cells in the mixture containing the patient's serum by the average number of bacteria in the white cells of the mixture containing the normal serum. This was an adaptation of the method, referred to above, developed by Leishman to study the phagocytic power of leucocytes.

Wright was firmly of the opinion that the opsonic index was an accurate measure of the patient's resistance to infection. He claimed it was low when the patient presented but that a rise in the index after vaccination was a clear indication of a good response and increased resistance. The fact that sometimes the index was actually *lower* after vaccination, a phenomenon he termed the negative phase, he explained as a result of the initial dose of vaccine being too large. In any case he claimed that it was rapidly replaced by a rebound to a level much higher than that before vaccination. In his subsequent work he insisted that the dose of vaccine be controlled by constant reference to the opsonic index so that production of the negative phase, when he conjectured that the patient would be more susceptible to infection, could be avoided. It is regrettable that he made no allowance for the considerable natural variability of the index that occurred from time to time in any given subject, and that he made no attempt at any statistical assessment of his results. Wright's work on opsonins did not go unchallenged. In 1908 Watson Cheyne, a surgeon at King's College Hospital who had some training in bacteriology, questioned the significance of opsonins.[17] He asked why there was no difference in opsonic content of serum between age groups when it was known that resistance to infection varied according to age. The two men were to cross swords again over the treatment of wounds during the Great War.

Wright's method has been described in some detail because it was to form the foundation of a system of diagnosis, prognosis and treatment for infections — vaccine therapy — that was to last for 40 years. As well as stimulating intense controversy in the medical profession and having considerable implications for the staffing and structure of hospitals, it was to form the subject of two important works of contemporary literature[18]: Shaw's *The doctor's dilemma* and Sinclair Lewis's *Arrowsmith*. Thus it was both unfortunate and ironic that the resolution of the acrimonious debate concerning the cellular and humoral theories of immunity, the main purpose of the paper by Wright and Douglas, had little effect on the main thrust of medical research in the area of cellular function in the immune reaction. Indeed for the next 40 years cellular immunity and the synergism between cells and serum factors was largely ignored. At late as 1933 the cellular contribution received little more than a passing mention in a standard work on immunity.[19] Research workers became obsessed with the nature and function of antibodies and complement to the exclusion of all else. This in spite of ignorance regarding the cellular site of antibody production, a lack of knowledge that was not to be rectified until the 1950s. A review of the controversy between cellular and humoral protagonists reveals how medical and biological investigations into immunological phenomena were neglected in favour of 'studies and theories of the ever chemically oriented Ehrlich, and given a strong push by the famous chemist Svante Arrhenius'.[20] Such studies had the added attraction of not involving patients and could be confined to the test tube in an isolated laboratory. Similarly clinical bacteriologists, convinced that antibody and complement investigations were the key to all infectious disease control, were able to carry out their work by culture of the offending organism and examination of the patient's serum without resorting to the apparently more difficult techniques involved in studying living cells and histological sections. The ease with which these antibody studies could be conducted without the physical presence of the patient resulted in their receiving a disproportionate amount of attention.[21] The cellular response to infection, evidenced by the polymorphonuclear leucocytes in acute infections and the predominance of mononuclear cells and giant cells in some chronic infections, was largely ignored and its significance unquestioned.

Wright failed to follow up the cellular phenomena in infections by, for example, investigating the role of mononuclear cells in chronic infections such as tuberculosis. By 1902 he was convinced, rightly, of the results of anti-typhoid inoculation and had formed the decided, but erroneous, opinion that such vaccination could be used not only in prevention of disease but also in the treatment of established infections. The idea of stimulating the body's defences was admirable but the means whereby he hoped to secure this were flawed and based on totally inadequate evidence. Yet Wright's misguided judgment must be viewed in the context of the times. The pattern of disease at the end of the Victorian age and the beginning of the 20th century was radically different from that in the late 1990s. Infections formed the principal illnesses among children and young adults, and death from such infections was common. Hospital wards were filled with young men and women dying of pneumonia; staphylococcal infections were frequent and, if complicated by septicaemia, usually fatal; maternal mortality due to streptococcal infection (puerperal fever) was the bane of obstetric practice and carried a 30 per cent mortality; other streptococcal infections, particularly those of the upper respiratory tract, with their serious complication of rheumatic fever and the common sequel of chronic cardiac disability, were all too familiar in general practice. There was a complete absence of any specific treatment for these conditions. In the 1903 edition of his textbook Osler[22] described pneumococcal lobar pneumonia as 'a self-limited disease which can neither be aborted nor cut short by any known means at our command'. Treatment was bed rest in 'a bright light room', 'thoroughly well ventilated' and a diet of 'plain water or lemonade given freely'. And this in a disease which in 1890 in the United States had an annual death rate of 189.94 per 100,000 of the population. Infectious diseases of all types were the main cause of death as is well illustrated by the figures for tuberculosis. In the USA in 1900 the mortality from tuberculosis was 110 per 100,000 of the population. (By 1950 the figure had been reduced, as a consequence of public health measures and antibiotics, to 5.4 and by 1975 was 1.2 per 100,000.[23]) It is thus understandable that in such an era anything that had a claim to specific treatment, even if based on flimsy scientific evidence, would catch the attention of the medical profession.

And the evidence was flimsy. In 1902, before his arrival at St Mary's, Wright published a paper in which he claimed that staphylococcal vaccine effected a cure in localised chronic staphylococcal infections of the skin, such as boils, furunculosis (infection of hair follicles), sycosis (barber's rash) and acne. He prepared the vaccine from bacteria cultured from the patient's lesions. This he did by growing the organism, usually *Staphylococcus aureus*, in nutrient broth for three weeks. He then killed the organisms by heat and the addition of dilute lysol. After demonstrating that the dead bacteria were non-toxic when injected into guinea pigs, he proceeded to inject the vaccine into the patient's flank, starting with 1 ml and giving two further injections of 1.5 ml at intervals of two weeks. Coincident with this he, or rather Leishman who was working with him, estimated the phagocytic power of the patient's white cells, which Wright claimed was increased as a result of his inoculations. In his paper Wright reported results of his treatment on six patients, all suffering from recurrent boils or other infections of the skin and subcutaneous tissues caused by staphylococci. In four patients lasting clinical improvement was claimed; in the other two cases there was marked, but only temporary, regression of the lesion which he attributed, in a later paper, to 'deficient power of response to the inoculation'. It was on these six patients that the whole edifice of vaccine therapy was established. This paper was described by Foster[24] as 'one of the most important in the history of medical bacteriology', not because of its scientific value (which he dismissed, with justification, as worthless) but because of its influence on development of medical bacteriology. When one considers the numerous controls, the extensive statistical trials and the endless committees on safety that any new drug has to pass through before it is allowed on to the market today, it does indeed seem remarkable that this mode of therapy was adopted without any critical assessment. But at the beginning of the 20th century such safeguards were not in place. One point in favour of vaccine therapy was that it seemed safe. This was in contrast to serum therapy, based on injecting serum taken from an actively immunised animal, which on occasions in sensitised subjects produced alarming symptoms of anaphylactic shock with acute respiratory distress, vascular collapse and even death. This process of passive immunisation had been successful in neutralising the toxic conditions of tetanus and diphtheria, as already mentioned, but it was of no use in other bacterial infections.

A year after publication of his paper with Douglas, Wright gave a lecture[25] to the Medical Graduates College and Polyclinic making strong claims for vaccination as a treatment. He started this lecture with a passage that was to be much quoted in years to come. It gives an impression of the crusading zeal twinned often with uncritical dogmatism that characterised much of Wright's work:

'The therapeutic method which I propose to consider with you today is a method as yet almost unexploited. None the less it is a method which is, if I am not mistaken, destined to revolutionise our ordinary practice in dealing with localised bacterial invasions. In dealing with these our treatment has in the past consisted in making repeated applications of antiseptics or, in the case where this is impracticable, extirpating the seat of infection . . . The time will come when, before embarking on either of these methods of treatment, and above all before acquiescing in a policy of leaving the bacterial invasion unchecked, an endeavour will be made in every case to arrest the invasion and to prevent its recurrence by calling into action the forces of resistance which lie latent in the organism (ie man). The physician of the future will, I foresee, take upon himself the role of an immunizator.'

In this lecture Wright revealed his obsession with what he termed the *negative phase*, when the opsonic index appeared to be reduced and the patient's resistance actually diminished. He claimed this was always followed by enhanced resistance or, as he put it, 'a higher base line of immunity'. He also extended the field of infections that could be treated to include those he considered as due to the colon bacillus, *Escherichia coli*, in patients with gall bladder disease, appendicitis, cystitis and other urinary tract infections. It seems to have escaped the notice of many doctors that in fact the recovery of patients might be due to their own innate powers of resistance rather than to vaccine therapy. This could readily have been established in a simple statistical trial using appropriate control subjects. Yet this crude form of vaccine therapy was adopted with profound implications for medical practice which will be considered in the next chapter.

Notes

1 Tauber AI, Chernyak L. *Metchnikoff and the origins of immunology*. New York: Oxford University Press, 1991.
2 Behring E. Unter suchvenger ueber das Zustande Kommen der Diphtherie-Immunität und der Tetanus-Immunität bei Thieren. *Dtsch Med Woch* 1890; **16**: 1145.
3 Behring E, Kitsato S. Ueber das Zustande Kommen der Diphtherie-Immunität und der Tetanus-Immunität bei Thieren. *Dtsch Med Woch* 1890; **16**: 1113.
4 Nuttall G. *Z Hyg* 1888; 4: 353.
5 Buchner H. *ZentralBl Baccteriol* 1889; **6**: 561.
6 Ehrlich P. *Proc Roy Soc* 1900; **66**: 424.
7 Fudenbereg HH, Stites DP, Caldwell JL, Wells JV. *Basic and clinical immunology*. Los Altos, California: Lange Medical Publications, 1978.
8 Bordet J. *Ann Inst Pasteur* 1895; **9**: 462.
9 Pfeiffer R. *Z Hyg* 1895; **18**: 1.
10 Silverstein AM. Cellular versus humoral immunity. *Cell Immunol* 1979; **48**: 208.
11 Tauber AI, Chernyak L. *Metchnikoff and the origins of immunology* p104. New York: Oxford University Press, 1991.
12 Leishman WB. *BMJ* 1902; **i**: 73.
13 Wright AE, Douglas SR. *Proc Roy Soc London* 1903; **72**: 357.
14 Wright AE, Windsor F. *J Hyg* 1902; **2**: 357.
15 Wright AE. *Handbook of the technique for the teat and capillary glass tube* pvi. London Constable and Co, 1912.
16 Ibid p62.
17 Cheyne WW. *Lancet* 1908; **1**: 1816.
18 Lowy I. *Med Hist* 1988; **32**: 314.
19 Topley WWC. *An outline of immunity*. London, 1933.
20 Silverstein AM. *Cell Immunol* 1979; **48**: 208.
21 Humphrey JH, White RG. In: *Immunology for students of medicine*. 3rd edn p44. London: Blackwell's Scientific Publications, 1970.
22 Osler W. *The principles and practice of medicine* p109. New York and London: D Appleton and Co, 1903.
23 Beeson PB. In: *Oxford Companion to Medicine*. Walton J, Beeson PB, R Bodley Scott, eds. Oxford University Press, 1986.
24 Foster WD. *A history of medical bacteriology and immunity* p142. London: William Heinemann, 1970.
25 Wright AE. *BMJ* 11903; **i**: 1069.

Chapter 6

Vaccines, Polemics and Greenwood

Convinced of the efficacy of vaccines, not only in prevention but also in treatment of infections, Wright proceeded to make them in large quantities. At first their production was confined to a small room in the basement of the old medical school at St Mary's Hospital; later, much larger quarters were to be occupied for this purpose. The principle involved in making a vaccine appeared to Wright as pleasingly simple. He classified vaccines into two broad types. The first, autogenous vaccine, was a sterilised pure culture of bacteria obtained directly from the patient's lesion. The second, known as stock vaccine, was a sterilised culture of the same species of bacteria but not from a specific patient. The organisms were grown on solid media and then suspended in normal saline. They were sterilised, preferably by heating to 55°C or 60°C but sometimes by addition of an antiseptic such as lysol. After test culture, to ascertain that the organisms were no longer viable, an appropriate dilution of the suspension was placed in a sterile glass bottle which was then sealed with a sterile rubber cap. When vaccine was required, it was withdrawn by plunging a needle through the rubber cap after the latter had been sterilised by wiping it with an antiseptic.

This method of storing sterile fluids for injection, invented by Wright, was in use until after the Second World War. Wright also devised a method for sterilising hypodermic needles so that they could be used repeatedly, with a single syringe containing vaccine, on a series of patients — helpful if a large number of people were to be inoculated against, say, typhoid in the army. Indeed this method had first been employed at Netley for just that purpose. Wright had a small oil bath provided with a 'regulator' that kept the oil constantly at 140°C. The hot oil was then drawn up through the needle into the syringe. Some at Netley had expressed doubts as to whether this was sufficient to kill all pathogenic organisms. Wright demonstrated its efficacy in a dramatic manner. He took a needle and syringe, plunged the needle into some horse manure, then sterilised both needle and syringe by the heated oil method and followed this by using the syringe and needle to inject a quantity of saline into his own thigh with no ill effect.[1] This method of sterilising hypodermic needles was still in use in many units in the British and other armies in 1940.

Wright was much in demand as a lecturer. Indeed, it was mainly through his lectures and writings that vaccine therapy became widely known to both the medical profession and the lay public. His own reputation was enhanced considerably by the favourable publicity and by his knighthood. His private practice increased, and society hostesses became desirous of his company at their dinners and receptions. Although he found these occasions irksome they generated numerous donations, which played a major role in financing his department. His lecture tour of the United States and Canada, undertaken from September to November 1906, spread the gospel of vaccine therapy to the New World[2] and was one of the factors in securing the lucrative agreement with Parke Davis.

One of the most significant and lasting results of Wright's advocacy of vaccine therapy affected the staffing and construction of British hospitals.[3] At the beginning of the 20th century, in contrast to France and Germany, pathology in England and Wales, though not in Scotland, was carried out by clinicians as a part-time activity. Although by the early 1900s there were a few specialist pathologists, mainly at London teaching hospitals, it was not until vaccine therapy became popular that it was deemed essential to have whole-time specialists in the subject. This form of treatment, which necessitated not only isolation of the organism responsible for the patient's infection but also preparation of the vaccine and control of its usage by means of the opsonic index, required the undivided attention of a bacteriologist. The division of pathology into its various disciplines — diagnostic histopathology, haematology, clinical biochemistry and bacteriology — was not generally recognised and the pathologist had to cover all aspects of the subject. The predominance of infectious disease, and with it the possibility of vaccine therapy, ensured that bacteriological interests had pride of place in the pathology laboratory.

In 1903, out of 186 non-teaching hospitals and dispensaries in London, only 11 listed a pathologist as a member of staff. In only one of these, the Central London Throat, Nose and Ear Hospital, was the holder of the post specified as a bacteriologist — he is listed as Mr St G Reid. In the teaching hospitals there were pathological departments but the head of the laboratories was often not a member of the consultant staff; indeed Wright himself was not elected to the staff when he first arrived at St Mary's. In the provinces the position was no better. The large cities, Liverpool, Manchester,

Newcastle, Sheffield, Birmingham and Bristol had pathologists at their central hospitals but, as in the case of Manchester Royal Infirmary and the Royal Infirmary in Newcastle, they were not always members of the consultant staff. Aside from these there were no appointments and much of the pathology, which for the most part was diagnostic bacteriology, was the responsibility of the local medical officer of health, whose laboratory was often situated some distance from a hospital. By 1920 the position had changed. In London there were 15 consultant pathologists outside the teaching hospitals, and this in spite of a decrease in the total number of such hospitals and dispensaries. In the provinces there were 48 specialist consultant pathologists, some of these specifically listed as bacteriologists; at the Bristol Royal Infirmary there was, in addition to a consultant pathologist, an assistant for pathology vaccine treatment, one Dr J M H Munro. These increases in medical staff were accompanied by an inevitable recruitment of additional non-medical technical staff and construction of new buildings, or conversion of old ones, to house laboratories. Much of this expansion, which was to continue in the following years, can be traced to Wright's zeal in promoting his subject. He was tireless in furthering the interests of his staff and used his reputation to effect. On 25 July 1912 Douglas was elected an additional member of the staff at St Mary's[4] but it was not until 1916 that Freeman achieved this status[5]; a year later Fleming was officially appointed[6] as a pathologist and assistant medical officer to the venereal disease department.

By 1910 interest in vaccines as therapeutic agents, as opposed to prophylactics, was intense. Sir William Church, recently retired as senior physician at St Bartholomew's Hospital, convened a series of six special meetings of the Royal Society of Medicine, of which he was president, to consider the value and limitations of the method — something unprecedented in the history of that body. The whole of the first session was devoted to an address, perhaps more accurately described as a harangue, by Wright.[7] He used the occasion to plead the cause of bacteriology as a separate discipline and, more especially, for physicians to be educated in the subject. He considered applied bacteriology to be 'the essential and indispensable part of medicine, and that the practice of medicine must be recognised upon that basis'. In the most forceful manner he pointed out that accurate diagnosis of infectious disease depended on bacteriology, illustrating his argument by drawing attention to its crucial role in typhoid fever, diphtheria and tuberculosis. Physical signs elicited by the physician at the bedside were not enough, and in any case were frequently apparent only when disease was far advanced. Bacteriology often provided, in addition to an accurate diagnosis, an early diagnosis. Pleading for adequate education in the subject he argued that 'No one should qualify as a medical practitioner without some elementary knowledge of bacteriology, and no one should proceed to any of the higher qualifications without a thorough training in this science.'

In those days infectious disease formed the major part of medical practice, and Wright maintained that bacteriological work was called for in nearly every case. This necessitated the consulting physician delegating the skilled work of diagnosis, that is, ascertaining the nature and identity of the organism causing the infection, to a bacteriologist who in many instances did not himself confront the patient. Instead he would be presented with a specimen, often obtained in an inappropriate manner and from an inappropriate site, by the physician and be expected to issue a report without being fully informed as to the nature of the problem he was expected to solve. He was seldom allowed to advise on the most suitable specimen to be examined or on the method whereby it should be obtained. The bacteriologist was being treated as a second-class citizen. The physician would reassure the patient that he would find out 'what was the matter', meaning all too often that someone else would do so while he, in those days of almost universal private practice, pocketed the fee. Wright put the matter bluntly, referring to ' the case of the man whose studies have not covered the whole of his professional work and who arranges to delegate to others that portion of the work which he has omitted to learn, while retaining for himself responsibility for the whole along with the higher scale of rewards which goes with that responsibility.' He compared this state of affairs to patients being treated by unqualified practitioners. This was indeed strong stuff and was delivered to the large number of physicians from Harley Street and its environs, many of whom he considered 'in everything that appertains to bacteriology more uninstructed than the educated layman'. It is unsurprising that Wright was not liked by this branch of the profession.

Wright based his case firstly on the fact that it was not possible to administer vaccine therapy without precise knowledge of the infecting organism. Indeed the vaccine had to be prepared in many instances from the bacteria isolated from the patient to whom it was to be administered. Secondly, he maintained that it was not possible to administer the vaccine without controlling its dosage. This control was achieved by reference to the opsonic index, thus enabling the vaccinator to avoid Wright's much-loved 'negative phase' when, following inoculation, the patient's resistance to infection could actually decrease for a short time. He spoilt his case not only by insisting on this test, which was to be totally discredited, but also by the grossly exaggerated claims he made for the efficacy of this form of therapy. He maintained, on the basis of a few uncontrolled case reports, that it was of value in such disorders as epilepsy, burns and cystic disease of the breast, in which there was no proof that primary bacterial infection played any role.

Wright's address received a mixed reception but adverse criticism was in the main reserved for his comments on the role of the physician rather than for his claims as to the therapeutic value of vaccines. Yet there were cautionary voices on the latter point. Kingston Fowler, senior physician at the Middlesex and Brompton Hospitals, said[8] that if he were 'pressed to produce from his personal experience the evidence upon which my belief in their value [ie that of vaccines] is founded, I fear I should be unable to do so'. Fowler had an extensive practice among well-to-do patients with tuberculosis and had not seen a single case where benefit had resulted from use of vaccine. Indeed one of the greatest disappointments and scandals relating to vaccine therapy was in the treatment and prevention of this disease. Robert Koch had identified the cause when he isolated the tuberculosis bacillus in 1884. Under circumstances of great secrecy he produced a vaccine, tuberculin, from a glycerine extract of killed bacilli. This, he claimed, could protect from, and even cure some forms of tuberculosis. Koch announced his discovery at the International Medical Congress in Berlin in 1900.[9] Alas, sound evidence that tuberculin was effective was lacking and it had the disadvantage of producing unpleasant side-effects. Yet the doctrine of 'if it isn't hurting it isn't working' applied and it remained in use in some clinics up until the 1930s. Tuberculin did have some use in a diagnostic skin test, but it was not until the production of BCG (*Bacille Calmette–Guérin*) that an effective vaccine was produced. Mistakenly Wright maintained that tuberculin therapy was of value, especially in the non-pulmonary forms of the disease, and administered it until after the Great War.

The most telling comments at the Royal Society of Medicine, however, were made by T J Horder[10], later to be Lord Horder. At that time he was physician to the Great Northern Hospital but only a medical registrar at St Bartholomew's, where he was elected assistant physician in 1912 and a full member of the staff in 1921. He was the greatest clinician of his day and was noted for his caustic criticism of his seniors. In the discussion of Wright's lecture he drew attention to the lack of scientific evidence as to the value of this form of treatment and to the glaring absence of any proper control series. He suggested that in order to obtain a sufficient number of patients for statistical analysis a group of physicians should cooperate and pool their experience in a coordinated trial. The idea was in advance of the time and fell on stony ground.

Horder argued strongly against reliance on the opsonic index. This index was another of Wright's ideas that was admirable in concept, in that it was an attempt to introduce an element of measurement into therapeutics, but poor in execution. As such it had excited widespread interest but some formidable critics.[11,12] Prominent among the latter was Dr Major Greenwood — 'Major' was his Christian name, not his rank — who was to become one of medicine's most distinguished statisticians. He subjected to rigorous statistical analysis the raw data provided, freely it must be said, by Alexander Fleming who had performed many of the estimations in Wright's laboratory, and by Strangeways and his colleagues in Cambridge.[13] He showed that much of the evidence 'ostensibly advanced to prove the trustworthiness of the opsonic index does in fact assume the truth of what is demonstrated'. There were two serious sources of error: those of technique and those of sampling.[14] With regard to technique there were considerable difficulties in making suitable preparations, owing to the great variation in the number and distribution of the bacteria exposed to the phagocytes. Examination of individual cell counts revealed a strikingly skewed frequency distribution, providing a strong indication that the sampling procedure was faulty and far from random. There was a marked bias towards counting only those cells that were easily identified as containing bacteria. Greenwood found that variations in the index that were attributed to infection could be accounted for by chance. This view was later to be supported by workers in other centres. Physicians listening to Wright in May and June 1910 had already come to the conclusion on intuitive grounds that vaccines could be given safely without reference to the opsonic index and, apart from the laboratory at St Mary's, the procedure was completely abandoned. Behind his back medical colleagues referred to him as Sir Almost Wright or as Sir Always Wrong.[15]

The absence of specific treatment for most infections ensured that vaccine therapy kept a place in the physician's therapeutic armamentarium until the advent of sulphonamides in the late 1930s. Its use had been severely criticised by this time, particularly when employed in acute infections. Dudgeon, professor of pathology at St Thomas's Hospital, in a monograph on the subject[16], wrote that he was 'directly opposed to vaccine therapy in the acute stages of generalised infections' and furthermore there was 'no proof that an injection of an autogenous or stock vaccine had any therapeutic value'.

Figure 16
*Major Greenwood, one of the founders of medical statistics. (Dunhill
M.* Medical Dictators. *London: Keynes Press)*

In chronic or relapsing infections, as in recurrent staphylococcal boils,
it was considered by some medical men that treatment shaded into
prophylaxis and perhaps the use of vaccines might be of more value.[17]
After the Second World War, in reviewing the whole era of vaccine
therapy, it was customary to dismiss the entire concept as fraudulent.[18]

And yet in the first years of the 21st century, perhaps we can allow
ourselves second thoughts. The concept of giving a vaccine after the
patient has become infected is not after all so bizarre. Rabies vaccine
has until recently always been administered after the patient has
received a dog bite. More recently, hepatitis B vaccine is given before
symptoms and signs of disease are manifest. There are increasing
efforts to treat those infected with the human immunodeficiency virus
along the same lines and there is some optimism that there are
possibilities for developing vaccines for non-communicable diseases,

such as cancer, by producing them with new methods of peptide synthesis, recombinant DNA technology and genetic manipulation.[19] Increasing resistance of organisms to antibiotics has generated renewed enthusiasm for prophylactic vaccines in prevention of infection, and the handbook on *Immunisation against infectious disease* issued by the British Department of Health in 1996 listed 22 infections where preventive vaccination is recommended.[20] It may be that in the future physicians will look back on Wright's efforts, primitive though they were, as a significant milestone in therapeutic endeavour.

Wright's international reputation was such that in 1911 he was invited by the Chamber of Mines of Johannesburg to visit South Africa. The gold and diamond mines in the Transvaal were a source of considerable wealth but the mines themselves were difficult to work. Large numbers of black Africans were brought into the area to perform this dangerous task but proved very susceptible to respiratory disease; and the directors of the mining companies were anxious to discover a method of prophylactic inoculation against 'the scourge of pneumonia which decimates the fresh arrivals among the workers in the Transvaal mines'. They sent a request for Wright to visit South Africa and he at once asked for leave of absence from St Mary's. The matter must have been considered one of some urgency as the chairman of the board of management of the hospital 'in the absence of the board, consulted two members of the staff who considered it desirable, partly in the interests of the hospital, to give Sir Almroth Wright the requested leave'.[21] There is no indication of any hidden significance conveyed by the words 'partly in the interests of the hospital'; nor is there anything to suggest that the two persons consulted were the physicians who walked out in disgust when Wright gave his inaugural lecture at St Mary's. It was thought, no doubt correctly, that Wright having been summoned by an organisation commanding immense wealth it might be of distinct advantage to a hospital in straitened circumstances though, as with so many such financial arrangements connected with the inoculation department, no records exist. Stewart Douglas was placed in temporary charge during Wright's absence, with Dr F C Martley as his deputy. This latter appointment was not well received by the laboratory staff,[22] as Martley was by no means a great bacteriologist. He did have other virtues including genius in financial matters, a point greatly in his favour as the laboratory was self-financing and needed a reliable person to keep the books in order during Wright's absence. Some members of the staff threatened resignation but nothing came of it. Colebrook in his diary records that Wright was seen at his worst over this appointment.

Wright embarked on 9 September 1911, accompanied by two of his assistants, W Parry Morgan and R W Dodgson. It is not known what fee Wright received, but the financial inducements to his assistants were sizable: they collected £150 a month and all expenses. On arrival in Johannesburg Wright stayed at the Little Athenaeum Club, but the assistants were put up at the noisy and uncomfortable Carlton Hotel. It is understandable that Colebrook, who was hard up, should be upset at not being included in the party, although he was given first refusal should one of the others decline the invitation. Unsurprisingly they did not. By the beginning of November, however, Wright cabled for additional help and Colebrook, much to the annoyance of Douglas who was left seriously short of staff, sailed on RMS *Walmer Castle* and arrived in Johannesburg on 6 December. The month-long voyage proved an emotional disaster; while on board he fell violently in love with one of his fellow passengers, a Miss Dumbleton who was a 'cello-playing manic depressive. For the next few months, totally distracted from serious work, he spent most of his time consoling her in a series of 'nervous breakdowns'. It says much for Wright's patience, and his regard for Colebrook, that he looked upon this unsatisfactory state of affairs with benign amusement.

From a medical point of view the South African expedition was notable for two reasons. Firstly, it gave Wright first-hand experience of chemotherapy, which was adversely to bias his judgment against this form of treatment for the rest of his life. Secondly, it provided further insight into the problems of prophylactic inoculations.

Ehrlich,[23] working in Frankfurt, was convinced that the answer to treatment of infection lay in chemotherapy. He hoped to produce drugs that acted against pathogenic bacteria but were harmless to normal body tissues and cells. This was his concept of the 'magic bullet'. To this end he developed a series of arsenical compounds which he and his assistants tested on *Treponema pallidum*, the microbe responsible for syphilis. By 1909 one of these, 606 or Salvarsan, was proved to be effective though it did have painful side-effects. The success of this treatment stimulated him and his colleagues to try other compounds in a variety of bacterial infections. Pneumonia, with its high mortality among young people, was an obvious choice for their investigations and in 1911 Morgenroth[24], working in Berlin, reported that 'aethylhydrocupreinhydrochlorate', known more conveniently as optochin, was effective against *Pneumococcus*, the bacterium responsible for lobar pneumonia. Its potency was established both *in vitro* and in experimental animals. Wright[25] gave great praise to Morgenroth for this work:

'These experiments are destined to stand out as a landmark in the history of pharmacotherapy, because they furnish the first demonstration of the possibility of preventing and curing a bacterial — as distinguished from a protozoal or spirochaetal — infection by the administration of a drug.'

Interestingly, Morgenroth used mice as his experimental animals, as Florey was to do 35 years later with penicillin, to demonstrate the effectiveness of his drug. He infected a group of mice with pneumococci, treated one half of the group with optochin and left the other half untreated, and found that all the latter died whereas the vast majority of the treated group survived. Wright knew of this work, and furthermore news reached him that the drug was effective in humans. He was sent a supply of optochin and carried out a series of experiments similar to those of Morgenroth. The effectiveness of the drug was obvious but disturbing features soon became apparent, in both Germany and London, when it was given to humans. Morgenroth cabled to Wright in South Africa that of 21 patients with pneumonia treated by him three had developed amblyopia, that is impaired vision. All recovered when the drug was discontinued. Wright's patients were less fortunate in that two of the eight cases he treated developed visual defects and one of these became completely blind. In London Dr John Parkinson had a similar experience. The drug, although bactericidal to pneumococci, was toxic to the optic nerve and thus too dangerous to employ in practice.

Wright was severely shaken by this episode and it coloured his view of chemotherapy to such a degree that he discouraged work on the subject in his laboratory. It was thus ironic that two of his assistants, Colebrook and Fleming, were to achieve international renown in this or closely related fields. Wright insisted that the only reliable method of combating infection was by enhancing the body's natural defence mechanisms by vaccine therapy. Predictably, he used this unfortunate saga to launch another attack on statistical methods of examining therapeutic results.

In his report to the Witwatersrand Native Labour Association [26] on their problems with pneumonia, Wright employed the optochin affair to illustrate the inappropriateness of statistics in assessing medical matters. He claimed that the experiential method, 'that is taking into account the whole complex of impressions which have been left upon the mind by experience', was of superior merit.[27] He considered that the experience of a few patients with optochin was quite sufficient to provide the necessary information as to its potency and its toxic side-effects. In this he was correct, but he totally ignored the fact that statistics never claimed anything else. Where he was wrong was in extrapolating this 'reasoning' to include areas of therapy where conclusions were less clear-cut. He also railed against the statistical method by use of the specious argument that 'it is the exception to find in connexion with clinical material either a really critical feature by reference to which the cases can be sorted into successes and failures, or a significant feature which is universally present and which lends itself to arithmetical evaluation'. This was rubbish. In a severe infection recovery or death are two obvious features which can be 'sorted into successes or failures'.

Wright placed great store on 'authoritative opinion'. Yet in all walks of life this has often proved untrustworthy, and nowhere more so than in the medical profession. Doctors in the past had all too often ascribed the favourable outcome of a treatment as being the result of their ministrations, and ignored less favourable results or attributed the latter to some ill-defined defect in the patient's constitution. Wright thought that: 'The fact that the medical profession, so far as it has experience of these remedies, is unanimous in its favourable verdict is evidence that they are signally effective.' Unfortunately, he poured scorn on the statisticians' reply to this argument, which he quoted: 'Unanimity of opinion does not furnish any guarantee of truth. If it did, the medical profession would not, time and again, have accepted unanimously — as it did for instance, in connexion with blood-letting — experiential conclusions which the progress of knowledge has compelled it to abandon.' To the impartial onlooker the statisticians' line of reasoning is very persuasive but it was dismissed by Wright on the grounds that blood-letting ceased because experience alone showed it in an unfavourable light when it was compared with results obtained when patients were not bled. He went on to assert that when several experts register the same impression, 'the correctness of such record is established beyond doubt'.

The disappointment in the drug treatment of established pneumonia led Wright and his colleagues back to the use of vaccines both as a form of treatment and as a prophylactic measure.[28] His investigations into the diagnostic bacteriology of pneumonia among the native labourers was surprisingly sophisticated for the time. He used blood culture, which yielded pneumococci in only approximately 25 per cent of cases, and also employed lung puncture, a daringly innovative technique, where positive cultures were obtained in over 60 per cent of cases. By these means he established that the pneumonia that was afflicting the miners was the result of infection by pneumococci rather than by any other respiratory pathogen. In order to assess the effectiveness, if any, of a pneumococcal vaccine as a therapy he divided the patients in the Native Labour Association Hospital who were suffering from pneumonia into two groups: one group that was given vaccine and the other receiving 'expectant' treatment, that is good nursing. There were 159 cases in the vaccine-treated group with 50 deaths, and 149 in the untreated group with 48 deaths. It was thus obvious that vaccine treatment was useless. Wright naively attributed this to the 'very low power of resistance' of tropical natives and to the difficulty in deciding the correct dose of vaccine.

Disappointed with his therapeutic efforts, Wright turned to prophylactic inoculation; and here he achieved limited success. In a series of what he termed 'mass experiments', many thousands of native labourers were inoculated and were compared with an equal number of uninoculated labourers; both groups were living under similar conditions. There were six of these mass experiments, each one differing somewhat in the dose of vaccine and the number and timing of the inoculations. The administration involved in following up so many men presented considerable difficulty but this was overcome by the perseverance of Dr W Parry Morgan, a colleague of Wright who had been a mathematician at Cambridge before studying medicine. In the groups who received the vaccine, there was a reduction in the death rate among those developing pneumonia of between 31 and 60 per cent and a reduction in the incidence of the disease of up to 50 per cent when compared with those who were unvaccinated. Wright attributed this only moderate success to the 'naturally non-resistant' population with whom he was dealing. While this may have been a factor there was a much more fundamental defect, which concerned the nature of the infecting organism. Wright did not appreciate, indeed it was not known at the time, that there was more than one type of *Pneumococcus* and that, although the majority of pneumonias are caused by a limited number of types, immunising against one variety does not confer immunity against all types. It is generally true that unsuccessful prophylactic immunisation is the result of failure to realise that there are often several antigenically distinct strains of a given organism. *Pneumococcus* is a particularly appropriate example of this, though this was not fully understood during Wright's sojourn in South Africa. *Pneumococcus* has a polysaccharide capsule and there are over 80 different capsular types; immunising against one type is useless in protecting against infection by another. It is true that most human pneumonias are caused by one of ten types but unless each of these is included in the vaccine little protection is afforded. After Wright and his colleagues left South Africa work was continued by Spencer Lister,

later to become director of the South African Institute for Medical
Research, who demonstrated that at least three types of *Pneumococcus*
were involved and that a combined vaccine against all three was much
more effective than the vaccine used by Wright. In fairness, it must be
stated that the classification and typing of pneumococci was ill-
understood in 1911; indeed, the seminal paper on prevention of
pneumococcal pneumonia by immunisation with specific capsular
polysaccharides was not published until 1945.[29] Today, readily
available vaccines offer protection against 23 types of *Pneumococcus*,
which account for approximately 90 per cent of those causing
pneumonia.[30]

Wright's party, except Parry Morgan who stayed behind to collate
results, travelled at the end of February 1912 to Cape Town where
they were invited to a wine tasting. Wright, who seldom drank alcohol,
refused to attend and the visit was cancelled to the intense
disappointment of the others. They embarked on RMS *Saxon*.
Throughout the voyage home Wright's peace of mind was disturbed
by Colebrook's infatuation with Miss Dumbleton to whom he had
become engaged. He was fearful for the future of one of his most
promising assistants and tactfully drew attention to her shortcomings.
This must have had its effect as the engagement was broken off on
return to Britain and she receives no further mention in Colebrook's
diary.

Wright published the first part of his report to the Witwatersrand
Native Labour Association, dealing with the pharmacotherapy of
pneumonia, in the *Lancet* on 14 and 21 December 1912. This
contained his severe strictures on statistics when applied to
medicine, as has been mentioned above. Colebrook in his diary
records that members of the department advised him to modify his
remarks, but to no avail. Three weeks later the *Lancet* carried a
devastating response from Major Greenwood, entitled 'On methods of
research available in the study of medical problems with special
reference to Sir Almroth Wright's recent utterances'.[31] Publication was
a courageous move. Greenwood was the son of a general practitioner in
the East End of London[32] and had been reluctant to follow in his
father's footsteps. In 1913 he claimed to be the only medically
qualified practitioner holding a post expressly created to further the
application of biometric methods in medicine and pathology. He was
statistician to the Lister Institute, where he had been appointed with
the special task of testing the validity of conclusions with regard to
prophylactic and curative treatment in medical practice. Eighteen years
junior to Wright, and not possessing a degree in medicine — he held

the conjoint qualification — it was an intrepid act directly to question such an acknowledged 'expert'. This he did in no uncertain terms but tactfully prefaced his paper by writing: 'If in the heat of conflict or the vanity of authorship I have used any expression unseemly in discussing a vast and complex subject with an older and abler man, I beg the offence may be attributed to carelessness, not to malice.' In the course of seven closely printed pages he then proceeded to dissect again Wright's claims with regard to the opsonic index. The details of his argument need not concern us; suffice it to say that it was accepted by the scientific community both then and now. To a great extent Wright invited criticism by adopting a high moral tone. Thus, in the introduction to his report on pneumonia, when considering drug administration, he wrote of those who give such treatment without proper evidence:

'Such practice is from the standpoint of strict science, clearly indefensible, and we as a profession regard it as indefensible. For we reprobate in quackery, not only the fact that it has a low standard of financial rectitude and that it proclaims its merit in public places, but also the fact that it proceeds upon assumptions which are either demonstrably false or scientifically unjustified.'

Wright failed to see that in using vaccine therapy he was guilty of these faults himself, though there was never any reason to doubt the sincerity of his beliefs. Greenwood maintained, correctly, that Wright's views on statistical method were based upon ignorance of the subject. Moreover claims that the medical expert alone is competent to say what his experiments did or did not prove were not merely unscientific but anti-scientific. He quoted Karl Pearson in saying that 'the day of authority in any branch of science has gone' — harsh words about one who was a Fellow of the Royal Society and the recognised leader in his field.

Wright's response to this onslaught was to ignore it. The second part of his report published in 1914 contains no reference to Greenwood. Not all members of the inoculation department at St Mary's were convinced by their chief's arguments and, although Colebrook loyally supported him, Parry Morgan with his mathematical background had grave doubts that were to cause serious disagreement at a later date. The remainder kept silent. Personal relations between Wright and Greenwood at this time were, not unnaturally, somewhat arctic so it is pleasant to record that towards the end of their lives they were completely reconciled on a personal basis and that Greenwood, who was considered by some to be cold and cynical, wrote in the warmest terms of Wright.[33]

Notes

1 Romanes G. Personal communication.
2 Wright AE. *Lancet* 1907 **i**: 493.
3 Foster WD. *A history of medical bacteriology* p127–223. London: William Heinemann, 1970.
4 St Mary's BOM vol 7 1912: 99, 107.
5 Ibid p549.
6 Ibid p592
7 Wright AE. *Proc Roy Soc Med Gen Reports* 1910; 1 (23 May 1910).
8 Fowler JK. Ibid p107 (8 June 1910).
9 For a full description of the circumstances under which Koch made his announcement see the excellent account in: Dormandy T. *The white death* pp139–44. London: Hambledon Press, 1999.
10 Horder TJ. *Proc Roy Soc Med Gen Reports* 1910; 139.
11 Fitzgerald MP, Whiteman RI, Strangeways TSP. An inquiry into the value of the opsonic index. *Bulletin of the committee for the study of special diseases* 1907: **1** no 8.
12 Greenwood M, White JDC. *Biometrika* 1909; **6**: 54.
13 Greenwood M. *Proc Roy Soc Med* pathological section 1909: 145–55.
14 Greenwood M. *Lancet* 1909; **i**: 614.
15 Opsonisation baths were still being advertised in catalogues of medical instruments and equipment as late as 1934, although it is dubious who was buying them. (Brown K. Personal communication.)
16 Dudgeon LS. *Bacterial vaccines and their position in therapeutics*. London: Constable, 1927.
17 Topley WWC. *An outline of immunity*. London: Edward Arnold, 1933.
18 Foster WD. *A history of medical bacteriology* p143. London: William Heinemann, 1970.
19 Ada G, Ramsay A. *Vaccines. vaccination and the immune response*. Philadelphia, New York: Lippincott-Raven, 1997.
20 Salisbury DM, Begg NT. *Immunisation against infectious disease*. HMSO, 1996.
21 St Mary's Hospital BOM 1911; **6**: 679.
22 Colebrook L. Diary entry for 3 September 1911.
23 Ehrlich P. *Studies in immunity* 2nd edn. London: Chapman and Hall, 1910.
24 Morgenroth, Levy. *Berl Klin Wochenschr* nos 34, 44.
25 Wright AE. *Lancet* 1912; **ii**: 1633.
26 Wright AE. Ibid.
27 Wright AE. Ibid.
28 Wright AE. *Lancet* 1914; **i**: 1.
29 MacLeod CM, Hodges RG, Heidelberger M, Bernhard WG, *J Exp* Med 1945; **82**: 445.
30 Salisbury DM, Begg NT. *Immunisation against infectious disease*. HMSO, 1996.
31 Greenwood M. *Lancet* 1913; **i**: 158.
32 Hill AB. *The introduction to* The medical dictator *by M Greenwood*. London: Keynes Press, 1986.
33 Greenwood M. *Lancet* 1947; **i**: 642.

Chapter 7

Women, St Mary's and the Suffrage Question

Wright is remembered today, if indeed he is remembered at all, on two counts: firstly as a misogynist and anti-suffragist, and secondly as the model for Sir Colenso Ridgeon in Shaw's play *The doctor's dilemma*. Both these labels are based to a large extent on misconceptions. Certainly he was not a misogynist. His attitude to women would today be considered absurd but at the beginning of the 20th century his views were applauded by many of both sexes. And in Shaw's play Ridgeon is little more than a distorted caricature of Wright, principally serving to personify the very real medical problem of which patients to treat when available resources are limited.

Wright's attitude towards women was largely formed by his upbringing in a predominantly male evangelical Christian household in which women occupied a subservient position. His mother devoted herself to the welfare of her husband and sons and saw to it that the domestic servants, all female, did the same. She instilled into her children the doctrine enunciated in the third chapter of *Genesis*: 'Thy desire shall be thy husband and he shall rule over thee'. It is well reflected in the words of Earl Percy in a Parliamentary debate in 1873 when he stated, 'The real fact is that man in the beginning was ordained to rule over the woman, and this is an eternal decree which we have no right and no power to alter'.[1] Wright was thus conditioned from an early age to women occupying a secondary role, and he had no contact with girls of his own age and intellectual attainments until he left Trinity College, Dublin. Indeed the educational opportunities offered to women in the last part of the 19th century were few. It was considered by many that a 'separation of spheres between the sexes had been ordained by God and/or Nature'[2] with women occupying a deferential and even servile role. Leading men of science confirmed this viewpoint; both Huxley and Darwin considered women inferior to men. The mother of a family occupied a managerial role within the house but her whole *raison d'être* was the glorification and satisfaction of her husband. The influential Victorian sage Thomas Carlyle, whose deeply unhappy marriage was common knowledge after Froude's publications in the early 1880s, had held the view that 'the true destiny of woman . . . is to wed a man she can love and esteem and to lead noiselessly, under his protection, with all the wisdom, grace and heroism that is in her, the life presented in consequence.'[3] This principle of the noiseless spouse was wholeheartedly embraced by Wright although, unsurprisingly, it did not appeal to his lively, intelligent and educated Irish wife.

Another factor influencing and lending support to Wright's attitude to women is to be found in the sentiments voiced by members of his profession. There was a powerful group of doctors opposed to entry of women into medicine. Their prejudice was fuelled by the prospect of unwelcome competition in private practice, which provided their only source of income. This was especially true in the fields of obstetrics, gynaecology and childhood diseases. Many women objected to intimate physical examination by a man. Indeed it was unusual for a practitioner to conduct such an examination, and empirical 'treatment' was often instituted without an attempt to establish a diagnosis by physical means. An excellent example of this excessive scruple to delicacy is to be found in Michaela Reid's fascinating biography of Sir James Reid, Queen Victoria's personal physician.[4] It is clear from this account that although Reid attended the Queen almost daily for over 20 years he never examined her. When she died he was surprised to discover that she had a large umbilical hernia and a complete prolapse of the uterus — conditions which must have caused her considerable discomfort. In gynaecological matters many women preferred to suffer rather than to submit to a vaginal examination by a man[5] but would endure the ministrations of unqualified midwives. When women finally entered the profession they achieved considerable success in gynaecological and paediatric practice.

Towards the end of the 19th century London University and the Apothecaries Society had opened their doors to women, but they were denied entry to the prestigious royal colleges. In 1895 a petition was presented by the officers and teachers of the London School of Medicine for Women — better known as the Royal Free Hospital Medical School — pleading for admission of women to the Conjoint Diploma of the Royal College of Physicians of London and the Royal College of Surgeons of England. On 22 October 1895, 14 of the most senior physicians in the London college submitted a memorandum to the Conjoint Board recommending that women should not be admitted to examinations for their diploma. They stated that:

'In common with a large body of medical men — probably a great majority — we hold . . . that the admission of women to the medical profession is most undesirable: and whilst fully admitting the ability of women to comply with the mere examination tests, we are none the less convinced that they are by nature unfitted for the pursuit and practice of the medical profession.'[6]

They went on to contest the argument that admission was inevitable because other medical institutions in the United Kingdom had opened their doors to women. Indeed they considered that the very fact that they had done so was 'sufficient to secure a full and complete trial of what at present is but an experiment which another generation may show to be a mistake.'[7] They viewed with horror the possibility that if women were admitted to the licentiateship they would have the right to proceed to the membership and even to the fellowship and, under such circumstances too terrible to contemplate, 'to the counsels and administration of the College.' Among those who signed this letter were Samuel Gee (senior physician at St Bartholomew's Hospital and at Great Ormond Street Hospital and later physician to King George V), William Jenner (already mentioned as one of the first to distinguish between typhoid fever and typhus, who was at this time a physician to the Queen and the Prince of Wales and had been President of the college from 1881 to 1888) and Patrick Manson (the leading authority on tropical disease). A special Comitia of the college was held on 24 October to consider the matter and the petition by the London School of Medicine for Women was rejected but, in view of the status of those against it, by the surprisingly close vote of 59 to 50. It was not until 17 January 1908 that a resolution was passed admitting women to all the College examinations. The first woman member, Miss Ivy Woodward, was admitted in 1909, followed in 1910 by the first woman licentiate, Miss Dossibhai Patell. Yet it was only in 1934 that the College elected its first woman Fellow and it was not until 1943 that the first woman councillor, Janet Vaughan, was chosen.[8]

The main London teaching hospitals excluded women medical students until the Second World War and there was no greater bulwark against change than St Mary's, in spite of persistent attempts to alter the position. On 6 December 1901 the minutes of a meeting of the board of management record a resolution urging female representation on every hospital board and house committee.[9] Women were essential for the smooth running of the hospital. The nurses were a devoted group, grossly underpaid and overworked. Women moreover played an essential role in fund-raising for the hospital, which was in severe financial difficulties. The nursing staff took a major part, when off-duty, in flag days and, together with wives and others related to members of the medical staff and management board, ran an almost continuous series of charitable fund-raising events. In spite of this, and the resolution mentioned above, it would seem that by 1910 no woman had been elected to the Board of Management. In that year Mr H A Harben, chairman of the board, proposed 'That it is most desirable that the board of management should consist partly of women.'[10] Harben was also chairman of the Prudential Insurance Company as well as being a most generous benefactor of both the hospital and medical school — he had rescued the latter from bankruptcy, following gross financial mismanagement, with a large personal donation in 1903 — and clearly his influence was considerable. The proposal, seconded by Mr J A Bryon, was passed.

Harben was seriously ill and on 18 August he died, to be succeeded as chairman by Mr Austen Leigh. The possibility of women members on the board was highly distasteful to Wright and he went to work on the other members to get the proposition rescinded. He found a ready ally in the senior physician, Sir John Broadbent,[11] and at the meeting on 12 January 1911 they moved 'That the resolution of the board on 16 June 1910 affirming that it is desirable that the board should consist partly of women be rescinded.' The meeting of that day was poorly attended and the motion was lost, there being two votes in favour and six against.[12] After a decent interval Austen Leigh, on 17 October 1912, proposed that Mrs Harben (the widow of H A Harben) and Mrs Percy Harris be elected to the board. On this occasion Wright and his colleagues were well prepared and the proposal was thrown out, with eight votes in favour and ten against. Leigh immediately tendered his resignation.[13] The proposal had been made at a time when feelings in the country were running high on the question of woman suffrage and the violent actions of the suffragettes. It followed Wright's letter to *The Times*, discussed below, and the rejection by the House of Commons of the Bill to give votes to certain classes of women on 28 March 1912.

The lay members of the board of management persisted and on 23 January 1913 Mrs Harben and Mrs Percy Harris were elected. The medical establishment restricted their activities, however, and the two were not permitted to take part 'either by way of discussion or voting in any question affecting the status or duties of the honorary medical or surgical staff or affecting management of the medical school'.[14] Even with these restrictions the presence of women on the Board was too much for Wright to stomach, and on 24 January 1913 he resigned.

This first modest breach in what was a bastion of male prejudice was enlarged during the Great War, when women students were admitted,

mainly as an overflow from the Royal Free Hospital Medical School.[15]
By 1915 St Mary's Medical School was again in severe financial
difficulties owing to the loss of fee income following enlistment of
many students in the armed forces. It was this that provided the
impetus for the school authorities to agree to admission of women. The
fees that they paid were a major factor in resuscitating the school's
finances.[16] Facilities for women medical students in London were
primitive and were concentrated at the London School of Medicine for
Women at the Royal Free Hospital. More doctors were needed and
fewer men were available owing to the demands of the army. There
were many women desirous of medical training and on 25 July 1916
Asquith, Balfour and Curzon, all noted anti-suffragists before the war,
wrote to the *Observer* asking for financial help from the public towards
building larger laboratory accommodation for the women's medical
school. As the Royal Free Hospital had not the space for an increased
intake of medical students, particularly in the clinical years, some were
admitted to St Mary's. This was not popular and on 2 August 1917 a
deputation of male students asked the board that:

(a) No women students be admitted as long as eligible men were available.

(b) Men be given preference in the house appointments at the hospital.

(c) When hostilities cease women shall have their appointments terminated within
one month.

(d) An official announcement on the whole question be made by the board.

The board is recorded as receiving these requests sympathetically.[17]
The question of admission of women medical students rumbled on for
several years, even though the agreement between the Royal Free
Hospital and St Mary's Medical School officially terminated on
30 September 1919. Matters came to a head in 1924 under
somewhat bizarre circumstances. Sporting activities at St Mary's had
in recent years reached a low ebb and there had been no successes in
inter-hospital competitions. This provided the stimulus for the male
students to petition the medical school committee with a
memorandum, which began as follows:

'The recent, but apparently habitual defeat of St Mary's in the Rugger Cup-tie,
calls for serious consideration. If this fact is taken in conjunction with the general
discontent and entire lack of public spirit now prevalent, it must seem that
something is radically wrong. The principal cause of dissatisfaction among the men
students at St Mary's, and in their opinion, the root of all the evil is the fact that we
belong to a 'mixed' hospital. From various points of view the presence of women
causes much harm. Athletically we are paralysed by them . . . and the constant
bickering between men and women is enough to upset the efforts of any mixed

committee. Further, the fact that most men dislike serving under women HPs [house physicians] and HSs [house surgeons] and on mixed firms is not conducive to smooth running.'[18]

There followed more in the same vein, and they drew attention to other more successful London hospitals which restricted their intake of students to men. At one point they stated that 'academically speaking women may be a success, but surely there are other essentials in the well-being of a community such as ours', a reference presumably to sporting prowess. The medical school committee and the hospital board of management held a special meeting to consider the matter and a motion was passed 'That the admission of women be discontinued'. The admission of women ceased[19] but the matter did not end there. There was pressure from the University of London on their medical schools to admit women, as all the provincial schools were doing by the 1920s. The dean, C M Wilson (later Lord Moran), exhibited the tactful deviousness for which he was later to become so celebrated, in replying to the University that St Mary's was prepared to admit women 'provided that all Metropolitan Medical Schools do the same'.[20] Here he was on safe ground as Guy's, St Bartholomew's, St Thomas's, St George's and the Middlesex did not admit women and had no intention of doing so, and the London Hospital had just decided to admit no more women. That remained the position until the Second World War.

Wright never allowed women to work in his laboratory. He claimed that 'if they are ugly they annoy me, if they are pretty they trouble me.' Yet there was a vibrant social life in the all-male laboratory. Until 1948 most of the staff were financially dependent on private practice and this they carried out in the mornings. The afternoons were devoted to hospital work and it was the custom to meet every afternoon at four o'clock when tea would be served. This gathering provided a forum for discussion of a wide range of subjects often outside purely laboratory matters. On occasion friends of Wright would be guests, Bernard Shaw being the best-known example, but other notable visitors from politics and the arts included Balfour, Haldane, Gilbert Murray and Granville Barker, as well as Ehrlich, Wassermann and Metchnikoff from the scientific fraternity. Opinions were freely expressed and Wright does not appear to have taken offence at criticism levelled at him or his work by junior members of his staff.[21] In this he must have been almost unique as the hierarchical nature of the medical profession in Edwardian days seldom encouraged differences of opinion between the chief and his subordinates.

Particularly in the years up to 1918 relationships between members of the laboratory staff were close. Freeman, until his marriage in 1907 and sometimes afterwards, lodged with Wright at 7 Lower Seymour Street; when Wright later moved to 6 Park Crescent, he and Freeman were joined by Leonard Colebrook, who stayed until his marriage in 1914. Members of the laboratory staff often went away together. Such expeditions might take the form of long weekends in Dorset, where Colebrook and his sister had a cottage, or longer breaks in Switzerland or Scandinavia. On such occasions, Colebrook recorded in his diary there was much talk of women. Switzerland was the preferred destination for Wright and he went there every year. A keen amateur botanist, he delighted in alpine gentians, anemones, rock roses, geums, globe flowers and crocuses. He was usually accompanied by one or more colleagues, and he seems to have enjoyed the mixed company in the hotels. Although he seldom drank wine or spirits he spent the evenings with the other male and female residents in the bar. This irritated Colebrook, who wrote that Wright 'preferred to endure the chatter of the dozen or so uninteresting people staying in the pub rather than to go unharnessed with plans alone with a donkey like RLS'.[22] Even so Wright was not above expressing anti-feminist views and openly disapproved of Freeman's wife wearing breeches for skiing; he considered it indicated freedom of expression 'which women should not have'.[23]

Physical exercise was not one of the joys of Wright's life and he avoided it whenever possible. Little of his time in Switzerland was spent walking; he had no head for heights, and when he did go on a ramble with Colebrook, who was a keen walker, he could manage only three or four miles. By 1911, aged 51 years, he was experiencing angina of effort but even this was not allowed to interfere with his professional or social life over the next 36 years. He was a frequent guest at dinner parties, notably those given by Lady St Helier. This remarkable lady had in 1881 married (as his second wife) Sir F H Jeune, an ecclesiastical lawyer who became a high court judge and was raised to the peerage as Lord St Helier. He died in 1908 and his wife proceeded enthusiastically to engage in public life. She became an alderman on the London County Council and later described herself in *Who's Who* as 'indefatigable in the service of the poor', and indeed she was concerned with raising money for St Mary's, for which she was formally thanked by the board of management in 1908. She also depicted herself as notable 'in society for her brilliant entertaining'. She gave frequent dinner parties for the great and the good. Sir Almeric Fitzroy, secretary to the Privy Council, recorded in his diary on 25 June 1911: 'Last night I dined with Lady St Helier, the Midletons, Winston Churchills, Godfrey Barings...Sir Almroth Wright and two or three others whose names I did not learn. It was amusing, after the ladies had gone upstairs, to hear Winston Churchill silenced on the subject of female suffrage by Sir A Wright.'[24] Churchill at this time, no doubt in part influenced by his wife, was in favour of giving the vote to women.

Lady St Helier lived at 52 Portland Place, only a few doors away from Wright's house in Park Crescent; it was probably through her that he met Miss Robinson, a lady deeply concerned with the care of the poor with whom he developed a very close relationship. There can be no clearer indication of his warm feelings towards women than his behaviour during her last illness. She suffered from some form of intestinal disorder complicated by obstruction and underwent a series of operations at the hands of Sir Arbuthnot Lane[25] in the early months of 1914. Her last days were recorded by Colebrook in his diary[26]:

'A very heavy time had gone over his [AEW'S] head with home troubles and the slow death of Miss Robinson. I was privileged to see a little towards the end of his struggle for her life and the infinite tenderness of his care for her. Lane had operated to close an enterostomy fistula. Obstruction followed and another operation, at which AEW marvelled at the surgeon's workmanship and courage under difficult circumstances. Lane however did not sew up the abdominal wall, or only very superficially, and in a few days everything parted and finally allowed the bowel to present — this with a good deal of pus formation about the wound and some mysterious source of pain involved the poor lady in some very terrible weeks through which AEW was constantly nearby, nursing, helping, comforting and she was quite wonderful — never for a moment allowing her brave spirit to lower its flag always thinking of those around her and their interests...At times she was pulling the Old Man's leg as to the intellectual and moral desirability for her feeling a little tired and piano...On the last Sunday...she refused morphia which she had been having in biggish doses for many days, saying she wanted to die with her wits about her. The Old Man went back to see her in the evening and she said a quiet goodbye to him and her folk, then the day's pain brought delirium and the poor tired body gave up the fight.

It was the most wonderful death bed I have ever known by a very long way and very beautiful to see her love for her old friend and his for her. He told me after how she had worked writing on the Poor Law through years of pain.'

The description of Wright's behaviour and reaction to this episode is hardly one that could be described as that of a misogynist. His reputation as such was acquired because of his staunch opposition to woman suffrage. Yet as Brian Harrison has emphasised, it would be wrong to equate anti-suffragism and misogyny.[27] Many of those, both men and women, who opposed giving women the vote did a great deal to promote women's rights in the fields of education, divorce and the care of children. Women's higher education was actively promoted by Mrs Humphry Ward who gave the name to Somerville College, Oxford. Curzon, who raised money for the National League for Opposing Woman Suffrage, supported women's admission to Oxford, and F E Smith helped reform divorce law and was favourably disposed to women pursuing a legal career. None of these could be called a misogynist, but all were in favour of what Harrison pertinently terms separate spheres of influence for men and women.

Relations between Wright and his wife were far from easy after their arrival in London. His habit of working late into the night and often into the early hours of the following morning were hardly conducive to conventional family life. They had two sons and a daughter but his children saw little of him — they spent a considerable amount of time in Dorset or on their mother's estate in Ireland. Freeman related how Wright's daughter, a pupil at Roedean, wrote in an essay on family life: 'It's awfully jolly if Daddy can manage to get down on a Sunday to see how his family are getting on.' One son, Edward, suffered from a club foot and spina bifida and by 1912 he was growing weaker; sitting up caused pain and he spent considerable periods lying on his abdomen.[28] Wright, when he was in Belfast to receive the freedom of the city, took the opportunity of travelling to the west coast of Ireland in order to find a suitable home for the boy. The lad did not improve and died following a revolver wound to his chest; the injury was described as accidental but there was a strong suspicion of suicide.[29] After 1912 Wright and his wife separated, and it was natural that he turned elsewhere for female companionship.

A serious point of contention between the Wrights was woman suffrage, of which she was an ardent advocate and to which he was implacably opposed. In the first decade of the 20th century this was a subject of much acrimonious debate fuelled by the militant methods of the suffragette movement led by the Pankhursts, the Pethick-Lawrences and the Women's Social and Political Union (WSPU). Not all suffragettes espoused violence; most of the women activists belonged to the National Union of Women's Suffrage Societies, an entirely constitutionalist pressure group led by Mrs Millicent Fawcett. A further faction was the Women's Freedom League, a body split off from the WSPU and led by Mrs Despard, sister of Field Marshal Sir John French, which favoured ordered or constitutional militancy such as refusing to pay taxes. Meetings held by both those in favour of woman suffrage and those against it were often disrupted by the opposite party. Medical students were prominent in such forays, doctors in their larval stage being peculiarly addicted to rowdiness. Students from St Mary's were to the fore in such incidents. On 16 December 1907 the local secretary of the London Society for Woman's Suffrage wrote an irate letter to the medical school committee complaining of disturbances at a meeting of the society held at Paddington Baths. As no convincing proof was forthcoming that the students of St Mary's had taken part, the committee resolved that a reply be sent expressing regret but refusing to take any action.[30] This was consistent with the general hostility of the profession to admission of women to what they preferred to keep as an exclusive male preserve.

The interest of medical students was no doubt further stimulated by the increasing numbers of women admitted to the profession and in particular by their being allowed to sit for the conjoint examination. It is thus not surprising that in January 1910 the St Mary's Medical Students Society arranged a debate on woman suffrage and invited George Bernard Shaw and Wright to be the principal speakers. The occasion, christened 'Man and Superman', took place after dinner. The library where the meeting was held was packed with 130 men and visitors. Precautions taken to exclude women were not entirely successful: to quote the *St Mary's Hospital Gazette* of the day, 'An old lady who spoke was reported to have been crushed by a gentleman in the front row' and later removed to the casualty department.[31]

The report of the debate in the *Gazette* was couched in facetious terms but the line of argument put forward by Wright rested on two main points.[32] Firstly, that in the final analysis physical force was necessary to maintain law and order, and in this men would always dominate over women. This was a widely accepted argument at the time, epitomised by the Victorian philosopher Herbert Spencer's remark to Lady Amberley that if women could not fight they should not vote.[33] Secondly, and here he employed coded language, women suffered from emotional instability associated with menstruation, pregnancy and the menopause. He considered women intellectually inferior to men, and when faced with those women who said 'Educate us for a few generations and we will be your equals,' he replied that acquired characteristics are not inherited.

Shaw's arguments were not reported in detail — perhaps the student reporter neither followed nor sympathised with them — but the line he took can be gleaned from other sources.[34] His opinion that women were the intellectual equals of men was supported by his experience of those involved in literature, 'in which there is no question about the ability of women to stand side by side in all branches of the art with men'.[35] It being a medical audience, he pointed out that the world being an epicene place he saw no reason to suppose that the diagnosis reached by women from a specimen viewed down a microscope should be any less reliable than that reached by a man. Women were at this time involved in movements to improve social conditions (as were Lady St Helier and Miss Robinson) but he maintained that far too much female talent 'instead of being applied to our social problems — those problems which affect both sexes alike — is wasted in this agitation', that is the struggle for female franchise.[36] If this could be granted the energies of these women could be concentrated on the more urgent social problems of malnutrition, homelessness, unemployment and poverty. Shaw's debating style was generally both effective and entertaining and, though the report is non-specific on this, he could seldom resist a witticism. This is well illustrated by his comments made at a public meeting in 1912 to consider the Wilks case. Mr Wilks was married to a lady doctor with a considerable income. Along with other suffragettes she embarked on a campaign of civil, non-violent disobedience and refused to pay her income tax. For this her husband, who was held responsible for his wife's actions, was sent to prison. At a protest meeting against this action by the authorities Shaw is reported as saying: 'As a man I have been able to bear with a certain amount of equanimity the delay of the reform, so long as I saw before me the inspiring spectacle of a number of women heroically sacrificing themselves: but now that the women have taken to sacrificing the men things are rather altered.'[37] At St Mary's it is perhaps not surprising that Shaw did not comment on the cyclical female phenomena mentioned by Wright, and indeed these were little understood — Starling had coined the word 'hormone' only in 1905 and the sex hormones as such were undiscovered. In any case such matters would have been referred to in phrases of great delicacy; contraception and sexual matters in general were definitely not for dinner-table conversation or public debate in spite of the agitations of neo-Malthusians such as Charles Bradlaugh and Annie Besant in the late Victorian period.

Needless to say the vote in the debate went in Wright's favour, though it was reported as close. One final remark on the occasion is of interest. Before the meeting Dr Charles Wilson said he felt sorry for Wright having to oppose such a celebrated speaker as Shaw, but after hearing both he felt embarrassed that Shaw, the guest speaker, had been so completely out-classed.

The House of Commons had been debating the issue of votes for women on numerous occasions. Thus, in 1904 both Lloyd George and Churchill had voted for woman suffrage in a debate in which the motion to grant it was carried by 182 votes to 68 but no further action was taken.[38] Yet motions were put down on a yearly basis, sometimes to be talked out, sometimes to be passed, but no legislation was enacted. The Liberal Party's attitude to extension of the franchise was ambiguous. An educated democracy was their ideal, but they were hesitant over how to achieve this. For all the noise and fuss over woman suffrage the major question, though seldom voiced, was universal male suffrage. At the time approximately two-thirds of men had the vote, and the third that did not were almost entirely drawn from the working classes. It was feared that the latter if given the vote would cast it in favour of the Labour Party, thus splitting the anti-Conservative opposition and allowing the Tories to win power on a minority vote — as indeed happened later in the century. Press interest in female suffrage grew when the militant campaign got under way. By 1909 hunger strikes among suffragettes in custody and the accompanying forcible feeding were newsworthy, as were the numerous acts of stone-throwing — the windows of West End stores such as Robinson and Cleaver, Swan and Edgar, and Swears and Wells, patronised by the well-to-do middle classes, were the focus of these attacks. There were serious clashes between police and demonstrators in Parliament Square in 1911, during which 200 women were arrested, including their leader Mrs Pethick-Lawrence. Such incidents had the reverse effect of that intended and antagonised public opinion.

The Times was particularly opposed to giving women the vote and on 16 March 1912, in a leading article entitled 'Insurgent hysteria', the paper questioned the sanity of the suffragettes. Significantly, the leader-writer commented 'Upon some phases of the movement which has culminated in senseless outrages against property and other acts of hooliganism, physicians could speak with more authority and insight.'[39] It mentioned doctors 'with large experience who come across many cases in which there is so much mental instability that any public excitement disturbs the balance and produces nervous tension and fits of hysteria, showing itself in violent conduct or violent loquacity.' It was considered that hysteria on a mass scale was new and among those largely responsible were 'women who have not married and who have no domestic duties...who find themselves with abundance of leisure.' These were considered ready recruits for window-smashing activities. Unmarried women were anathema to

Wright and his fellow anti-suffragists. Indeed many from all walks of life thought that the protests of women 'were merely the whimperings of those who had failed to get the real prize in life — a man.'[40]

Feelings were running high. At four o'clock in the afternoon of 1 March 1912 there had been an outbreak of concerted violence: nearly every shop window in Oxford Street, Regent Street and the environs of Piccadilly had been broken by suffragettes wielding hammers or throwing stones. Mrs Pankhurst in the company of two other ladies meted out the same treatment to the windows of 10 Downing Street. *The Times* leader was in part a reaction to this and in part a shot across the bows of those Members of Parliament who were considering casting their votes in favour of woman suffrage in a debate planned for 28 March. This debate was on a Bill which proposed only limited female suffrage — it was severely criticised by the WSPU because it did not include equal or full adult suffrage for women. It was proposed to confer voting rights only on women who were inhabitant occupiers of separately rated houses or tenements. Women were not to be disqualified by marriage but husband and wife were not to vote in the same constituency.

According to Colebrook, Wright was asked by anti-suffragette friends to write to *The Times*.[41] He spent eight days composing a letter that occupied two and a half columns, and which was highly commended in an accompanying leading article. In the first decade of the 20th century explicit matters relating to sex were not openly discussed either in 'society' or in the press.[42] This provides a striking contrast to the position in the last decade, with its daily dose of nudity in the tabloids, and the pages of medical information, often of a specifically gynaecological nature, found in *The Times* and other broadsheets.

In his letter Wright based his case on physiological and psychological differences between men and women which he claimed 'mystified' men.[43] These he categorised as 'periodically recurring phases of hypersensitiveness, unreasonableness and loss of the sense of proportion' — coded language for what is now termed premenstrual tension. In 1912 this was a taboo subject in any conversation between the sexes, and to write about it in the broadsheet press was regarded as outrageous. He went on to mention mood changes during pregnancy and the menopause, referring euphemistically to the latter as the 'change of life'. The conventions of the day were captured in his opening paragraph where he wrote 'No man can close his eyes to these things: but he does not feel at liberty to speak of them.' Wright's real contribution to the subject was to bring it into the open. He stated (wrongly) that these normal physiological phenomena caused dangerous 'upsetting of mental equilibrium' and concluded there was much 'mental disorder' in the suffragette movement.

Like many of his contemporaries Wright had a certain contempt for the unmarried woman, considering that she was the main source of the problem and that she constituted a recruiting field for the suffragist; he thought them 'lifelong strangers to joy', and sexually embittered. His naive solution to the 'problem' of the unmarried woman, of which there were half a million in the United Kingdom, was that 'they had better long ago have gone out to mate with its complement of men across the sea' in the Colonies — the counterpart of the 'fishing fleet' of young women who sailed to India each autumn in search of a husband. This conveniently ignored the very large number of suffragettes who were married women and indeed that the campaign was led by at least four such Mrs Despard, Mrs Pethick-Lawrence, Mrs Fawcett and Mrs Pankhurst.

Conceivably it might be argued that there was a germ of truth in Wright's thesis that there was some temporary mild depression during periods of hormonal disturbance associated with menstruation, pregnancy and the menopause, but these things were ill-understood at the time. It was not until 1931 that Frank[44] suggested that the tension, irritability and depression experienced by some women in the premenstrual period, sometimes accompanied by breast swelling, abdominal swelling and even oedema, were hormonally induced. That this was not a universal phenomenon, nor by any means always a debilitating one, was ignored.

Wright was particularly harsh on girls' schools and colleges staffed, he maintained, by unmarried suffragists who taught 'that woman had suffered all manner of indignity at the hands of man'. He ignored the achievements of women in fields such as literature, where, for example, Jane Austen and George Eliot had exercised a profound influence, or in medicine, where Florence Nightingale had revolutionised the nursing profession. In those areas where women worked alongside men Wright was vehemently opposed to them receiving equal pay, a proposal he dismissed as 'fatuous' even when they were performing the same tasks. He based this extraordinary opinion on men having 'a much larger reserve of physical strength', claiming that 'as soon as a time of strain comes a reserve of strength and freedom from periodic indisposition is worth paying for'. He even maintained that women were unfitted to work alongside men in the medical profession because it was necessary to keep up 'some of the modesties and reticences upon which our civilisation has been built up' — another legacy of his Calvinistic upbringing. He considered women as a class were quite incompetent to adjudicate on political issues, that they could not effectively back up their votes by force and that granting them the vote might 'seriously embroil man and woman'.

Those opposed to granting women the vote had to overcome the evidence from Australia, Canada and the Colonies where women had the franchise and no evil had come of it. Wright dealt with this objection in a wholly unsatisfactory manner by stating that in the Colonies 'man there sees his women-folk voting practically everywhere in accordance with his directions and lending him a hand to outvote his political opponent'. The grounds on which he based this argument were not given; it is difficult to see how any proof could be forthcoming when there was a secret ballot. In any case he asserted that 'In England everything is different', because if woman suffrage came in it would be as a result of 'very violent feminist agitation'. Like most of the population he deplored the use of female physical violence in furtherance of the suffragist cause, and condemned it as against natural law. Although we can see that Wright's arguments were in the main specious, here he did have a point; in later years it was acknowledged that women might well have achieved the vote earlier in the 20th century if they had not resorted to such militant methods in pursuit of their aims.

On the same day that Wright's letter appeared in *The Times* another signed 'Vera Collum' put the women's viewpoint in a concise and cogent manner.[45] Deploring the methods of the WSPU and the damage to private property, the writer claimed that the perpetrators of the recent window-breaking expeditions constituted only a very small minority of suffragists. Her arguments for giving women the vote were based on the obvious injustices in the arrangements operative in 1912. Firstly, there should be no taxation without representation, yet the single or widowed woman householder had to pay income tax and rates but had no vote. This argument might be faulted in that it ignored the whole question of indirect taxation. Secondly, the woman distinguished in the arts, science or public service again had no vote in spite of her intellectual attainments and was ranked below 'a partially illiterate man'. Thirdly, a mother with children had 'as important a stake in the country as her husband' and was denied the vote. Fourthly, and this she considered of paramount importance, the working woman who was increasingly expected to support herself economically and whom circumstances had forced into the open labour market, often in competition with men, was denied the franchise, and in addition did not have the backing of the trade union movement. These were potent points and were certainly not adequately addressed by Wright. It should be emphasised that women were playing an increasingly important role in social services. The first woman Poor Law inspector was appointed in 1872 and several more in 1883.[46] Asquith, when Home Secretary, appointed the first female factory inspectors in 1895.[47] Women were prominent on school boards. Social welfare and voluntary charitable works were an accepted sphere of influence for women, but increasingly central government was taking responsibility for such matters. In 1906 a Bill was passed to enable local authorities to provide meals for schoolchildren, and in 1907 it became the duty of local education authorities to have children in their care medically inspected.[48] After 1869 women had been able to vote in local elections — it was not until 1907 that they could stand as candidates — but this invasion of areas which were of deep concern to women made them increasingly desirous of representation in central government.

Regrettably Vera Collum's letter did not receive much attention, whereas Wright's was given considerable publicity by other national newspapers; for example, on the evening of 28 March the *Pall Mall Gazette* carried the headline 'Plain speaking by Sir Almroth Wright' and in a long article both reported and endorsed his letter.[49] In the House of Commons that night the Conciliation Bill, as the Bill to grant a limited female franchise was called, was defeated by 222 votes to 208. The defeat of the bill was attributed by some to Wright's letter, which that morning had been reproduced by the National League for Opposing Woman Suffrage and handed to every member. More probably defeat was due to the Irish Nationalists voting against it as a block. They were frightened of franchise reform as, ever since the famine of the 1840s, they had been grossly over-represented at Westminster. The number of their seats had been fixed at 120 by the Act of Union in 1800 and their population had fallen dramatically as the result of emigration. Their tax contribution did not merit such representation, and they did not care for this to be highlighted. Several English members failed to give their support because they were revolted by the violent methods of some of the suffragettes. *The Times*'s leading article the next day expressed relief that the Bill had been rejected. The leader-writer regarded it as a 'stalking horse' that presaged giving the vote to all women without distinction 'and consequent swamping of the male by the female vote'.[50] Woman suffrage had never been before the country at a general election and this in itself the paper regarded as reason enough for rejection.

During the following days the correspondence columns were filled with comments on Wright's letter. Senior members of the medical establishment were quick to dissociate themselves. Sir Richard

Douglas Powell, a past president of the Royal College of Physicians and physician to the King, protested at Wright's impropriety in referring to such delicate matters as female physiology, which he considered had been gleaned from experience in the medical consulting room.[51] Viscount Helmsley[52] had been reported as commending Wright's letter as 'extraordinarily able and interesting'; this infuriated Victor Horsley, professor of clinical surgery at University College Hospital, a Fellow of the Royal Society and one of the founders of neurosurgery. He had been superintendent of the Brown Institution, where Wright had worked before going to Australia. In *The Times* of 1 April he described Wright's views as 'most repulsive' and his statements and allegations as ' essentially pornographic'.[53] Not all medical correspondents expressed their views in such language. Agnes Savill, a prominent physician at the Royal Free Hospital, turned the tables on Wright and patronisingly pointed out that when the specialist leaves his field to pronounce on 'the philosophy of humanity' he always affords amusement to those who listen. She asserted that the average woman performed her daily duties come what may; her family noticed no difference in her behaviour and this was also true of nurses, matrons of large institutions, students and female doctors. She further declared that men were frequently swayed by irrational prejudice and sentiment, as well as being subject to phases of irritability 'during which flattery alone can prevail'.[54] Wry humour was also supplied by an adjacent letter that suggested that the solution to the whole question was to abolish the female sex altogether, concluding: 'Cannot science give us some assurance, or at least some ground of hope, that we are on the eve of the greatest discovery of all — ie how to maintain a race of males by purely scientific means?' This was signed 'CSC (one of the doomed)'[55]; the attempt at anonymity was of little avail as it soon became public knowledge that the initials stood for Clementine Spencer Churchill.[56] Winston had voted against the bill.

Yet Wright was not without supporters from the ranks of both sexes. In *The Times* Mary Duff acknowledged 'the deep debt of gratitude my sex owes to Sir Almroth Wright for his very lucid and outspoken letter'.[57] She lamented that the most cogent reasons against woman suffrage could not be produced in mixed company. She also wrote that 'it is generally taken for granted that we anti-suffragists approve the present franchise and consider it right that George Eliot should be shut out and her gardener admitted, but many of us think that her gardener should share her fate', illustrating how class was a more important question than sex to many of the antis. The subject remained a topic for the columns of *The Times* for the next two weeks. Too many correspondents devoted space to reprimanding Wright for his indelicacy in raising such matters as the assumed effects on mental stability of normal female bodily functions. Calling his letter obscene did not constitute an argument against his case. Support for his frankness in bringing vagaries of female physiology to the attention of the public came on 11 April from Professor T Claye Shaw, who was on the staff of St Bartholomew's Hospital. Claye Shaw was one of the most enlightened psychiatric physicians of the day and a keen advocate of mental clinics in general hospitals. He thought Wright's letter 'was dictated with singular felicity and courage' and, while not agreeing with all the sentiments expressed, he considered that in arriving at a solution to the problem of granting women the vote 'the temperate and full consideration of all the qualifications of women' was needed. For this 'full illumination was required'[58].

The suffragette press was predictably incensed by the attitude taken by *The Times*. On 4 April *The Common Cause*, a weekly suffragette journal, carried a leading article entitled 'Our Little Brother' containing a rebuttal of Wright's letter.[59] It began by stating that there were two sides to the problem, an obvious but in this case a pertinent point, as Wright throughout his life was reluctant to acknowledge anyone else's side in an argument. On the matter of physical force it was agreed that it was an offence to civilisation for a man to strike a woman but it was notorious — and this was also raised in *The Times* by a distinguished scientist, Sylvanus Thompson[60] — that the courts exercised double standards when such matters came before them. The trivial sentences passed on men convicted of assault, the inadequate protection against forcible seduction as well as the inequality in the treatment between men and women in the divorce courts, provided glaring examples of this. No doubt newspaper discussion would have continued but the early morning of 15 April saw a catastrophic event that drove all other matters from the headlines. The *Titanic*, the pride of the British passenger fleet and the world's largest liner, struck an iceberg on her maiden voyage and sank with the loss of 1635 lives.

Characteristically Wright did not let the matter rest and proceeded at once to write a book on the subject. *The unexpurgated case against woman suffrage* was published at the end of September 1913.[61] He had asked the editor of *The Times* to print it in four instalments but Dawson, newly appointed in succession to G E Buckle in the second half of 1912, refused to do so. The book, 86 pages in length, adds little of substance to his original letter, although marked by coarser exaggeration. Despite the declaration in the preface that 'I am very far from laying claim to any dogmatic authority', the whole work is permeated by undiluted assertive male chauvinism. Wright supplements his arguments concerning physical force by adding a financial factor stating, 'For no upright mind can fail to see that the woman who lives in a condition of financial dependence upon man has no moral claim to unrestricted liberty.'

In the book Wright purports to deal with arguments for and against granting the vote to women and his final section suggests a 'palliative or corrective' for any of the discontents of woman. Much of the work is taken up with semantics — Wright considered himself a philosopher. Thus he draws a distinction between women's rights and women's claims. He discusses at length the meaning of the word 'justice' and concludes that whether it is just to refuse the suffrage to women 'will be determined by considering whether the classification of men as voters and women as non-voters is in the public interest.' He concludes 'It would be for the electorate (ie man) not for the woman suffragist to decide that question.' His case against the suffragists' plea that taxation without representation represented a tyranny was even weaker as he answered this by, firstly, drawing attention to peers and foreigners who paid taxes and had no vote and, secondly, by claiming that rich women had anyway derived their fortunes and incomes from men rather than by work with their own hands.

He went on to assert that a woman's vote would not represent physical force, and that it was by physical force alone that the nation protected itself 'against foreign interference, upholds its rule over subject populations, and enforces its own laws.' Such an opinion, written in all seriousness, vividly reflects the difference in the frame of mind between those living in the first and last decades of the 20th century. To talk of 'rule of subject populations' was the mark of an imperial nation at the height of its power and represents an attitude repugnant to popular opinion today. Yet it does much to explain the favourable reception of Wright's views by a considerable number of his contemporaries, both male and female. (His book sold well: 5000 copies were printed in Britain, a further 1000 went to Australia and there was a separate American edition.[62]) Wright thought, and many thought with him, that 'no virile and imperial race' would brook any attempt at forcible control by women. He feared that military foreign nations would cease to believe in the 'stamina and firmness of purpose' of our island race. He emphasised, as in *The Times* letter, the periodic temperamental instability of females which he considered led to 'defective moral equipment'. Here was set out his afterwards notorious remark that 'One would not be very far from the truth if one alleged that there are no good women, but only women who have lived under the influence of good men'! One of his most telling submissions concerned the immorality — morals were a favourite subject in Wright's conversation — of the violent methods adopted by suffragettes, which threatened to alter the regulation of relations between the sexes that had been built up by civilisation. He maintained, and against the evidence, that 'the happy wife and mother is never passionately concerned about the suffrage'. His solution to the 'problem' of the discontented and, as he thought unfulfilled, woman remained the same — emigration. Claiming there were three million unmarried women in England and Wales, he urged many of these to leave for the Colonies; the practicalities of this mass transfer of population were not discussed.

These bizarre opinions were not thought out of the way when the book was published by Constable — Constable's had been threatened with violence if they accepted it, but in the event nothing untoward occurred — though its reception was mixed. *Punch* of 8 October included a cartoon of Wright at the top of a fire-proof tower with a suffragette trying to gain admittance;[63] the same journal commented on his statement that there are no good women: 'This is a bit rough on his mother — if the rumour that he has one is true.'[64] The more serious weekly journals carried discursive reviews. The anonymous reviewer in the *Spectator*[65] did not consider it a good book or that his line of argument against the suffrage was sound or expedient, but added 'we are also bound to say that the tone and temper in which it is written afford one of the most poignant and powerful arguments that could possibly be adduced in opposition to the suffragist agitation in its later phases.' The fact that Wright had been goaded into writing the book at all was the result of the anti-male invective that permeated the speeches and writings of some women suffragists. The latter were thought to be in danger of instigating a sex war which would be 'the most terrible disaster that mankind has ever endured'. Such alarmist language was not unusual and was the direct result of the window-breaking, arson and direct personal assaults on Government ministers by the militant suffragettes. The most potent criticism of the book was that it generalised from the behaviour of a small section of the adult female population — the *Spectator* thought five per cent — to womankind as a whole without any justification. 'Deceit lurks in generalities' and it seemed that 95 per cent of women were indifferent to the controversy. The *Saturday Review* commended the book as the soundest discussion of the woman suffrage yet written — 'Sir Almroth says clearly and well — in brutal truth — what the majority of men and women today are thinking about the feminist franchise agitation.'[66]

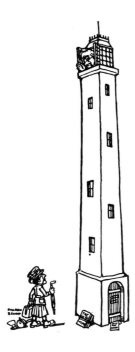

Figure 17
Cartoon from Punch, *1913. The caption reads:
'History in the Making: the unchivalrous Sir
Almroth Wright denying his identity to a fair caller
at the fire-proof retreat where he is retiring after the
nervous strain of writing "The Unexpurgated Case
against Female Suffrage"' (London:* Punch*)*

The most penetrating critique came from a fellow doctor. Ronald
Ross was Britain's most distinguished medical scientist. He had
discovered the life history of the malarial parasite in the mosquito, had
been awarded the Nobel prize for medicine in 1902 and was director of
the Hospital for Tropical Diseases; in addition he had published a
novel and several volumes of poetry. In *The Nation* of 11 October he
took Wright to task for his complete lack of scientific impartiality in
dealing with the woman suffrage question, the very title of the book
suggesting 'not impartiality but advocacy'.[67] Even so, Ross's own
words carried a strong whiff of male prejudice, even of paternalism,
when he compared women with men. Thus on the question of intellect
he considers it 'probably a fact that the highest male intellect is a little
superior to the highest feminine intellect', although this did not imply
that 'the average of one is higher than the average of the other'. Only if
it could be demonstrated that the highest feminine intelligence was
lower than the lowest male one would it be justifiable to exclude
women on the grounds of intelligence.

Similarly Ross took issue on the question of women's disability in
the matter of morality applied to public affairs. In his experience of
appointments, giving of contracts and so forth, favouritism, nepotism
and personal influence all carried weight with men; women were
certainly no worse than men in being moved by such personal
emotions. Indeed he thought that if probity with regard to such matters

was a serious consideration, as no doubt it should be, then 'a large number of women would have to be included, and a very large number of men excluded' from the franchise. He conceded that what he termed the 'physical disability' of women was a strong argument against giving them the vote but doubted whether it was strong enough — 'we vote with our brains, and not with our bodies'. As to Wright's assertion that wealthy women with property had only obtained their wealth from a male and should thus be denied the vote he pointed out that this could also be used as an argument against giving the suffrage to innumerable men who had inherited wealth. Finally Ross castigated Wright for ignoring the question as to why the vote should be given at all — that is that in a democracy it should reflect 'the representation of interests'. Wright had made no effort to counter the proposition that 'the introduction of women to the electorate and even to parliament . . . will bring into the councils of mankind a vast body of experience from exclusion of which those councils now materially suffer.'

This careful assessment by Ronald Ross contrasted with the somewhat frivolous review by Bernard Shaw in the recently founded *New Statesman*.[68] Perceptively Shaw labelled Wright as 'a particularly innocent and, at bottom, rather chivalrous Irishman'. He noted that many arguments that Wright deployed against women having the vote applied equally to men. Thus both sexes are over-influenced by individual instances, arrive at conclusions on incomplete evidence, lack a sense of proportion, accept the congenial as true and the uncongenial as false, and take the imaginary that is desired for the reality. He commended the book, not as a contribution to the question of woman suffrage but as 'a criticism of the political competence of mankind'. Shaw's most serious point was that Wright produced 'no evidence that the qualities for intellect and character needed for political organisation are any more specifically sexual than digestion or blood circulation or cell structure.' In spite of all his long-winded pseudo-scientific and pseudo-philosophical musings, Wright's case rested purely on subjective impressions. Shaw concluded that, as women had all the faults of men, giving them the vote 'would no more achieve the millennium' than had giving the vote to manufacturers and working men in the past. As to the book, it could safely be left on the drawing-room table in both country house and parsonage.

In all the social turmoil that this controversy caused Wright himself did not escape torment from the militants. His postbag was filled with abusive correspondence; the postcard that most delighted him called him 'a lewd slug'. Some letters were complimentary, including one

from Gilbert Murray—himself a supporter of the suffragette cause—
who considered the book the best contribution on the subject to date.
The attentions of the window-breaking brigade Wright might not have
found so amusing. He narrowly escaped assault by one of the most
distinguished women of the age, whose life and achievements
constituted a living rebuttal of his contention that women were
intellectually inferior to men.[69] Ethel Smythe, later Dame Ethel, had
by the age of 54 achieved, against much opposition, distinction as a
composer. Her Mass in D, written in 1893, was later praised by the
music critic Donald Tovey when he wrote 'no choral work in modern
times is more independent of all classical and modern antecedents'.[70]
She also composed several operas as well as a concerto, an oratorio
and, most notably in 1912, a *March of the Women* which she is reported
to have conducted, using a toothbrush as a baton, from a cell in
Holloway prison. At the height of Wright's unpopularity she was
detailed to throw a stone through the dining-room window of his house
at 6 Park Crescent. She overslept and by the time she arrived at the
house the police were on guard. Thus she failed in her mission. Many
years later she related this incident to John Freeman who told her that
had she succeeded she would have hit him as he was sleeping in that
room at the time. She replied 'That wouldn't have mattered; we should
have made friends through the hole just the same!'

Publication of Wright's letter and book seems to have provided the
final catalyst in the breakdown of his marriage. He and his wife had
been living more and more apart; she was spending much time in
Ireland. Although very much in love when they married they failed to
share an intellectual life; Colebrook reports a friend as saying 'The
great qualities of Almroth were such as did not appeal to Ina and vice
versa.'[71] By 1913 there was much bitterness on both sides and Lady
Wright was contemplating divorce. Another factor was the death of
their son in Dublin. Lady Wright wrote of this on 26 October 1913 to
Mrs Fawcett. Clearly she was heartbroken—'My dear son has left me
after nearly twenty-four years of constant thought and care—just as
everything was brightening and he was stronger and happier than he
had ever been. I was looking forward to spending some quiet happy
days with him later on when he had a house of his own'.[72] This was the
house that Wright hoped to purchase for him. In his will the son left
£500 to the WSPU and according to Lady Wright he was a firm
supporter of their cause—'nothing would please him more than to see
us marching forward undaunted.' He had not thought it correct to
work for woman suffrage while he was wholly supported by his father.
As far as one can tell the donation, a considerable sum in 1913 (worth

upwards of £25,000 in 1998) was never made public and Wright remained in ignorance of it.

Although suffragist agitation continued throughout 1913 it ceased almost entirely the following year, when the catastrophe of war engulfed the nations of Europe. In Britain women joined the workforce in unprecedented numbers in factories and on the land, replacing men who had been recruited into the armed services. The enormous contribution that women made to the war effort completely failed to alter Wright's views. It was rumoured that there was an understanding between the suffragette leaders and the Government that, if women displayed a sense of responsibility during the war, their claim to suffrage would be favourably reviewed. Indeed Asquith wrote to Mrs Fawcett on 7 May 1916 reassuring her that bygones would be bygones and that in dealing with the suffrage question the militant events of the past decade would not be used as an argument against granting women the vote.[73] In 1917 a Bill was passing through the House of Commons — it did not become law until 1918 — extending the franchise to women with property; this stimulated another long letter from Wright, on this occasion to the Conservative *Morning Post*. He concentrated all his arguments on the issue of physical force. It was his firm view that 'the equitable principle is that only those who count as a force, and are prepared to back their opinions, should vote.' In his opinion this excluded not only women but also Quakers, clergymen and conscientious objectors. He wrote that 'Many a woman, who explains to you that she is well educated, will asseverate that the two things — voting and physical force — have absolutely no connection. She might just as well explain to you that the jury which brings in the man guilty of murder has nothing to do with his sentence of death.'[74] No doubt in some quarters there remained support for his views, on the grounds that women with the forces in France were in positions less exposed to danger than the men who were being slaughtered in their thousands in the trenches. This was taken to reinforce the concept of separate spheres for the sexes. In addition the large number of men being killed was increasing the existing majority of women in the proposed new electorate, thereby augmenting the fear that the male electors would be seriously outnumbered and out-voted. But the enormous war efforts of women in munitions factories, in military hospitals and in auxiliary positions in France converted many die-hard anti-suffragists to the view that women had earned the vote. The argument for denying this right to women grew weaker with every day the war continued. Yet it was not until 1928 that universal franchise, that is equal voting rights for adult men and women, was adopted. It was ironic that, after all the fuss, giving the vote to women made little immediate difference to the composition of the House of Commons. In 1951 there were only 17 women members, and at that time only four women had achieved ministerial status. Indeed it was not until the massive Labour Party victory in the 1997 general election that women entered Parliament in really significant numbers.

Wright's letter to the *Morning Post* excited little comment in 1917. Minds were concentrated on the appalling events in Flanders, and Wright himself was heavily embroiled in a polemical controversy over the treatment of the wounded, which brought him, as in 1906, into direct conflict with the army hierarchy. Yet his contribution to the treatment of war casualties was considered, even by his enemies in the medical profession, to be his greatest bequest to medicine.

Notes

1 Percy. House of Commons debate, 30 April 1873. Cited by Harrison B. *Separate spheres* p58. London: Croom Helm, 1980.

2 Harrison B. *Separate spheres* p56. London: Croom Helm, 1980.

3 Quoted by Harrison B. Ibid p68.

4 Reid M. *Ask Sir James* pp212–13. London: Hodder and Stoughton, 1987.

5 Porter R. *The greatest benefit to mankind* p676. London: HarperCollins, 1997.

6 West C *et al.* Petition to Royal College of Physicians of London 22 October 1895.

7 Ibid.

8 Cooke AM. *History of the Royal College of Physicians of London* vol 3. Oxford, 1972. Gives a full account of the struggle women experienced in gaining admission.

9 BOM 6 December 1901.

10 Ibid 16 June 1910.

11 At this time Broadbent was against admitting women but later he must have changed his mind. Following admission of women medical students during the Great War, he wrote of them in enthusiastic terms in the *St Mary's Hospital prospectus* for 1918. (Quoted in Garner JS, ref: 16.)

12 BOM 12 January 1911.

13 Ibid 17 October 1912.

14 Ibid 23 January 1913.

15 Ibid 17 February 1916.

16 Garner JS. The Great Experiment: the admission of women to St Mary's Hospital Medical School 1916–1925. *Med Hist* 1998; **42**: 68–88. This article gives an excellent account of the triumphs and difficultire experience by these women.

17 BOM 2 August 1917.

18 St Mary's Hospital Medical School Archives. MS/AD 46/14.

19 BOM 16 October 1924.

20 Ibid 28 February 1926.

21 Carmalt Jones DW. [Obituary] *Lancet* 1947; **i**: 930.

22 Colebrook L. Diary entry for 6 June 1911. Contemporary Medical Archives, Wellcome Institute.

23 Ibid 5 June 1911.

24 Fitzroy A. *Memoirs of Sir Armeric Fitzroy* vol 2 p414. London: Hutchinson & Co, 1923.

25 Arbuthnot Lane was a surgeon at St Bartholomew's Hospital and an enthusiast for the 'radical and heroic' type of surgery made possible by the Listerian gospel and the revolution in anaesthesia.

26 Colebrook L. Diary entry for 14 May 1914.

27 Harrison B. *Separate spheres* p91. London: Croom Helm, 1980.

28 Colebrook Diaries 1912.
29 Ibid February 1913 (retrospective entry).
30 Minutes of St Mary's Medical School Committee 16 December 1907.
31 Wilson CM (later Lord Moran). *St Mary's Hospital Gazette* 10 January 1910 p6.
32 Ibid p7.
33 Quoted in Fulford R. *Votes for women* p78. London: Faber & Faber, 1957.
34 Shaw GB. Why all women are peculiarly fitted to be good voters. *New York America* 21 April 1907.
35 Ibid.
36 Ibid.
37 Quoted in Fulford R. *Votes for women* p266. London: Faber & Faber, 1957.
38 Ibid p121.
39 *The Times* 16 March 1912 p9.
40 *The Times* 18 March 1912 p9.
41 Colebrook L. Diary entry for 6 August 1912 (retrospective entry following return from South Africa).
42 There was concern in the late 19th and early 20th centuries about the full reporting of divorce cases.
43 *The Times* 28 March 1912 pp7, 8.
44 Frank RT. The hormonal causes of premenstrual tension. *Arch Neurol Psychiatr* 1931; **26**: 1053.
45 Ibid p9.
46 Ensor R. *The Oxford history of England: England 1870–1974* p130. Oxford University Press, 1936.
47 Jenkins R. *Asquith* p85. London: Collins, 1964.
48 Ensor R. *The Oxford history of England: England 1870–1914* p397. Oxford University Press, 1936.
49 *Pall Mall Gazette* 28 March 1912 p1.
50 *The Times* 29 March 1912 p9.
51 Ibid 1 April 1912 p6.
52 Charles William Reginald Duncombe, MP for Thirsk and Malton from 1906 to 1915 when he became 2nd earl of Feversham. He died in 1916.
53 *The Times* 1 April 1912.
54 Ibid.
55 Ibid.
56 Soames M. *Clementine Churchill* p79. London: Cassell, 1979.
57 *The Times* 1 April 1912.
58 *The Times* 11 April 1912.
59 *The Common Cause.* Unsigned leading article. 4 April 1912, pp880–1.
60 *The Times* 29 March 1912.
61 Wright AE. *The unexpurgated case against woman suffrage.* London: Constable & Co, 1913.
62 Colebrook Diaries 1913.
63 *Punch* 8 October 1913 p312.
64 Ibid p299.
65 *Spectator* 18 October 1913 pp612–13.
66 *Saturday Review* 11 October 1913 pxiv (unsigned review).
67 Ross R. Man and woman. *The Nation* 11 October 1913 pp933–4.
68 Shaw GB. Sir Almroth Wright's polemic. *New Statesman* 18 October 1913 pp45–7.
69 Freeman J. In Cope Z. *Almroth Wright: founder of modern vaccine therapy* pp162–75. London: Nelson, 1966.
70 Howes F. *DNB* 194150 pp804–5.
71 Colebrook L. *Almroth Wright: provocative doctor and thinker* p214. London: William Heinemann, 1954.
72 Letter from Georgina Wright to Mrs Fawcett. Fawcett Library, autograph letters vol viii E.
73 Letter from Asquith to Mrs Fawcett. Fawcett Library, autograph letters.
74 *Morning Post* 15 June 1917.

Chapter 8

The Wounds of War

War came as something of a surprise to the inoculation department, as it did to many in the rest of the country. Colebrook's diaries give no indication that war was imminent.[1] The department was fully occupied with developing vaccine therapy and with raising money via private practice, not only for themselves but also to finance research. Yet there were strong military connections. All the assistant staff were in the Territorial Army. Stewart Douglas, having retired from the Indian Army Medical Service due to ill health, was on the reserve list and would retain the title of captain up to and beyond 1918. John Freeman had fought in the ranks in the Boer War. In 1900 Alexander Fleming had enlisted, as a private soldier, in the London Scottish Rifle Volunteers. He took a full part in both the social and the professional activities of the regiment; he and his brother were outstanding shots and formed part of the team that won the Daily Telegraph Cup at Bisley.[2] They also played water polo for the regiment. Fleming showed no ambition for promotion or military responsibility and remained a private until the pressure of professional work forced him to resign — fortunately for medicine — in April 1914. Colebrook had enlisted in a Kensington volunteer regiment as medical officer, thoroughly enjoying life in the mess and 'having a great time' at the annual camps. He particularly savoured the luxury of having a horse. By the summer of 1914 his mind was occupied with the question of marriage. Wright had introduced him to Dorothy Scarlett Campbell, a well-connected lady, with whom he had gone on holiday earlier in the year to Montserrat. They married on 24 September from Wright's house at 6 Park Crescent and after a three-day honeymoon Colebrook left to join his regiment.[3]

Wright had considerable knowledge of the army and its ways from his days at Netley. He also knew Kitchener and was pressing him to introduce compulsory anti-typhoid inoculation for all troops serving abroad. He wrote a long article in *The Times* of 28 September 1914 forcefully drawing attention to the dangers to troops fighting in northern France where the disease was endemic. He pointed out that 'an army, on going out on active service, goes from the sanitary conditions of civilization straight back to those of barbarism'.[4] As we have seen in a previous chapter he was successful in persuading Kitchener in the matter of anti-typhoid inoculation. In furtherance of his aims Wright placed the entire resources of his department, which was of course financed independently from the hospital by sale of his vaccines, at the disposal of the Government. This offer was accepted, though not without some resistance on the part of diehards in the RAMC; and, mainly due to the organisational skills of Douglas, over ten million doses of vaccine were prepared. The results of this vaccination programme were spectacular and the incidence of typhoid on the Western Front was negligible compared with that encountered by troops in South Africa during the Boer War (see Chapter 3). Epidemics did occur among uninoculated civilians, most notably at Malasse where a camp had been set up by the Society of Friends for the large number of Belgian refugees who had crossed the border after the bombardment of Poperinghe.[5]

Wright also advocated, and supplied, vaccines against the septic infections caused by staphylococci and streptococci, but here he was less successful as scientists had no knowledge of the ineffectiveness of these, there having been no controlled trial of their use. The director general of the Army Medical Services, Sir Alfred Keogh, was doubtful as to the value of these antiseptic vaccines but realised that sepsis was going to prove a major problem and that control of wound infection would play a vital part in treatment of casualties. He asseverated in October 1914, 'We have, in this war, gone straight back to all the septic infections of the Middle Ages.'[6] He proposed that Wright should set up a research laboratory to investigate wound sepsis at the base hospital in Boulogne. This offer was readily accepted and Wright, who was now employed by the newly formed Medical Research Committee (see Chapter 10), was seconded to the RAMC with the rank of colonel. His influence was such that he managed to take with him most of the staff of the inoculation department. This was not easy as those in the Territorials or on the reserve had been asked at once to join their units. Douglas was due to join the Indian base hospital, Parry Morgan was drafted to Netley, Colebrook to his regiment and Freeman, given the rank of Lieutenant-Colonel, had been sent to Russia to obtain cultures of the cholera *Vibrio* in order to produce a vaccine. Only Fleming, given an immediate commission as a lieutenant, was available to accompany Wright to France. It is an indication of Wright's influence and determination that he was able to persuade Kitchener to recall Colebrook from his regiment — a fortunate move as the regiment 'was

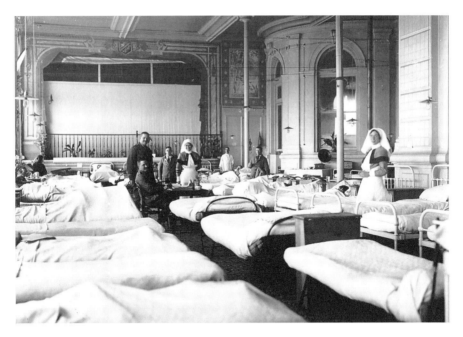

Figure 18
The casino at Boulogne converted into No.14 British Military Hospital. Wright had to walk through these wards each day to the laboratory. (The Imperial War Museum, London)

badly cut up at Loos' and many of Colebrook's friends killed — and draft him and the others to Boulogne. Douglas, whose health was always suspect, was taken ill late in September and on recovery was allowed to remain at St Mary's supervising vaccine production.

The casino at Boulogne had been converted into No.14 British Military Hospital, but no satisfactory provision had been made for laboratory work. The official allocation of pathology staff for such a hospital was one medical officer and one laboratory assistant. The latter was a regular soldier, Sergeant William Clayden, who left a description of conditions when Wright arrived with his staff and a considerable quantity of apparatus.[7] Initially the laboratory was in an annexe on the ground floor. A drain with several inspection traps ran through this room and the stench was intolerable. At 6 am Clayden would remove the inspection trap covers and pour diluted cresol down the drain, repeating the process several times during the day. Despite these measures the malodorous atmosphere persisted and Wright, after protesting vigorously, obtained permission to move to the top floor which before the war had been used as a fencing school. This was well ventilated and lit through skylights but had no gas, water or benches. Clayden appears to have been a resourceful scrounger and before long

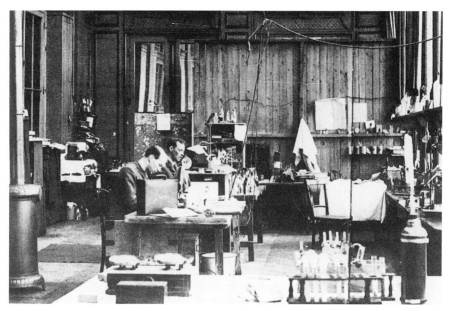

Figure 19
The laboratory above the casino; it had previously been the fencing school. (The Imperial War Museum, London)

he had begged, borrowed or stolen benches and seats. It was in situations such as this that Fleming's ingenuity showed to great advantage. Large Winchester containers were filled with water and then fitted with glass and rubber tubing for slide washing; methylated spirit burners replaced Bunsen burners. Oil heaters were brought into service as incubators. Working conditions were far from pleasant. It was bitterly cold in winter. When the wind was in the wrong direction the laboratory was liable to fill with fumes from the three inefficient oil stoves used to heat the room. Although these stoves were later replaced with more suitable models the place was never really warm, but such was the *esprit de corps* that everyone accepted these conditions and there were no complaints. Eventually a tank was installed in the roof and they had running water.

It must have seemed tough and primitive to a group of doctors drafted into the army from what was, for those days, an efficient, well-run laboratory in a London teaching hospital. Douglas with his experience of the Indian Army was in charge of the administrative side and kept up morale by always having a joke and encouraging the laboratory assistants though, according to Clayden, he could also use 'forceful words'. His early departure back to England meant that Fleming, who at first seemed excessively reserved, had to take over the administration. In time the other ranks grew to respect his judgment and were stimulated by his ingenious technical methods. One instance of this, subsequently of importance in the study of wounds, was his construction of an apparatus for glass-blowing from an old petrol can, glass and rubber tubing and a foot bellows.

Wright, although given the rank of full colonel, was totally unsuited to the military life. His appearance in uniform provided something of a shock to the conventional Sergeant Clayden who would give Wright the 'once over' every morning when he came to the laboratory to see that his belt was straight and his shoes and buttons polished. Yet nothing was allowed to interfere with the laboratory work. One incident will serve to illustrate the contrast between the regular soldier and the temporary commissioned officer.[8] One morning when Wright arrived in the laboratory Clayden was horrified to observe there was a large tear in the seat of his trousers. Deeply shocked Clayden went to Fleming and said, 'Sir, the seat of the Colonel's trouser is torn and his shirt is hanging out, I think you had better draw his attention to it'. This Fleming suggested would come better from the sergeant. Clayden then went up to Wright, sprung sharply to attention and saluted — a procedure that always brought a smile to Wright's face and a twinkle to his eye — and said: 'Sir, the seat of your trousers is hanging out.'

Wright looked up and replied: 'What phraseology, sergeant. Do you think the nurses will be upset? Now tell me what I should do.'

'I suggest we send the car driver down to the billet for another pair and you can change in the cubby hole.'

'What a brain,' said Wright and work was resumed at once.

The reference to nurses is significant because in his approach to the laboratory Wright had to pass through the wards, indeed he was in charge of one, seeing at first hand the severely septic wounds and the extreme distress of the young soldiers. Much of this was due to the excruciating pain caused by removing dressings that had become adherent to the open wounds. Alleviation of this agony was brought about by an ingenious procedure invented by Douglas,[9] who remained in close contact with Boulogne throughout the war. He found that if the wound was covered with a layer of thin perforated celluloid, rendered both sterile and pliable by soaking in 5% cresol and then washed in sterile saline, it could be lifted off the surface of a wound without causing pain. All the discharges from the wound passed through the perforations — which were 1.5 mm in diameter, with four perforations per square centimetre — leaving the surface of the wound clean. Furthermore when the wound was dressed the celluloid was found to have regained its original stiffness, thus making an accurately fitting splint which kept the wound in a complete state of rest.

Figure 20
Wright in the uniform of a full colonel at the laboratory bench
(The Wellcome Library, London)

The billet referred to by Clayden was a house in the Boulevard
Daunou that Wright had rented. It was close to the Seamen's Institute
founded by his father in the 1870s. All members of the laboratory lived
there while working in Boulogne and they were looked after by a
woman who cooked for them and by her daughter Lucienne, who
acted as a parlourmaid. Social life centred round the drawing-room
where they received many distinguished visitors.

The RAMC approach to the battles in Flanders in 1914 was based
on their experiences in the Boer War. There the impression had been
formed that antiseptics had solved the problem of wound infection.
This was a serious misjudgment. The South African campaign was
fought over an uncultivated sandy and rocky terrain that carried little
risk of infecting wounds. The wounds were usually caused by penetration of high-velocity Mauser bullets and, providing a vital organ or
blood vessel was not hit, healed rapidly. There was some disagreement
over treatment of abdominal injuries. McCormac, consulting surgeon
to the army in the Boer War, considered that they should be treated

conservatively and should not undergo operation. His much-quoted aphorism was: 'A man wounded in the abdomen dies if he is operated on and remains alive if he is left in peace.'[10] This became official RAMC policy and was in force at the beginning of the Great War. It was a view that did not go unchallenged. The professor of surgery at Netley, W F Stevenson, was of the opinion that abdominal wounds should be explored to ascertain if the bowel had been punctured and could be repaired.[11] In the Russo-Japanese war a Russian woman surgeon, Princess Vera Ignatievna Gedroitz, had operated near the front line on abdominal wounds, with considerable success.[12] In spite of this knowledge the official policy in the British army was not altered until the successes achieved by younger civilian volunteers, such as Souttar and Gordon-Taylor, showed that early operation could result in recovery.[13] In the first week of August 1915 official policy was altered, and rapid evacuation of abdominal wounds and early operation was recommended as the correct treatment.[14]

Conditions in France and Flanders were entirely different from those on the veldt in two fundamental aspects. Firstly, the terrain was an intensely cultivated area which over centuries had been heavily manured and was rich in pathogenic organisms including not only the common pus-producing *Staphylococcus* and *Streptococcus* species but also bacilli responsible for tetanus and, most sinister of all, the anaerobic bacillus *Clostridium perfringens*, responsible for gas gangrene — a condition unknown in the Boer War.

Secondly, the type of wound sustained in France was not at all similar to that received in South Africa. Simple puncture wounds caused by bullets were much less frequent than the multiple wounds, so often encountered from 1914 onwards, that resulted from numerous fragments of shrapnel from high-explosive shells. These jagged pieces of metal could penetrate limbs in several places and carry with them muddy layers of khaki clothing. The resultant wound would be irregular in outline with many deep crevices and heavily infected from the start. Most of these injuries were in those who had been living in waterlogged, muddy, insanitary trenches and who often received their wounds when crossing no-man's land — a quagmire pocked by shell holes filled with foul-smelling, faecally contaminated water. During daylight it was often difficult or impossible to retrieve these men and it was only after dark that stretcher-bearers could bring them back to the regimental aid post. From there they would be slowly transported to the casualty clearing station, often several miles behind the front line, where surgical help was available. Incessant shelling of roads and lines of communication further delayed movement to the rear. It was often

24 hours or more before the wounded man reached the surgeon, by which time infection had established a firm hold. Mortality was high — 80 per cent or more in compound fracture of the femur. The medical profession faced with this situation could rely only on Lister's 19th-century doctrine and apply more and stronger antiseptics. The results were catastrophic.

The antiseptic treatment of wounds was vigorously advocated by the hierarchy of the surgical profession and by no one more ardently than its leader, the President of the Royal College of Surgeons, Sir William Watson Cheyne.[15] Cheyne had been born in the Shetlands, orphaned at an early age and brought up by his uncle, a Presbyterian minister on the Shetland island of Fetlar. He was educated at Aberdeen Grammar School and King's College, Aberdeen before entering Edinburgh University to study medicine with a view to becoming a ship's surgeon. Here he came to the notice of Lister, who made him his house surgeon. When Lister was appointed to King's College Hospital in London he took Cheyne with him. Lister was not universally welcomed in the capital and Cheyne, who at first was resident in King's College Hospital, faced considerable hostility. He remained fiercely loyal to his chief and this paid rich dividends: before long he was appointed to the staff, and from that moment his future was assured. Yet he was not endowed with originality and was inflexible in his views. He clung rigorously to Lister's principles of antisepsis, and was incapable of realising that the conditions of the wounded on the Western Front required a new approach. Lister had used chemicals, mainly diluted carbolic acid, to destroy bacteria on the surface of the skin and on instruments and dressings. His doctrine alerted surgeons to the dangers of germs and resulted in the use of face-masks when operating, the universal sterilisation of instruments and dressings as well as the wearing of operating gowns and, eventually, of rubber gloves. All this had a dramatic effect on the incidence of post-operative infections but had little effect on established infection. Yet by the end of 1915 Cheyne had written no fewer than six papers advocating that wounds sustained in the mud of Flanders should be treated with stronger and stronger antiseptics.[16] He wrote to Sir Anthony Bowlby, consulting surgeon to the expeditionary force, recommending packing wounds with a paste containing 2% cresol. Such procedures seem to have been slavishly followed by many surgeons in France, with results that were far from satisfactory and in many instances frankly disastrous. By the end of 1914 the army medical services were overwhelmed by the large numbers of wounded coming in from the battles of Mons, Ypres and the Marne, many of whom were dying from wound infection.

Cheyne, who was consulting surgeon to the Navy, had no practical experience of injuries sustained by the soldiers in France. He wrote from a limited experience in South Africa and from observations on a relatively few wounded in naval actions where there was no contamination by infected soil. By 1915 he should have accepted that conditions on the Western Front were different from those experienced in any previous conflict. Indeed Bowlby himself wrote on 30 November 1914 to the *Lancet* in vivid terms describing the plight of the wounded man left lying in 'wet mud of manured fields until their torn trousers and their wounds were so soaked in a mixture of blood and dirt that it was impossible even to get the torn muscles mechanically clean let alone aseptic'.[17] The casualty clearing stations, often three or more miles behind the front line, were the first place at which casualties could undergo operation. These stations were equipped to treat 200 cases a day but even in 1914 'the total number of wounded treated at the clearing stations was at the rate of more than 1200, and on one day was over 3000.'[18] This was a situation beyond the comprehension of surgeons in London teaching hospitals, where a busy surgeon might operate on six to eight cases in an afternoon in comfortable surroundings and with ample assistance.

By the end of 1914 the delay in treating wounded men, the paucity of surgeons and facilities, and the high death rate from sepsis among the wounded who were recovered from the battle field were causing alarm in London. Between 12 October 1914 and 16 January 1915 a series of private reports on the medical services in France were sent to the Secretary of State for War, Lord Kitchener, by Col Arthur Lee MP.[19] These were essentially reassuring. Complaints concerning treatment of the wounded 'widely rumoured in the drawing rooms of London' were considered to be 'either much exaggerated or based upon a lack of appreciation of the difference between war and peace'. Much blame was unjustifiably put on the French, who were said to have commandeered all the trains that were needed to carry the wounded to the Channel ports whence they would be taken back to England. In war conditions this was a lengthy process and by the time the men reached the ports they were all too often either dead or *in extremis*. In a letter of 21 October 1914 Lee claimed there were 'very few cases of tetanus or gas gangrene' and stated 'nor can I gather any evidence to justify the sweeping statements in Sir Anthony Bowlby's original complaint.' One wonders what evidence he obtained. What was required was treatment in France as near as possible to the front line. Bowlby, a surgeon at St Bartholomew's Hospital and a major in the Territorial Army since 1908, understood this and had written to the director general of the Army Medical Services, Keogh, asking for more surgeons in France. This request was supported by Sir Berkeley Moynihan, the Leeds surgeon generally acknowledged to be the most able operator in the country and also a consulting surgeon to the Army. Keogh's reply clearly demonstrated that the authorities in London were out of touch with the situation at the front. He began his letter, dated 26 February 1915, to Bowlby 'I have no more intention of sending out surgical teams to France than I have of sending out baked potatoes.'[20] Moynihan had suggested sending to France mobile teams composed of surgeons, assistants and nurses, a system successfully adopted in the Second World War. When Keogh confided this proposal to Sloggett, the director general of medical services to the expeditionary force and a regular RAMC officer, the scheme was resisted. It seems that both Keogh and Sloggett were particularly 'concerned to guard the interests of our good young surgeons' — that is, the regular RAMC officers.[21] Keogh was convinced that 'selected RAMC officers were as good as anything that the civil profession can produce in France'. This sensitivity with regard to the ability of the regular army surgeons and the implied wish to exclude civil surgeons with temporary commissions was to cause trouble throughout much of the war.

Antagonism between regular and temporary RAMC officers was one of many factors leading to difficulties encountered by Wright when pressing his views on treatment of wounds. Faced with the appalling sepsis among the wounded in the hospital in Boulogne, Wright and his colleagues adopted a scientific approach to the problem. They realised at an early stage that indiscriminate application of antiseptics was doing more harm than good. Wright now stimulated Alexander Fleming to carry out an investigation into the bacteriology of wounds.[22] Swabs for bacterial culture were taken from all wounds and also from the men's clothing remote from the injury, so that contamination by purulent discharge from the wounds might be avoided. Culture of the swabs from the clothing revealed a variety of organisms similar to those found in the wounds. It was apparent that the men's own soiled clothes, fragments of which had been driven deep into the tissues by shrapnel, were the main source of infection. The types of bacteria isolated were of the greatest significance. In over 90 per cent the organism isolated was *Clostridium perfringens*, which causes gas gangrene. In some 30 per cent of cases *Clostridium tetani*, the organism whose toxin is responsible for tetanus was also found; in addition, species of the pus-forming bacteria *Streptococcus* and *Staphylococcus* were present in 40 per cent and 15 per cent of cases respectively. Both the gas gangrene and tetanus organisms are plentiful in horse manure and in the well-fertilised fields of northern France. These organisms cannot grow in the presence of oxygen (that is, they are anaerobic). In normal tissues they are unable to proliferate but in war wounds there are two conditions under which they can cause disease. Firstly, Fleming was able to demonstrate that if both the gas gangrene bacillus and streptococci or staphylococci were present in the wound, the last two organisms would consume all the oxygen and thus provide favourable conditions for the growth of the gas gangrene bacilli. Secondly, if damage to its blood supply had caused death of muscle in the depth of a wound, that muscle would provide an excellent culture medium for anaerobic organisms.

In the first months of the war, during the battles of the Marne and the Aisne, many of the wounded contracted tetanus. This unpleasant complication, often following very small wounds, is characterised by symptoms of severe muscle spasms involving the face and limbs, difficulty in swallowing and distressing painful contortions of the body. There follows rapid wasting, exhaustion and death with the patient conscious to the last. Fortunately, with the introduction of anti-tetanus serum, owing mainly to the influence of Wright's old adversary Bruce, the incidence of this disease was greatly reduced. During the whole period of the war on the Western Front there were 1,907,199 wounded and only 2549 (0.127 per cent) cases of tetanus[23]. By far the highest incidence was in the period August to November 1914.

No such effective prophylactic existed for gas gangrene. Before the war this condition was so rare in civil wounds as to be thought almost non-existent. In the South African war it was so unusual that it is not referred to in surgical writings on that campaign. In 1914 it became not only one of the most frequent but also the gravest complication of gunshot wounds. Its onset could be sudden with severe pain at the site of injury. It affected small, apparently insignificant, soft-tissue limb wounds as well as larger injuries. It was noticeable that men who had been in the trenches for long periods, and whose clothes had been subjected to the insanitary conditions prevailing there, were more likely to develop the complication. The infection could spread with alarming rapidity within the tissues. Men hit in the legs only eight hours previously were found to be gangrenous up to the level of the umbilicus. Sweating and febrile with an ashen appearance about the face, blue lips and watery eyes, yet alert and orientated until the end, their death was rapid. Those arriving at a casualty clearing station, or a base hospital, with a bandaged arm or leg would cry out in pain as the

gas formed by the organisms caused swelling of the limb. Removal of
the dressings would disclose a grossly swollen and discoloured arm or
leg; on palpation of surrounding skin there would be crepitations due
to underlying foul smelling gas which might be seen exuding from the
wound itself. In such cases immediate amputation offered the only
hope of survival. Those left out in no man's land presented an even
more grotesque sight. They appeared as 'one bloated gangrenous
mass'.[24] The swelling of the limbs was so rapid and extensive that the
tunic, trousers and even the boots burst open revealing the greenish-
black blebbed skin. The experience of passing through the wards each
day remained with Wright and his colleagues for the rest of their lives
— it constituted the 'pain in the mind' often spoken of by Wright.[25]
After hostilities had ended they could seldom bear to recall the horrors
of those years.

It was a principle, adhered to by Wright throughout his life, that
treatment should be aimed at assisting the body in its natural defence
mechanisms against infection. As described in Chapter 4, one of the
main arms in such defence lies in the active mobile cells of the body,
known as macrophages, and in the neutrophil polymorphonuclear
leucocytes of the blood. Fleming, with Wright's encouragement, in
addition to culturing organisms from clothes of wounded men, also
studied microscopically the purulent exudate from the wounds. They
discovered that those wounds not treated with antiseptics contained
numerous macrophages and neutrophils actively engaged in ingesting
and destroying infecting organisms. In wounds treated with antiseptics,
only a few dead and dying macrophages could be seen and organisms
were proliferating freely. The antiseptics were killing the macrophages
and neutrophils. Although this work by Fleming was not published
until 18 September 1915, Wright was already enunciating the basis for
wound treatment in an address to the Royal Society of Medicine on
30 March.[26] He listed the types of organism causing infection,
emphasising their origin from animal and human faeces. He then
elucidated the principles upon which treatment might be based namely
(a) antiseptics, (b) physiological methods — 'procedures such as
opening and draining of the wound, which bring the anti-bacterial
powers of the blood to bear on the infecting microbes', (c) vaccine
therapy. He concluded emphatically:

'I believe it is really beyond all question that of these the second is beyond all
comparison the most important, and I would submit that, all loud talk about
antiseptic treatment notwithstanding, this is at best an ancillary method of
treatment. And, of course, the same applies to treatment by vaccine.'

Considering his firm belief in vaccine therapy this statement was not only courageous but showed a commendably impartial approach to the problem.

At this meeting, which drew a large audience of surgeons, physicians and pathologists, Wright described in detail the experimental laboratory methods and results on which his opinion was based. Wright's statement regarding antiseptics went against all the prejudices of the surgeons and were especially offensive to the closed mind of Sir W Watson Cheyne. Yet Wright was not alone in his views. Just two weeks after his address the *BMJ* carried a memorandum 'On the treatment of bacterial infections of projectile wounds' under the names of Col F F Burghard, Sir William B Leishman, Sir Berkeley Moynihan and Wright.[27] This recommended freely opening up the wound, removing all foreign bodies, slough and blood clot and inserting a wide-bore drainage tube. Wright further recommended washing wounds with sterile hypertonic saline, which by osmosis would promote the flow of lymph, containing antibodies and phagocytic cells, into the wound. 'The leucocyte is the best antiseptic' became a favourite maxim of his. Leucocytes also played an essential part in ridding the wound of its coating of scab and fibrin by promoting separation of the slough. This they did by releasing an enzyme, trypsin, which acted by 'cleansing digestion resolving the products of inflammation in the infiltrated tissues and severing the connecting strands by which sloughs are bound to the face of the wound'.[28] Wright considered that trypsin was liberated into the wound when it was irrigated with strong, that is hypertonic, saline that disrupted the membranes of the leucocytes discharging the enzyme. Once this had occurred, and the slough had separated, he advocated irrigation with normal saline until the wound was 'clean' and secondary suture could be undertaken.

But there was still much opposition to overcome, and not only among army surgeons. In Wright's own laboratory in Boulogne Parry Morgan, the mathematician turned bacteriologist, quarrelled with his chief. He disagreed with Wright on the theoretical question as to whether saline solutions affected the flow of lymph and cells into the wound and on the use of saline to promote the removal of pus.[29] On the question of antiseptics he concluded that: 'For the purpose of washing out a wound neutral hypochlorous solutions are by far the most potent of the antiseptics usually employed', but these are almost immediately converted to saline, i.e. the solution Wright was recommending, as soon as they contact the wounded tissues. Parry Morgan received strong support from Zachary Cope, a surgical colleague of Wright's at St Mary's, but neither his paper [30], which was refuted by Fleming[31], nor Parry Morgan's had any long-term influence on wound treatment. Parry Morgan left Boulogne to take up a post as bacteriologist in Cardiff. His opinions were not corroborated by other members of the laboratory staff.

Wright followed up his address of 30 March with a lecture accompanied by a laboratory demonstration at the Royal Society of Medicine on 8 and 14 October 1915.[32] He started by making the point that surgeons in civilian life were essentially concerned with the avoidance of infections in operations. They achieved this by sterilising the skin with antiseptics before incising it, using sterile instruments, gloves, gowns and so forth. These admirable measures were not applicable to the treatment of wounds already the seat of septic infection. After a year of war, he reasoned 'there are on that point very few illusions left'; yet conventional surgeons were unable to understand why chemical antiseptics could kill bacteria in a test tube but were unable to do so in shrapnel wounds on the Western Front. One factor was the jagged nature of the wound itself with its many crevices. Fleming, who was an expert glass-blower, devised an ingenious experiment to illustrate this point. He produced a model artificial wound by taking a test tube and creating a series of spiked recesses in its wall to resemble the crevices of a real wound.[33] He filled the tube with fluid heavily infected with bacteria. The tube was then emptied and filled this time with an antiseptic solution, which was left there for 24 hours. The tube was again emptied and filled with a culture medium and incubated. Lo and behold, the bacteria grew prolifically! The antiseptic had not touched the organisms in the recesses. Fleming and Wright deduced that it was even less likely that penetration by antiseptics would take place in a shrapnel wound, with its more complex crevices. In addition they demonstrated that antiseptics were removed rapidly by absorption on to the wound dressings and were neutralised by the pus and drainage fluids exuding from the wound. It was known that the bactericidal properties of antiseptics were counteracted if they came into contact with blood or serum.

Armed with these facts, Wright determined to campaign vigorously for a change in the accepted treatment of wounds. He recommended prohibition of all antiseptics likely to damage phagocytes, the earliest possible removal of dead tissue and foreign bodies, irrigation of the wound with sterile saline and application of a sterile dressing and immobilisation of affected limbs. This treatment was often effective if applied early enough but did not always work after infection had set in. It was a strong argument for treatment as near to the front as possible,

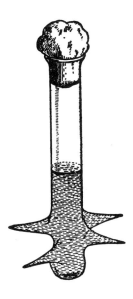

Figure 21
The glass model of a shrapnel wound devised
by Fleming. Organisms placed in the spiked
outpouchings were unharmed by antiseptics.
(London: William Heinemann, 1954)

a matter that was to occupy Wright for the remainder of the war. In cases already infected many surgeons insisted on irrigating the wound with a variety of antiseptics, but only one of these was in any way effective. This was the Carrel–Dakin solution containing sodium hypochlorite, an unstable compound that, as mentioned above, on coming into contact with the tissues was at once converted into sodium chloride — that is, the salt solution Wright was advocating.

Watson Cheyne was incensed, and many other surgeons found it offensive that Wright should consider that antiseptics were not only useless but actually harmful. If they were capable of killing germs in a test tube or on the surface of intact skin, and if they did not work at first in an infected wound, then surely the answer was to use more and stronger antiseptics. Cheyne published a long article in the *British Journal of Surgery* to this effect in which he castigated Wright personally.[34] The arguments he employed were pitiful, based mainly on anecdotes drawn from Lister's experience, over half a century before, of a few civilian patients with compound fractures of the femur. He rested much of his case on the fact that Lister 'found none of the horrible things which we are told by our colleagues in France happen to infected wounds when strong antiseptics are applied.' He completely ignored the conditions under which troops in the front line were living, and there is no evidence that he visited France at that time to see for himself. He wrote 'the antiseptic is used up in killing the bacteria, and that if we have a large number of bacteria in the wound we must use a correspondingly large amount of antiseptic.' He returned to recommending the use of antiseptic pastes, as he had done to Bowlby on an earlier occasion. Throughout the paper there were numerous sarcastic references to Wright, belittling his views and experimental work. He insisted that for success 'the surgeon must believe that such disinfection is possible' with antiseptics. Faith it seemed was more important than science.

The *British Journal of Surgery* invited Wright to reply; but when the editors read his strongly worded typescript, even though it had been slightly modified by his colleagues in Boulogne, they withdrew their invitation because such was the deference to the authority of the President of the Royal College of Surgeons that they considered the criticism of Cheyne unseemly. The *Lancet* had no such qualms. It had, after all, been founded by Thomas Wakley 'to expose the quacks and charlatans in medicine and to report on the bungled operations of famous surgeons'.[35] It published Wright's reply to Cheyne, unexpurgated, on 16 September 1916[36] but took the precaution of having an editorial leader in the same issue describing his phraseology as regrettable. The editor 'would have preferred to see certain crude expressions omitted in an argument between the President of the Royal College of Surgeons and a famous pathologist.'[37]

By the standards of today Wright's paper was excessively long, consisting of ten double-column pages of small type. Instead of replying in a sharp succinct manner, basing his argument on the firm experimental evidence available, he launched into a disquisition on the virtues of polemical criticism. Only then did he draw attention to the fallacy that wounds of the type seen in France could not be sterilised at once if treated with antiseptics; their jagged nature and penetration of the crevices in the deep tissues by infected clothing perforce precluded this. 'Sir W Watson Cheyne is, as it seems to me, blind' wrote Wright, and quoted from Dante: 'he has not seen the city we seek; not even sighted its tower from afar'. In the matter of the intellectual equipment required of a scientific worker Wright described Cheyne as 'being hopelessly short', and his views on the bacteriology of wounds as 'imaginative fiction'. He wrote that: 'Sir W Watson Cheyne's mental vision is never sufficiently acute to discriminate between two issues which are distinct but interconnected.' He accused him of 'confused cerebration and defective logic', and his writings as being those 'of a man who is blindfolded by prejudice or who sets out to lead his reader, if a fool, into pitfalls'. He categorised Cheyne as a 'man so obsessed with the old ideas as to extrude from the world, if he could, everything that is incompatible with them — suffering no new thing to come up which did not conform to tradition'. Two weeks later Cheyne wrote in

Figure 22
A group outside the casino in Boulogne. Seated are Wright and Harvey Cushing; standing are Colebrook,
Roger Lee and Alexander Fleming. Cushing and Lee were in charge of the surgical and medical divisions
of the Second Harvard University Unit, which took over some of the wards in the casino in 1916. (The
Wellcome Library, London)

a short letter to the *Lancet*, 'You will hardly expect me to reply to Sir Almroth Wright's personal attack on me by defending my own or dissecting his mentality.'

Wright's paper, termed by one professor as an 'unedifying rough and tumble',[38] was regarded as being in the worst possible taste and caused intense annoyance to older members of the profession. This reaction to what many saw, wrongly, as an unprovoked personal attack rapidly blinded them to the scientific merits of Wright's case. (It was after all Cheyne who had been the first to introduce the personal element into the discussion.) Among regular RAMC officers any questioning of orthodoxy as propounded by an authority, such as the President of the Royal College of Surgeons, was regarded as outrageous; yet support came from younger surgeons, such as the visiting American Harvey Cushing who shared Wright's opinion on antiseptics.[39] Wright was once more his own worst enemy for, by using what the *Lancet* had called 'crude expressions', he antagonised many who might have been sympathetic to his views. The controversy reached the general public and Wright's friend Bernard Shaw said that he had not only cut off

Cheyne's head but put his brains on the operating table to show that he had never learned how to use them! Cheyne's opinion of Almroth Wright's scientific competence cannot be ascertained, however; he withdrew from the controversy on the ground that it had entered the region of the unprintable.[40]

In spite of the hostility within the regular RAMC, Wright's recommendations received some support. One textbook on military surgery[41] published as early as 1916 included the following passage on dealing with wound infection:

> 'Much has been written in the past concerning infection of gunshot wounds, and it was thought that with modern methods of antisepsis and first aid dressings, combined with high velocity projectiles, infection would be reduced to a minimum. Unfortunately this has not proved so.'

By the end of the war Wright's views had gained wide acceptance. In 1919 H M Gray, consultant surgeon to the 3rd Army of the British Expeditionary Force, referred to 'Sir Almroth Wright's able and stimulating work having much influence in gradually weaning the profession from the established faith, and in fostering reliance, so to speak, on the powerful natural reserves which can be called upon to cope with invading organisms.'[42] Gray deplored the use of antiseptics in treatment of wound infection and asserted that 'the stronger the antiseptic the worse the result'.[43]

There is no doubt that Wright was responsible for a radical change in wound treatment but for this he has had little credit — a fate of many unpopular innovators. Perhaps the most fitting verdict on the whole episode was provided by *The Times* medical correspondent on 1 May 1919 when he quoted a confession by 'one of Britain's greatest surgeons', possibly Moynihan: 'We all said Wright was mistaken about his antiseptics: but it was we who were mistaken.' In the Second World War his recommendations for early operation, excision of dead tissue and foreign bodies, washing out the wound with sterile saline and immobilisation of the wounded part followed by secondary suture were largely adopted.[44]

Notes

1   Colebrook Diary. Wellcome CMAC PP/COL/A.3.
2   Macfarlane G. 1984 *Alexander Fleming, the man and the myth* p25. London: Chattto & Windus, 1984.
3   Colebrook Diary. CMAC PP/COL/A.3.
4   *The Times* 28 September 1914.
5   Cushing H. *From a surgeon's journal 1915–18* p65. London: Constable, 1936.
6   Colebrook L. *Almroth Wright, provocative doctor and thinker* p72. London: Heinemann, 1975.

7   Clayden W. Br Lib Add MSS 56214.

8   Ibid.

9   Douglas SR. *Lancet* 1916; **ii**: 558.

10 Gordon Taylor G. *Medical history of the Second World War: Surgery* p93. London: HMSO, 1953.

11 Stevenson WF. *Wounds in war.* 2nd edn. London: Longmans, Green & Co, 1904.

12 Cartwright FF. *The development of modern surgery* p109. London: Arthur Baker Ltd, 1967.

13 Till AS. *Ann Roy Coll Surg* 1974; **54**: 33.

14 Bennet JDC. J Roy Soc Med 1991; **84**: 554.

15 Cheyne WW. *Lancet* 1914; **ii**: 1185.

16 Cheyne WW. *Brit J Surg* 1915–16; **3**: 427.

17 Bowlby AA. *Lancet* 1914; **ii**: 1427.

18 Ibid.

19 Lee Reports. Wellcome CMAC RAMC 446/7. Arthur Lee was later elevated to the peerage as Viscount Lee of Fareham and donated Chequers and its contents to the nation for use by the Prime Minister.

20 Wellcome CMAC RAMC 365/2.

21 Ibid.

22 Fleming A. *Lancet* 1915; **ii**: 376 , 638.

23 Macpherson WG, Bowlby AA, Wallace C, English C, eds. *Official history of the Great War. Medical services, Surgery of the War* vol 1 p153. HMSO, 1922.

24 Hughes B, Banks HS. *War surgery from firing line to base* p140 *et seq.* London: Baillière, Tindall and Cox, 1918.

25 Colebrook L. *Almroth Wright: provocative doctor and thinker* p70 *et seq.* London: Heinemann, 1954.

26 Wright AE. *Lancet* 1915; **i**: 625

27 Burghard FF *et al.* 1915 Memorandum on the treatment of the bacterial infections of projectile wounds. *BMJ* 1915; **i**: 735.

28 Wright AE. *Lancet* 1916; **i**:1203.

29 Morgan WP. *BMJ* 1916; **i**: 685.

30 Cope Z. Fashions in wound treatment. *St Mary's Hospital Gazette* April 1916 p42.

31 Fleming A. Ibid May 1916, 60.

32 Wright AE. *Lancet* 1915; **ii**: 629, 670, 717.

33 Wright AE. *Lancet* 1917; **i**: 939.

34 Cheyne WW. *Brit J Surg* 1915–16; **3**: 427.

35 Quoted by Douglas C. *BMJ* 1998; **316**: 1991.

36 Wright AE. *Lancet* 1916; **ii**: 503

37 *Lancet* 1916; **ii**: 526 [Editorial].

38 Boycott AE. 1916 *Lancet* 1916; **ii**: 622.

39 Cushing H. *From a surgeon's journal 1915–18* p131. London: Constable, 1936.

40 Shaw GB. *Doctors' delusions, crude criminology and sham education* p14. London: Constable & Co, 1931.

41 Penhallow DP. *Military surgery* p23. Henry Froude, Oxford University Press, 1916.

42 Gray HM. 1919 *The early treatment of war wounds* p35. Henry Froude, Oxford University Press, 1919.

43 Ibid p107.

44 Porritt A. 1953 Treatment of war wounds. In: *History of the Second World War, United Kingdom Medical Services. Surgery* pp 927. HMSO, 1953.

Chapter 9

Over the Heads of the Generals

Had Wright restricted himself to preaching on the scientific treatment of war wounds it is possible that his views would have received earlier acceptance. He was incapable of such restraint. In France it seemed to him that administrative arrangements for the care of the wounded were not all they should be. Many of his friends, distinguished in politics, journalism and the arts, came to see him and even stayed in his house on the Boulevard Daunou. Colebrook, who lived there, mentions Princess Marie Louise, Berkeley Moynihan, William Osler, George Bernard Shaw, Granville Barker, J A Spender of the *Westminster Gazette*, Geoffrey Dawson, editor of *The Times*, and several others.[1] Friends in the army passing through Boulogne on their way to the front also enjoyed his hospitality. To all these people he communicated his doubts as to the effectiveness and efficiency of the methods used by the RAMC in the management of wounded men. These views reached ministers in London.

The RAMC in 1914 was an organisation designed for a small army involved in a war of movement. Yet it found itself serving an army of millions engaged in static trench warfare; it is unsurprising that it encountered administrative difficulties. By early 1915 these difficulties were all too apparent to Wright and he concluded his address on wound infection to the Royal Society of Medicine on 30 March that year with a penetrating analysis of the problem[2]. He considered it essential that some machinery should be set up for coordinating the work of medical officers engaged in treatment of the sick and wounded. He realised that the RAMC constituted three distinct services: Administration, Hygiene and Sanitation, and a service for the sick and wounded. The Administrative Service was concerned with transport of the wounded man from the regimental aid post at the front to the advanced dressing station, then in succession to the field ambulance, to the casualty clearing station, to the base hospital and back to England using stretcher-bearers, ambulances, trains, canal barges and hospital ships. The service also had to ensure supplies of food, clothing, medical and surgical stores and equipment. The

Sanitation and Hygiene Service was concerned with protection against epidemic disease by ensuring that pure water supplies were available and instituting a programme of inoculation against typhoid.

These two services absorbed nearly all the regular RAMC officers. Thus the service for the sick and wounded was staffed almost entirely by volunteer civilian practitioners who had enlisted into the Territorial Army or taken temporary commissions in the RAMC. These included nearly all the regimental medical officers as well as those staffing casualty clearing stations and base hospitals. The casualty rate among these men, particularly those serving with the regiments, was high. Wright in his address was concerned that there was no regulation or system in treatment of the wounded and there was considerable variation in therapy adopted by individual medical officers — as indeed there was in civilian hospitals — each officer having independent charge of his patients. Such a system was not advantageous in the unprecedented conditions in Flanders where the doctor was encountering unfamiliar problems of infection in multiple projectile wounds. Furthermore there was no means whereby the results of treatment could be followed as patients were whisked away down the line and back to England with all speed. Indeed he thought, with good reason, that regular RAMC officers considered their main function was to pass the patients on as soon as possible. There was a serious conflict of interest here. The medical profession then, and to some extent today, cherished the tradition that the doctor was there to institute whatever treatment he considered most suitable. In the case of the wounded man this meant that medical officers he encountered at various points on his journey to England might each favour a different form of therapy.

Wright proposed that it would be to the general public, patient and military advantage if control of the treatment of wounds was instituted so that it would be possible scientifically to assess results of various therapeutic procedures and thus draw up 'general instructions and recommendations for the treatment of different categories of cases'. Such regulation was already in place in preventive treatment where there was compulsory anti-typhoid inoculation for all troops serving overseas and also in the administration of anti-tetanus serum to all wounded men; the result of both these measures had been a resounding success. Wright proposed that, in order to supervise the trial of various wound treatments and to draw up appropriate recommendations, there should be a 'Professional Head of the Service for the Treatment of the Sick and Wounded' supported by an advisory committee, membership of which would be restricted to 'those who were actually at the seat of war'.

The idea that doctors, whether in the army or not, should forgo any professional freedom in order to promote more consistent and effective care for the wounded was abhorrent to the higher echelons in the profession, and these proposals were ignored. Many thought Wright was simply trying to secure for himself the post of 'Professional Head of the Service', as indeed he may well have been. In any event nothing was done and the authorities at home were further reassured by the bland letters, mentioned in the previous chapter, from Arthur Lee to Kitchener. Others were not so sanguine. Hector Munro the writer, better known as Saki, had enlisted in the ranks at the age of 44. As well as writing fiction he was a political satirist, at one time working on the *Westminster Gazette*. He moved in influential social and political circles but, having an aversion to the self-righteous and conventional, he did not hesitate when on leave in London to draw attention to unnecessary hardships suffered by the common soldier. This must have reached the ears of the director general of the Army Medical Services, Sir Alfred Keogh, because in a letter to Sir Arthur Sloggett, director general of Army Medical Services to the Expeditionary Force in France, he wrote: 'There is a Hector Munro I believe alarming the London drawing rooms'[3]. Munro was killed the following year, 1916, at Beaumont Hamel.

During 1915 casualties were increasing at an alarming rate, the battles at Neuve Chapelle and Loos resulting in particularly heavy losses. In October Wright gave another lecture at the Royal Society of Medicine, together with a practical demonstration, on wound treatment and returned again to the topic of defects in organisation in the RAMC.[4] The Army had appointed some eminent surgeons as itinerant consultant advisers, and Wright was of the opinion that it would have been much better to have made them an integral part of the Army Medical Service with appointments to specific hospitals. They could then be entrusted with selection of operating staff and made responsible for all operative treatment in the hospitals where they served. Also he thought it essential that men with both clinical and laboratory experience should be given appointments as physicians in charge of wards where infected wounds were treated.

All this had little effect; but discontent was mounting and particularly among civilian members of the medical profession who had received temporary commissions. As early as January 1915 Bowlby, one of the consulting surgeons, had approached Keogh on the question of promotion for such men who often had considerable experience and higher qualifications yet found themselves under the command of professionally inferior regular RAMC officers. Keogh replied on 24 January 1915 that he was of the opinion that consulting surgeons should not be promoted to the rank of surgeon general — a rank soon to be abolished but then the highest available to a practising surgeon — although he proposed that Bowlby himself should be so promoted.[5] It was a subject that was to recur over the next three years but in 1916, together with other shortcomings of the RAMC, it was forcefully drawn to the attention of the authorities in a memorandum drawn up by four of the most respected and experienced medical men of the day.[6] The four who signed the memorandum were:

- Sir Alfred Fripp, surgeon to Guy's Hospital and the King. He had served in the South African War and was a member of the advisory board on Army Medical Services appointed after that conflict.
- Sir Alexander Ogston was surgeon to the King in Scotland and had served both in the South African War and in Serbia in 1915.
- Sir Cooper Perry, Physician and Superintendent at Guy's Hospital. He had served in the South African War, been a motivating force behind the establishment of the Royal Army Medical College at Millbank and was later to become Vice-Chancellor of London University.
- Dr T J Horder, later Lord Horder, physician to St Bartholomew's Hospital and the most distinguished clinician of his day.

The paper that these men wrote was based on a tour of the battle zones in France and contained severe criticism of the Army Medical Services. They were concerned that: 'Most members of the profession who could speak best, or who would make pertinent enquiries, are silent because they hold commissions or because they feel lack of knowledge of RAMC organisation...Many again are deterred from comment or criticism by fear of an implication of lack of patriotism'. They found that care of the sick and wounded at base hospitals left much to be desired and that 'much is tolerated by patients because to expose deficiencies might suggest lack of pluck and self sacrifice.' They considered that much of the dissatisfaction among patients, civilian practitioners and junior RAMC officers was hidden from seniors of the Corps and even from highly placed officers of other branches.

Their most penetrating remarks concerned the position of the director general, Keogh. In those days when loyalty to regiment or corps and respect for seniority, inspired by the public school spirit and 'not letting the side down', were paramount, this was something that could be said only by a distinguished and impartial group such as Fripp and his colleagues. The medical and social problems occasioned by the war had become so complex that they represented too big a proposition for one man to deal with; and this they stated plainly. They suggested that there were many aspects that lay beyond the cognizance of the director general and that on these a properly constituted committee could shed light. No-one had more delicate questions to decide than the director general on matters of vital interest to the health, efficiency and morale of the armies in the field: 'Yet he is the only expert official of the Government whose views and decisions are not subject to expert criticism and revision by his own profession. He is answerable to no individual or body that is in a position to form a judgment upon highly technical questions.'

In addition to these general comments about the director general, they made a series of specific criticisms. Among these were the unevenness in staffing levels in hospitals, the anomaly of medical officers allocated to duties for which they were not qualified and consulting surgeons not being used in the capacity for which they were most fitted. They concluded that what was needed was an advisory board upon which the civilian profession would be represented. They considered that it would reassure the public and the medical profession if questions concerning the Army Medical Services were considered by a body of experienced men 'instead of, as at present, being decided by a single individual [Keogh] who is not even on the Army Council, is not represented in Parliament by any man versed in the technical knowledge which is indispensable for answering questions (surely the work and occasion call for this), and is so inundated with work that he cannot be easily accessible.'

All this was independent of any prompting from Wright and against the background of the unprecedented casualties produced in 1916 by the battle of the Somme, in which on 1 July alone 57,000 were killed or wounded.[7] Casualty clearing stations designed to admit between 150 and 300 casualties a day found themselves dealing with thousands. Only the most urgent cases could be operated on at these stations — 11,000 in the month of July, according to Bowlby.[8] The remainder were evacuated to hospitals farther behind the lines or to England, often taking days to reach their destination. The diaries of junior RAMC officers serving at the front reveal some of the great difficulties encountered. On 15 September Neil Cantlie, himself many years later to become director general, records that his division attacked at 6.20 am and that almost at once two regimental medical officers were hit. There were heavy casualties but 'many cases cannot be brought in until nightfall'. There were between 500 and 600 casualties that day on his

Figure 23
*General Sir Alfred Keogh, director general of the Royal
Army Medical Corps 1914–18. (The Wellcome Library,
London)*

front and after 24 hours 'about 200 cases from the 1st King's
Shropshire Light Infantry are still lying out in no man's land'. The
following day, 16 September, 150 cases were still not recovered and it
was becoming increasingly difficult to search for them at night as they
remained hidden in shell-holes. There was a very high casualty rate
among medical officers. On 24 September Cantlie noted that 14 were
lost from the 6th, the Guards and the 20th divisions. They were
replaced by six newly arrived doctors drafted from civilian practice,
'with no training of any practical sort. They did not even know how to
put on a steel helmet.'[9] On 5 October he wrote a letter to the quarter-
master general's office explaining the difficulties encountered by
stretcher bearers.[10] The attacks had taken place across a narrow
front with consequent bunching of troops, which resulted in numerous
casualties from machine-gun fire. Casualties had to be carried for long
distances, six to eight thousand yards being not uncommon, in bad

weather over slippery ground churned up by shells, with no tracks or paths. Horse transport had difficulty in getting up to the front due to absence of roads. There were numerous problems in locating wounded men in the shell-holes of no man's land. A major problem was the physical condition of the stretcher-bearers after 24 hours of continuous work. Cantlie considered that under these conditions a bearer could undertake only two journeys of 6000 yards a day. Having been collected, the wounded man had to be taken by horse or motor transport to an advanced dressing station, which was often four and a half miles away, and only then begin his protracted journey home. The diaries of Major W J Webster tell a similar story to those of Cantlie but are tinged with bitterness; thus the entry for 23 July notes: 'on the Somme 13,000 casualties mostly from our own fire, same old mistake'[11].

The ultimate responsibility for dealing with these problems rested with Keogh, director general of the RAMC, and Sloggett, director general of the medical services in France. Keogh came from an Anglo-Irish background, graduating from Queen's College, Galway and entering the army in 1880 at the age of 23. He had served in the South African campaign as commandant of a general hospital and been mentioned in dispatches. On returning to the United Kingdom he was nominated to represent the RAMC on the committee appointed by the Secretary of State for War, Brodrick, to reorganise the Army Medical Services. He achieved rapid promotion and was gazetted director general on 1 January 1905. During the next five years he played a key role in laying the foundations for putting the civilian medical services on a war-time footing. He visited many of the major hospitals in the land, persuading the staff to join the Territorial Army and thus obliging them to serve in time of war. He also surveyed many buildings such as schools, private houses and other institutions which, in the event of war, could be converted into military hospitals. All this work was to prove invaluable when war was declared. Keogh, however, retired in 1910 to become Rector of Imperial College, London. For the next four years Sir Lancelotte Gubbins took over as director general but on 1 June 1914 Gubbins too retired and was due to be succeeded by Arthur Sloggett. Unfortunately Sloggett was ill and could not take up his post at once. War clouds were gathering and it was realised that the director general would have to implement the expansion of medical services at home, planned years before by Keogh. On Kitchener's advice Keogh was recalled to resume the post of director general and Sloggett, when he recovered, was posted to France on 24 October 1914 as director general of the Army Medical Services attached to the British Expeditionary Force.

Sloggett was the same age as Keogh; he had joined the Army in 1881 and had served in many of its actions since that date. He was lucky to survive a chest wound at the battle of Khartoum, when his horse was shot from under him. In the Boer War he was in charge of the Imperial Yeomanry Hospital and afterwards was posted to Bombay, eventually being promoted director general of medical services in India. In many ways he was ideally suited to the post in France. He had seen much action, had a reputation as a gifted administrator and above all was said to be a shrewd judge of men. Sir George Makins, who served under him during the war and later became President of the Royal College of Surgeons, praised his unusual capacity for encouraging men to work together harmoniously and his breadth of view in assessing proposals made from diverse sources.[12] Yet he was not interested in scientific research and had little sympathy for Wright and his laboratory methods. It says much for both Keogh and Sloggett that they worked together in harness in what could have proved a difficult relationship, and there is no evidence that Sloggett resented his displacement by Keogh as director general. Yet both men were steeped in traditions of the regular army and the Empire. Orders were given and orders were obeyed without question. Men such as Keogh and Sloggett were unused to criticism; indeed any word of disagreement with their opinions by an officer junior to them in rank was taken at best as indicating disloyalty and at worst as gross insubordination. Both in France and at home the director general's word was accepted as law and, more than anything else, there must be loyalty to the Corps. Such an ethic might have prevailed had the medical services during the war been staffed solely by regular RAMC officers; but such was far from the case. There were only 1200 such officers and they were distributed over the entire Empire and all fields of war. In the Army in France Territorial officers and civilian doctors with temporary commissions far outnumbered the regulars. It is not surprising that there was some discontent among these new medical officers and that the complexity in dealing with the massive casualties brought unnecessary distress to the wounded.

The press was fulsome in its praise of the RAMC during the first years of the war but by the end of 1916 there were clear indications that all was not well. The *Field* of 9 December carried a leading article entitled 'Mobilised medicine' which praised the pathology services for their role in controlling typhoid and tetanus, urged the establishment of pathology laboratories in field hospitals and pointed out the essential role such laboratories had played in controlling a potentially devastating epidemic of dysentery in the Sinai peninsula.[13] All this had taken place 'in spite of much ignorance and malicious opposition'. The article concluded, without mentioning names, by hoping 'that those who are responsible for the medical direction of the army will take advice, or, if they will not take advice, will take warning.' The defects in the medical services were placed firmly at the door of the regular RAMC officers whose 'organising and administrative officialdom of the Service is entirely out of touch with modern medicine'. The system of seniority was largely to blame: 'It had put in high places a good many army doctors who belong to the unreformed era of the Boer War.' Such men had done little or nothing in the prevention of epidemics, 'rather have they on more than one occasion thwarted, hampered and choked the efforts of the scientific civilian element'. This was a clear reference to the opposition experienced by Wright when he advocated anti-typhoid inoculation prior to the war.

These were strong sentiments and the fact that Wright, among others, was praised and the entire article extolled the value and virtue of bacteriology, cast suspicion that it had been inspired from sources at the laboratory in Boulogne. Wright denied any personal involvement but Freeman, who enjoyed 'Society' connections through field sports, may well have expressed his views while in London. Criticism was not confined to the *Field*, which had a small though influential readership. *The Times* of Saturday 6 January 1917 contained an article from their medical correspondent on 'Health of the field armies' praising the role of the scientist in preventing epidemic disease during the war in France. The scientist was described as facing great difficulties, almost invariably underpaid and the recipient of second-class honours. The writer extolled the Medical Research Committee, which was formed as part of Lloyd George's National Insurance Act, in bringing this advance to preventive medicine, and he complimented Dr W Morley Fletcher, the secretary of the committee. He added: 'This record is so good that in the minds of many the idea has formed that the Medical Research Committee should have greater powers conferred on it. It should be associated definitely with the Army Medical Department as an advisory body. The use which this department has made of its services leaves no room for doubt that this reform would be welcome.' On the following Monday, 8 January, a leading article appeared in *The Times* that vigorously supported this proposition, stating that the Medical Research Committee should be appointed as 'expert advisers to the War Office in regard to disposal of staff and selection of suitable scientific officers'.

The report by Fripp and his colleagues, together with all these newspaper articles unanimously criticising the leadership in the

RAMC, must have left both Keogh and Sloggett feeling threatened and uncertain of their positions. The arrival on Keogh's desk of a memorandum that Lord Derby, the Secretary of State for war, had received from Wright, which had also been seen by the Prime Minister, completed their discomfort. Wright's memorandum[14] was relatively short — normally he was inclined to prolixity — being only six and a half foolscap pages of double-spaced typing. Also it was, for him, tactfully worded and under normal circumstances would not have caused any turbulent emotions in those to whom it was directed. But Keogh and Sloggett had been sensitised by the papers mentioned above, furthermore they suspected, wrongly, that Wright had inspired the articles in *The Times* through his close relationship with Dawson.

Wright began his memorandum by praising the administrative and non-professional work of the Corps but went on to doubt whether its general policy was promoting the welfare of the wounded. The medical administration, by which he implied the director general, in his view should not regard questions of treatment as matters for which they had no direct responsibility. Many of the medical officers at the front were inexperienced and had not received instruction in the treatment of the type of wounds they were encountering. He concluded that the medical administration ought 'to prescribe at any rate in broad outline the treatment to be adopted'. Wright had a strong argument here as the authorities already adopted this approach with regard to prevention, in that anti-typhoid inoculation was compulsory and anti-tetanus serum was given to all wounded men, both measures having given gratifying results.

His second main criticism concerned the policy of hustling the wounded from place to place until they reached England. He thought the RAMC was measuring its success by the fact 'that a hospital has passed so many thousands or tens of thousands through its wards, evacuating these in a minimum of time so as to be at the disposal of more patients'. He emphasised that the correct treatment of wounds necessitated early operation with excision of dead tissue followed by surgical closure when bacterial infection had been overcome. Before such treatment had been undertaken every journey was a setback for the wounded man. As emphasised in the previous chapter, there were divergent views on how wounds should be dressed so as to minimise damage associated with long journeys. Criticising the accepted policy of sending patients to England as soon as possible, Wright drew attention to the fact that base hospitals were rarely full and that under such circumstances it was 'not imperative to send out patients so long as there is sufficient staff to cope with the work'. The illogical nature of the policy of evacuation to England meant that many staff at hospitals in France were idle for long periods; yet surgeons were accumulating in France while the wounded were accumulating in an England that was drained of surgeons. Reiterating the point that all wounds should be operated on as near as possible to the front and as soon as possible, he quoted the example of an American surgeon, Carrel, who had invoked just such a policy with great success. Wounds involving compound fracture of the femur were frequent and carried a mortality approaching 50 per cent; Wright was of the opinion that there was a strong case for setting up special fracture hospitals where these patients could receive specialist treatment. At that time most fracture patients were under the care of general surgeons whose main expertise was in abdominal surgery.

In order to address these problems Wright made the constructive suggestion that a scientific staff standing in relation to the medical department of the Army should be appointed. Such a staff, which he called a medical intelligence and investigation department, 'while taking cognizance of all the different opinions, should plan and carry out such investigations as would be calculated to bring into clear light the effect of rival procedures.' This staff would also be able to investigate the many new problems such as gas poisoning, epidemic jaundice and trench fever affecting the armies in the field. He suggested further that the Medical Research Committee and (significantly in view of his previous struggles with Pearson and Greenwood) its statistical staff could provide the framework for such a body. He even went so far as to name the secretary of the Medical Research Committee, Morley Fletcher, a man with whom he did not always enjoy an easy relationship, as someone who could initiate these arrangements. (It should be remembered that Wright had been seconded from the Medical Research Committee for the duration of the war.)

Yet probably the suggestion made in Wright's memorandum which most offended the regular RAMC hierarchy was that the field ambulance should be downgraded or abolished. These units had been formed during the Boer War and, being entirely staffed by RAMC personnel, represented to officers in the Corps what the regiment did to an infantry officer — a source of pride to which unswerving loyalty was rendered. They were given the task of following up the Army, collecting the wounded and conveying them to the casualty clearing stations or hospital. Wright maintained there was little place for them in the relatively static trench warfare in Flanders. Indeed they were wasteful of medical personnel, with many doctors occupied in non-professional duties and concerned with matters such as transport. Furthermore, as they were divisional troops, when the division was in the rear both the field ambulance and its doctors were idle. Wright's observations and proposals were not those of an armchair critic sitting in a comfortable billet at the base. Colebrook records that in order to see conditions for himself he had spent some uncomfortable weeks at Choques, a village just behind the front line.[15]

On receiving Wright's memorandum from Derby, Keogh summoned a meeting on 15 January 1917[16], which was attended by 27 senior officers. The representatives from France were Colonel Galloway, a physician, Colonel Burghard, a surgeon, Colonel Lister, an ophthalmologist, and Surgeon General Macpherson, the Deputy Director General of Medical Services in France. Notable among the others were Bruce, who could be relied upon to disagree with any proposal put forward by Wright, Leishman, who had some responsibility for bacteriology in France, and Wright's friend Berkeley Moynihan. The meeting began with an address by Keogh expressing pained surprise that any criticism could be levelled at the efficiency of the RAMC and the charge that 'all we care about is the evacuation of the wounded soldier and the efficiency with which this is done'. Totally missing the point, he said that the public were 'always admiring the celerity with which the wounded are moved from France to England.' On the question of treatment, Keogh claimed that he had at all times taken heed of the opinions of his scientific advisers; he was clearly infuriated by Wright's proposal that a medical intelligence department should be set up at the War Office. His words on the subject, faithfully recorded in the minutes, have the authentic ring of the autocrat, a medical version of the Victorian mill-owner:

> 'Now, gentlemen, I do want to be quite frank with you about that. I am responsible for the care of the sick and wounded in the campaigns we are waging at the present moment, and I want it to be distinctly understood that I will do that work in my own way and not in the way prescribed by anybody else.'

He failed completely to grasp the changed nature of warfare and the wounds it inflicted. These required a new approach to treatment with a central body to give advice to medical men at the front faced with lesions the like of which they had never encountered. Bursting with indignation, he declared: 'I cannot and will not, as a medical man I would not, consent to issue orders from here as to how people should treat their cases.' He concluded by reading part of a letter from the secretary of the Medical Research Committee, Morley Fletcher, which to his everlasting discredit contained the following sentence: 'There is no reason to suppose and as I think the Chairman has already explained to you, every reason not to suppose, that the Committee would support the proposal made by Sir Almroth Wright if they were aware of it.'

Wright had sent Fletcher a somewhat longer version of his memorandum[17] and this, on 19 December, Fletcher had shown to Henry Dale, then the senior scientist at the MRC establishment at Hampstead and a future Nobel laureate. The following day Dale wrote to Fletcher advising him 'to dish' Wright's proposals.[18] Of Wright he wrote 'I give him full credit for believing he is the man to run the RAMC . . . I have always credited him with an honest belief in his call to run the MRC and all that belongs to it. But I am certain he is mistaken.' He acknowledged that Wright was clever and charming, impressing those who did not know the subject, and disarming those who did by his candour. But Dale concluded, 'He is quite incapable of honestly and impartially organising the work of others in a field he regards as his own . . . If you once let him get on top you will find him in the way of all your schemes for the future and for the present.' These opinions strengthened Fletcher's resolve to distance himself from Wright but they also had important consequences for the future of the MRC, as will become apparent in the next chapter. Fletcher was no friend to Wright and earned the reputation of being a somewhat duplicitous character. (Relations between the two men were not improved when on 26 March 1917 Fletcher wrote to Wright expressing pleasure on learning that Wright had been awarded the Le Conté prize by the French Academy 'for the part taken by him in the introduction of anti-typhoid vaccination into medical practice'. Wright took great offence at the words 'for the part taken by him', as he considered that he had brought about the adoption virtually single-handed against much opposition from the medical establishment. This was also the view of the French Academy, who had wanted to award him the more prestigious Osiris prize but were unable to do so as foreigners were not eligible to receive it.[19])

At Keogh's meeting the discussion that followed disclosure of Fletcher's letter was nauseating for its sycophancy. Lt Col Davy, who in civilian life was physician to the Royal Devon and Exeter Hospital, was of the opinion that 'this document is one of the most insulting and unjustifiable I have ever read'. His views were chorused by others; general revulsion was expressed that there should be any direction as regards treatment and an organised scientific attempt to assess the value of one method as opposed to another. Yet there was also reluctant, but heavily coded, approval for some of Wright's suggestions. Several of those present thought that the concept of specialist fracture hospitals a good one. Lt Col Sir Thomas Myles, a

Dublin surgeon, considered that a higher degree of specialisation in the treatment of compound fractures was desirable. He drew attention to the tendency for surgeons in France to be abdominal experts who were untrained and uninterested in fracture work. Moynihan, who had advocated early operation as near the front as possible, now claimed that this was taking place, although he conceded that many men had suffered during journeys to the base hospitals in France and England. Regrettably, he showed a complete lack of insight into the need for assessing and comparing various methods of treatment when he declared: 'It is true of surgery there are many ways of treating the same problem and every one of them is right.' A notable feature of the meeting is that there is no record of any contribution from Bruce. Possibly he agreed with Wright's proposals and criticisms but, as a consequence of past quarrels, was not prepared actively to support him. Generally a mood of undiluted self-congratulation permeated the debate.

In France the memorandum received a similar reception when it was sent by Keogh to Sloggett and his senior colleagues. Sloggett was incensed that Wright had submitted his paper to Keogh and Derby without reference to himself as director general of Army Medical Services in France. He regarded this as a breach of military discipline. Formally he had a point, though Wright energetically denied this. Sloggett called together his advisers and they sent Keogh a joint reply. In this they claimed that in certain areas close cooperation between scientists, pathologists and clinicians had already resulted in marked improvements in prevention and treatment. They cited the development of gas masks to avoid the effects of poison gas, an epidemic of jaundice that had been found to have originated from contact with infected rats in the trenches (it was Weil's disease) and in the alleviation of trench foot and trench fever. Yet they reacted strongly against all Wright's remarks on treatment of wounds and once again commended the use of antiseptics. They contested his assertions regarding evacuation of the wounded and claimed his arguments were based on ignorance. Wright's suggestions on field ambulances in his memorandum were deplored and their role was stated as essential not only in transport of wounded but also in the dressing and splinting of wounds. During periods when divisions were resting in the rear, they claimed that the medical officers were fully occupied in daily care of the sick and in running rest stations and convalescent camps. They concluded their report to Keogh:

'After carefully reading the memorandum we consider that Colonel Sir Almroth Wright is not in a position to make a comprehensive survey of the activities of the medical service in France, nor has he had at his disposal the necessary material or information on which alone an impartial estimate of work done can be based and a reliable judgment pronounced. The whole memorandum is inaccurate in its statements and unjustified in its conclusions, whether it deals with questions of evacuation, personnel or treatment and it is entirely unsupported by any evidence beyond the opinion of the writer.'

This was signed by Sloggett and seven senior officers including T P Woodhouse, G H Makins, A A Bowlby and W P Herringham.

At the time that Sloggett and his colleagues were composing this reply Wright seems to have been blissfully unaware of the emotions he had aroused. On 12 January he had penned a friendly note to Sloggett which began 'You are always helping me' and asked for additional staff for the laboratory in Boulogne.[20] One of his men, Captain Tanner, had drowned and three others had been recalled home. Wright asked for Freeman who at that time was also in England to be returned to France. On 15 January Sloggett replied to Wright's request for extra staff, also enclosing a copy of the document he and his colleagues had drawn up in answer to the memorandum.[21] The letter began: 'You really are the most astonishing person. Fortunately I have a keen sense of humour and delight in your eccentricities.' He went on to accuse Wright of going behind his back, of talking to Cabinet ministers, of engineering a press campaign and of launching bitter criticisms of the medical administration, which Sloggett took as a personal attack. He continued: 'Knowing you as I do and delighting in the playfulness of your cheery personality it is a real grief to me to say that I have no further use for you in France!' He suggested that Wright should send him a letter 'asking if you may be allowed to resign your appointment'.

Two days later Wright replied.[22] He strongly denied going behind anyone's back and pointed out that he had had a conference with Keogh and Sloggett some time previously at which both generals agreed 'there would be nothing inimical to the setting up of such an intelligence and investigation department as I had in mind'. He also stated that he had written to Keogh telling him he would like to see Lord Derby but that he would prefer Keogh to ask Derby if he could do so. This Keogh had done. Derby had agreed about the propriety of his sending the memorandum directly to him and Keogh. Wright denied that when speaking to Cabinet ministers and others he had criticised anyone personally. He disclaimed having fed information to journalists from *The Times* or any other paper. Finally he refused to resign.

Sloggett was not alone in taking the memorandum as a personal insult. The consulting surgeons and physicians in France thought it a slight on their professional ability. Makins, Bowlby and Herringham wrote to Sloggett threatening to resign unless Wright left the Army. In particular they resented the implication that they were neglectful of 'the lives and limbs of our soldiers'. This was surely reading too much into Wright's comments. Their over-reaction and hypersensitivity may in part be explained by a situation in which many of the surgeons were being overwhelmed by the volume of work carried out under difficult conditions. Bowlby's emotions were especially bizarre as later in the year, on 22 June, he was to echo Wright by protesting at the lengthy evacuation procedures to which the wounded were subjected. Bowlby drew attention to 'six cases of gas gangrene originating in one long journey of 17 hours' and pleaded for increased staff at casualty clearing stations.[23] Copies of all the correspondence between Wright, Sloggett, Keogh and the surgeons were sent to Derby. He was deeply disturbed and immediately took steps to placate the various parties.

On 25 January[24] Derby wrote to Sloggett reassuring him that Wright had not gone 'behind the back of the medical authorities' and pointing out that he, as Secretary of State, reserved the right to see anybody he pleased. He had also seen Bowlby. He had agreed to Keogh calling a meeting to consider the memorandum and reported that it was unanimous in its conclusion that Wright's criticisms were unjustified. Significantly, however, Derby firmly rejected any suggestion that Wright should resign his commission or be dismissed. He concluded his letter to Sloggett: 'This is not the time for dispute and quarrels. We are all out to do our best to help win the war, and I am perfectly certain Sir Almroth Wright had no idea in his own mind except to do what he thought was in the best interests of our sick and wounded men.'

On 5 February Derby also wrote to Sir George Makins and the surgeons who had threatened resignation unless Wright was dismissed. He wrote:

'I quite understand your feelings of irritation at Sir Almroth Wright's action; they are only natural, and I see it might, under ordinary circumstances, be difficult for you to continue your work with him, but I ask all three of you to forget the past, let bygones be bygones, and without any feeling of animosity towards him continue the admirable work you are doing. I am only the mouthpiece of the sick and wounded in making this request. It is they who will suffer if you in anyway abate your work, or remove your skilful treatment from them.'[25]

Keogh informed Bowlby of Derby's views, and of his not allowing Wright to be dismissed or resign his commission, and that there was to be no disciplinary action. Some insight into Keogh's personality — and into Derby's methods — can be gleaned from the closing lines of his letter in which he wrote 'There is no news except they are giving me the GCB tomorrow'.[26] Yet Keogh's mind remained unsettled. In a previous letter to Bowlby, enclosing the minutes of the meeting on 15 January which was unanimous in rejecting Wright's criticisms, he had written: 'You will have seen . . . the result of our meeting here. But I do not think we have by any means heard the end of it.' The significance of this was soon to become apparent.

Derby had the reputation of being all things to all men. Haig, writing to his wife, thought him 'a weak-minded fellow . . . like the feather pillow he bears the marks of the last person who has sat on him! I hear he is called in London genial Judas!'[27] Yet in this matter of the adequacy of treatment for the wounded he was to show determination in ascertaining the true position. Too many criticisms were surfacing for the matter to be ignored. A letter to him from Viscount Knutsford, written on 30 July[28], drew his attention to the depletion of staff in the voluntary hospitals in the United Kingdom even though they were taking in the wounded from France. Yet medical men were being sent to France from the United Kingdom only to find no hospitals and even no sites chosen for them. This directly corroborated Wright's point that the patients were in England and the surgeons in France. When asked for his views on this by Keogh, Sloggett replied on 4 August[29]: 'I really think at a time of pressure like this we should be protected at home from hysterical gas bags like Knutsford—his attack is on a par with the one he made about shell-shock cases—really we have other and more important work to do than the destruction of mare's nests discovered by faddists.' Sloggett seriously underestimated Knutsford, who was a hospital and social reformer of consequence, became chairman of the London Hospital and is remembered as 'practically the founder of modern hospital efficiency'.[30]

Sloggett's bluster no longer sufficed to deflect criticism and Derby took action. His sympathies lay with the soldiers. He had held a commission in the Grenadier Guards, served in South Africa and had afterwards been financial secretary to the War Office in the Conservative government of 1900. Now, in August 1917 he set up a Commission on Medical Establishments. It had the following terms of reference: 'To proceed at once to France for the purpose of inquiring into various matters connected with the personnel and administration of the Army Medical Services in that country. On their return they will carry out similar investigations in the United Kingdom'.[31]

The commission was headed by Major General Sir Francis Howard, who had served in the Rifle Brigade at Omdurman and in South Africa. He had retired in 1909 but in 1914 had been recalled as Inspector of

Infantry. The seven other members were all distinguished civilian practitioners and included the President of the Royal College of Physicians, Sir Fredrick Taylor and, most significantly, Wright's *bête noire* Sir William Watson Cheyne. The commission moved with commendable speed, crossing to France on 1 September and returning with their report on 27 September. It was a document of 133 pages containing 37 recommendations, and included a minority report. They visited 23 hospitals, eight casualty clearing stations, three field ambulances and two regimental aid posts. Though, tactfully, they commended the Corps for its work ('. . . the committee have found nothing seriously amiss or inconsistent with the high standard which the Army Medical Service has set before it') they did recommend changes, many of which chimed with those proposed by Wright. Thus they supported the 'systematic instruction in medical and military subjects . . . extending over a period of not less than three weeks' for newly commissioned doctors who were sent to France. The advice that separate hospitals under appropriate experts should be established for special diseases and wounds, such as compound fractures, was endorsed.

The use of medical officers for non-medical and administrative duties, such as transport supervision, was deplored and, notably, they considered that the number of medical officers in field ambulances should be reduced. The figure given for wastage of medical officers for 1916 alone was 1896, although the commissioners questioned this as they thought it included not only death, incapacity due to wounds, and resignations but also 'temporary absences'. Yet there was no escaping the fact that the figures for killed and wounded were high and were almost entirely among regimental medical officers. These men, as can be appreciated from the diaries of Cantlie and others, frequently went over the top with the combatants. They were reluctant to order their stretcher-bearers out into no man's land while not going themselves. This had resulted in an unacceptably high casualty rate among the regimental doctors and one of the commission's firmest recommendations was that: 'battalion commanders should be directed to adhere as closely as possible to the existing instructions which intimate that the right place for a regimental medical officer during an action is either at his aid post or with his commanding officer, and that he should not be allowed to go over the top unnecessarily.'

In the main body of the report (par 74, p60) it is recorded that one commissioner suggested that field ambulances should be reduced to mere 'off-shoots' of casualty clearing stations. He indicated that: 'This would save the necessity of changing the wounded from ambulance car to ambulance car, which now usually takes place.' This was almost precisely what Wright was suggesting. This commissioner (ironically it was Wright's bitter rival Watson Cheyne), felt so strongly about this that he issued a minority report. In this he came out strongly in favour of what he termed the radial system. He disapproved of the method whereby the wounded were moved from the front to the various hospitals in England. Under this system there were three independent zones of treatment and 'except for a few rough notes which come with the patient, the medical officers in the second and third zones have no exact idea (and often no idea at all) as to what line of treatment (and I refer especially to wound treatment) has been previously carried out. Most patients pass through the hands of several medical officers, each with his own view of what is the best treatment'. He then listed the various sites where different medical officers might treat the patient:

- the regimental aid post.
- the advanced dressing station.
- the main dressing station of the field ambulance.
- the casualty clearing station.
- the ambulance train.
- the general hospital in France.
- the hospital ship, and.
- the base hospital in England.

Cheyne went on to state that under this system: 'There can be no continuity in wound treatment . . . and no real advance can be made in the way of ascertaining what is the best line to adopt.' He suggested that the casualty clearing station was the most important part of the surgical system and should become the centre of surgical work under the direction of a leading consultant surgeon who would have complete command of the treatment, directing patients to specialist hospitals where needed, and training and supplying medical officers for regiments and dressing stations. The casualty dressing station would thus become more of a hospital. These criticisms could well have been written by Wright himself. Cheyne also deplored the system whereby consulting surgeons were really no more than 'wandering inspectors' whose skills were lost to the community. If they were instead placed permanently in charge of operating at a casualty clearing station their expertise would be fully utilised. This scheme would enable a large number of the wounded to be retained in the casualty clearing stations and advanced base hospitals in France. Cheyne was careful not to say that the field ambulance should be abolished but he was in favour of them retaining only a skeleton staff and the majority of their medical officers being returned to the casualty clearing stations and hospitals where they would have plenty of medical practice. He concluded: 'Thus instead of being idle, or perhaps told to build huts and make gardens, becoming discontented and forgetting their work while times are slack, they will keep up their interest in medical work and lead an active life.'

That these suggestions were made independently by two such opposed characters as Wright and Cheyne should have been taken seriously by the authorities, but there is little evidence that they were. The medical arrangements continued largely unaltered throughout 1917 and 1918. Sloggett no doubt resisted change. Yet some criticism found its target. In May 1918 when Sloggett reached retiring age, some of his staff wrote to the War Office pleading that he should be retained until the end of the war. There was precedent for this as Keogh, who was the same age as Sloggett, remained as director general until 1919. This plea was firmly rejected and Sloggett was replaced by C H Burtchael.

One consequence of Wright's and Cheyne's criticisms was that a more effective advisory council was set up to inform the director general on scientific matters. It continued to sit after hostilities ceased, and on 18 December 1918 a subcommittee met to consider '*Streptococcus* infection of wounds'[32]. They interviewed both Fleming and Colebrook. Evidence given by these two was to have great significance for the practice of hospital medicine in the years that followed. As a result of their work in Boulogne these two bacteriologists had found that *Streptococcus pyogenes* was the most frequent infecting organism in wounds. But of more importance was their discovery that on arrival in hospital only 15 per cent of wounds were so infected, but that the figure rose to 90 per cent after a week in hospital. They concluded that infection occurred in the majority while they were in the wards. They pointed to the dangers of human carriers and the importance of cross-infection from staff and other patients. This phenomenon of cross-infection was to achieve considerable notoriety in the causation of puerperal sepsis in civilian hospitals. Both Fleming and Colebrook were to play major roles in its conquest.

In the Second World War many of Wright's ideas were adopted. The director general had a consultants' advisory commitee, medical officers received instruction in wound treatment and when penicillin became available firm rules were laid down with regard to its use and administration. It is a pity that Wright's part in these advances has been accorded little credit.

Notes

1 Colebrook L. *Almroth Wright, provocative doctor and thinker* p71. London: William Heinemann, 1954.

2 Wright AE. *BMJ* 1915; **i**: 762.

3 CMAC: RAMC 365/1. Letter from Keogh to Sloggett 11 June 1915.

4 Wright AE. *Lancet* 1915; **ii**: 629, 670. 717.

5 CMAC: RAMC 365/6 Letter from Keogh to Bowlby 24 January 1915.

6 CMAC: RAMC 446/13 Memorandum containing severe criticisms of the medical services.

7 Ellis H. *Ulster Med J* 1991; **60**: 80–86.

8 CMAC: RAMC 365/1 Bowlby AA. Memorandum to committee of inquiry dated 7 September 1917.

9 CMAC: RAMC 242 War diary of Neil Cantlie.

10 Ibid.

11 CMAC: RAMC 2010 *With British forces in France*, being the diary of Walter Bentham.

12 Makins G. Sir Arthur Sloggett. [Obituary] *Lancet* 1929; **ii**: 1033.

13 Mobilised medicine.*The Field* 1916: 9 December p893.

14 Wright AE. Memorandum on the necessity of creating at the War Office a medical intelligence and investigation department to get the best possible treatment for the wounded; diminish invaliding; and return the men to the ranks in shortest time. CMAC: RAMC 365/4.

15 Colebrook L. *Almroth Wright, provocative doctor and thinker* p91. London: William Heinemann, 1954.

16 CMAC: RAMC 365/4.

17 PRO FD5/97.

18 PRO FD5/86 .

19 PRO FD/97.

20 Ibid.

21 Ibid.

22 Ibid.

23 Part of a letter from Bowlby. CMAC: RAMC 365/1.

24 CMAC: RAMC 365/4.

25 Ibid.

26 Ibid.

27 Quoted in Churchill R. *Lord Derby, King of Lancashire* p348. London: Heinemann, 1959.

28 CMAC: RAMC 446/20.

29 Ibid.

30 Gore J. Sydney George Holland, 2nd Viscount Knutsford. *DNB*.

31 CMAC: RAMC 1165/1.

32 CMAC: RAMC 365/1.

Chapter 10

Research and Teaching

After the Armistice Wright returned to London where he was to take up an appointment with the Medical Research Committee — it did not become the Medical Research Council until 1920. For reasons given below, he did not do this. The lack of facilities and personnel devoted to medical research in Britain had been a subject of concern since the latter part of the 19th century. In 1855, in a lecture to staff and students at University College, London[1] Burdon-Sanderson[2], first Waynflete professor of physiology at Oxford, lamented that: 'In England a scientific career is neither understood nor recognised.' He advised against staying in London and recommended young men to go to Berlin, Vienna or Paris to study pathology, to Prague, Strasbourg or Leipzig to pursue experimental medicine and to Berlin for research into pathological chemistry. Burdon-Sanderson himself had done his best to remedy this situation by his generous support for the Brown Institution, but this only offered hotel facilities for research and the research workers had to provide their own salaries and apparatus. In response to such strictures from Burdon-Sanderson and others the British Institute for Preventive Medicine was founded in London in 1891 — it was renamed the Jenner Institute in 1899 and finally the Lister Institute in 1903.[3] It was under-financed and appeals for money met with little response, in striking contrast to the generous response to appeals from hospital charities. This has been attributed to the intensity of anti-vivisectionism in Britain.[4]

When, in 1902, Wright arrived at St Mary's and established a new department, lack of financial support for his research became a primary concern. He needed money not only for apparatus but also for the salaries of his assistants and technicians. He was able to supply these needs from sale of vaccines, from his own private practice and from donations given by wealthy friends and grateful patients. But this took considerable time and effort, both of which he considered could be more profitably spent on research work itself. His frustration with this situation was expressed in an article he wrote in the *Liverpool Daily Post* of 30 August 1905. His choice of newspaper was not so eccentric as might be supposed. At that time there was no radio or television, and provincial papers of high standing such as the *Yorkshire Post* and *Liverpool Daily Post* were widely read in their particular regions; their opinions also registered at Westminster. In the article, entitled 'The world's greatest problem', Wright began by destroying any faith patients might have had in the curative powers attributed to their medical attendants. In his opening paragraph he wrote: 'If the belief is nurtured that the medical art of today can effectually intervene in the course of disease, this ought to be dismissed as an illusion.' He went on to argue that the 'thoughtful and conscientious physician' when confronted with an acute bacterial infection could not conceal from himself that he was 'quite in the dark' and could not foresee the outcome. Such sentiments, uncomfortably true though they were, did not endear him to physician colleagues in Harley Street. Neither did surgery, then prospering under Listerian antiseptic measures, escape criticism when he stated: 'It may be suggested that by surgical methods it is now said to be possible to cope effectually with any localised bacterial infection. That claim should be accepted with very respectful reserve.' He acknowledged that improved sanitation had diminished the incidence of typhoid fever and all but eliminated dysentery from the civilian population. In infectious diseases generally programmes of isolation, disinfection and evacuation had had limited success but no specific treatment was available. Furthermore there was 'no real knowledge of the morbid chemical processes which are associated with gout, diabetes and Bright's disease (nephritis)'. He asserted that the general practitioner was fully occupied with diagnosing and ministering to the sick and anyway had not time, or training, or opportunity for research. The same applied to consultant physicians who gave their services to their hospitals and had to earn their living in private practice.

In England, although there were Royal Commissions indicating the need for more research (for example, that on 'Hospitals for Infectious Diseases', 1883, and on 'Consumption of Tuberculous Meat and Milk', 1891), no concerted effort was being made to address the problem. Wright was of the opinion that the main difficulty was an economic one. Money was forthcoming only if business interests were being directly served — hence the support for research into tropical diseases by Liverpool shipowners and merchants. No career structure existed. A young man wishing to engage in research as a life-time work 'finds himself immediately confronted in his own person with those very fundamental and primitive problems of obtaining subsistence, and clothes, and a shelter over his head.' A few research scholarships, such as those provided by the city of London livery companies,[5] were available to open competition but these could be held only for a year or two and provided no long-term security. The problem was compounded by the illusion cherished by many of the wealthy and powerful, then as now, that when they or those dear to them fell victim to disease they would be cured by a fashionable physician in London or, failing that, one in Paris or Berlin. Wright thought that the wealthy should be disabused of this belief. They should realise 'that the wealth to which they trust will, when their dark hour arrives, be found impotent to purchase for them any effectual scientific aid against disease.' He appealed for funds to be directed towards attracting 'a proportion of the very best ability in every country' to medical research.

Not surprisingly this article, with its attack on the complacency of private practitioners, did not receive sympathetic support in the medical press. The *Lancet*, in a leading article in the issue of 9 September 1905, was distinctly cool towards his proposals. Many of his arguments were listed but then damned. It was particularly critical of his plea for financial support, stating: 'We are, nevertheless, entirely sceptical as to the possibility of developing a capacity for research by any means of such transparent simplicity as the mere provision of stipends for the workers.' Then, in what must be taken as a personal attack on Wright himself, the *Lancet*'s editorial went on, 'when ambitious mediocrity is placed in the chair we get a type of professor in whose person loquacity, not always inspired by accuracy, is made to represent the latest achievements of scientific labours.'

It would be wrong to give the impression that all medical men were indifferent to research. In 1891 a group of those interested in the subject had formed the Medical Research Club. On 1 July that year a meeting was held at the laboratories on the Victoria Embankment at which 15 medical men engaged in research gathered and founded the club. This meeting was chaired by Sims Woodhead[6] and among those present were Victor Horsley, Roy, Sherrington, who had succeeded Horsley as superintendent of the Brown Institution, and Martin, who later became director of the Lister Institute. Wright, recently returned from Australia and not yet appointed to Netley, attended and was to remain a faithful member throughout the rest of his life. The club was to consist of not more than 50 members — later this was reduced to 35 — all of whom should be actively engaged in medical research. The subscription was 10s. 6d. a year. Watson Cheyne was among the founder-members and took the chair at several of the early meetings. Although the name of the club indicated an interest in general medical research, and some of the early meetings heard papers on renal and endocrine diseases, the club came to be dominated by bacteriologists. This is unsurprising as at that time the main medical problems were centred around infections. In its first hundred years there were 224 members, of whom 129 were bacteriologists.[7]

The rule that members should be actively engaged in medical research was strictly adhered to and some of the original members were soon required to resign. Notable among these was Watson Cheyne, busily engaged in private practice, whose resignation was accepted on a proposal from Wright and Bulloch! By 1902, when Wright returned to London, initial enthusiasm for the club had waned and two meetings had to be cancelled due to lack of material for presentation. The subscription was reduced to five shillings to encourage younger members to join. Yet the poor attendance and low membership must have been mainly due to the lack of talented men able to devote their time to research. As Wright pointed out in his *Liverpool Daily Post* article, this was the consequence of a dearth of money available to support such work. In the United States this need for finance was well recognised. In 1897 F T Gates, adviser on philanthropic expenditure to John D Rockefeller, had written: 'Medicine can hardly hope to become a science until it can be endowed, and qualified men enabled to give themselves uninterrupted study and investigation, on ample salary, entirely independent of practice.'[8].

Wright circumvented these difficulties by becoming self-financing, but on a national level the problem was not addressed until the second decade of the 20th century. The lack of enthusiasm for charitable funding of medical research made it essential that central government should take a lead. The first steps towards this goal were achieved in Lloyd George's National Health Insurance Scheme, the Bill for which he introduced into the House of Commons on 4 May 1911. One result of the passing of this Bill was the formation of the Medical Research Committee under the chairmanship of Lord Moulton.

John Fletcher Moulton was a lawyer, and possessed of a formidable intellect. Lord Birkenhead, later Lord Chancellor, wrote that he had never been brought into contact with a mind that impressed him more by its 'brilliancy, scope and power'[9]. Moulton was a mathematician of note, being Senior Wrangler at Cambridge before being called to the Bar. While at the Bar he continued his scientific work, and was elected a Fellow of the Royal Society at the age of 36. Before going on the Bench he had been a Liberal member of the House of Commons and was admired by Lloyd George, who later appointed him to preside over a committee to oversee the manufacture of high explosives during the

Great War. Significantly, Moulton was an intimate friend of Wright;[10] he had provided strong support during Wright's struggles to found the inoculation department. When, in 1909, Moulton was asked to give the opening address to the Faculty of Medicine at Leeds University, Wright supplied much of the material for the speech. In it Moulton dilated on the dangers of infection, likening the body to a besieged city, and the weaknesses of natural forces resisting the invaders. He used the occasion to explain Wright's work on opsonins and antibodies and to press for anti-typhoid inoculation.The two men met frequently and Moulton was aware of Wright's desire for the establishment of a central funding agency for medical research. No doubt these views were conveyed to Lloyd George and had an influence on allocation of Treasury money earmarked for research when the National Insurance Bill was drafted. The idea that the State should have responsibility for such work was largely accepted in France and Germany but was a new concept in Britain; its establishment, independent of political interest, was revolutionary.

It was not until 2 July 1913 that the first meeting of the Medical Research Committee was held.[11] It took place in Lord Moulton's house, 57 Onslow Square. The precise number and names of those attending are not known; the only record consists of a few handwritten notes by Leishman who acted as secretary for the first meetings. One person who was mentioned as present on this occasion was Sir Robert Morant, a senior civil servant, a previous architect of the Education Act of 1902, and a man endowed with volcanic energy who was at this time chairman of the National Health Insurance Commission. He played a major role in obtaining support from the Treasury, which agreed to allocate one penny per member subscribing to the National Insurance Scheme. Furthermore he was instrumental in ensuring that the Medical Research Committee had freedom to spend the money on all forms of medical research — there had been a suggestion that the research should be limited to investigations into tuberculosis.[12]

The first official meetings took place on 24 and 25 July 1913 and continued, often at weekly intervals, until the outbreak of war. The original members of the committee consisted of two members of parliament and six medical or scientific men. The two MPs were Major Waldorf Astor and Dr Christopher Addison. Addison was another key figure in the establishment of the research committee. Being both a Liberal member of parliament and a doctor — he had held the chair of anatomy at University College, Sheffield and been a lecturer at Charing Cross Hospital, London — he was closely associated with Lloyd George in drafting the Health Insurance Bill.[13]

The other members were Clifford Allbutt, Regius professor of physic at Cambridge; C J Bond, a Leicester surgeon who was also a Fellow of University College, London; William Bulloch, professor of bacteriology at the London Hospital and a close friend of Wright; Matthew Hay, professor of forensic medicine at Aberdeen University and medical officer of health in Aberdeen; F Gowland Hopkins, professor of biochemistry in Cambridge; and William Leishman, an RAMC officer and Wright's former assistant at Netley.

Initially Moulton and Morant provided the general framework within which the committee operated. From the first meetings it became clear that there was to be a central laboratory, grants were to be available to research workers, who would reinforce clinical staff of existing hospitals, and there would be a statistical department. Moulton, accompanied by one or more of the medical members, visited universities throughout Britain, looking at research in progress and searching for suitable men who might be interested in working for the Committee. The subjects they considered most in need of investigation were nearly all related to infectious diseases. Among these tuberculosis was most prominent but also important were pneumonia, syphilis, measles, streptococcal infections, diphtheria and poliomyelitis. Hopkins pressed the case for investigating metabolic diseases such as diabetes mellitus and also mentioned rickets and tooth decay, but there is no reference to cancer[14], cardiovascular disorders or genetics — subjects which tax the medical research worker at the beginning of the 21st century.

At their second meeting the idea of having a hospital attached to the central laboratory was conceived. Moulton advocated taking over and adapting some large existing hospital, mentioning Netley as a possibility — surely the influence of Wright can be seen here. In the end they decided to purchase Mount Vernon Hospital in Hampstead; Addison thought it could be bought for £20,000 and he was asked to approach the hospital authorities. By 17 December 1913 the matter was decided and the formalities for the purchase and development of the hospital were under way. The contract for the freehold site of two and three quarter acres was completed on 25 March 1914. The price was £35,000 (about £1.5 million in today's money) spread over five years, but the hospital was in fact fully paid for by 1915. Utilisation of the building was delayed by the outbreak of war and because of a proposal for amalgamation with the Lister Institute on an alternative site which came to nothing.[15] During the war the hospital became the Hampstead Military Hospital and then, in 1917, the Central Hospital for Flying Officers.

Having decided on a site for the central laboratory the next question to be settled concerned the staff. This was discussed as early as 22 October 1913, and it was envisaged at this meeting that there would be an overall director of the central laboratory or institute. Wright was considered to be 'the only man satisfying the requirements for such a post' but, without any reason being recorded, this idea was quietly dropped.[16] On 1 December proposals for the directors of the four main departments in the Institute were discussed and it was decided to ask Wright to take charge of bacteriology, Henry Dale biochemistry and Leonard Hill physiology.[17] The post of director of the statistical department was not decided at this time but was eventually given to Dr Brownlee, physician superintendent at Ruchill Hospital in Glasgow and a disciple of Karl Pearson. The other important decision was that those appointed should have tenure and receive a pension.

By 21 January 1914 Wright had a firm assurance that he was to head the bacteriology department. The minutes of the meeting of that day record that he wished to attend the committee *de jure*.[18] It is also recorded that he wanted his own assistants at St Mary's (Douglas, Parry Morgan, Colebrook, Hayden and Fleming) to come with him and be on his permanent staff. He proposed that his own salary should be £1600 to £2000 (some £69,000–86,000 in modern money). In addition he wanted to bring with him his vaccine department, which was self-financing, and a number of 'unpaid' workers. He also volunteered the opinion that 'there should be no secretary (of the Committee) in the sense of a superior officer who administers in the name of, or under instruction of, the governing committee'. The reaction of the MRC to all this is not recorded but it was a portent of troubles ahead.

The MRC was indeed exercised about the appointment of a secretary. The matter had been under discussion for three months but the scope of the post had not been precisely defined. It was taken for granted that the secretary must be a medical man, but Landsborough Thomson in his history of the Medical Research Council states that 'the idea that he must also be a man of experience, and indeed eminence, in research had yet to be assimilated'.[19] After several names had been proposed it was decided on 19 February 1914 to approach Dr Walter Morley Fletcher, a physiologist and Fellow of Trinity College, Cambridge. He was unable to take up the position until 1 July but from 19 March attended meetings of the Committee. Fletcher was an inspired choice and undoubtedly the success of the Medical Research Council, as it became in 1920, is largely the result of the firm

leadership and guidance he gave it in its early years. He was endowed
with a first-class brain and considerable athletic prowess; together with
an intuitive sympathy with young research workers; by reducing red
tape to a minimum, he enabled them to do their work unhampered by
administrative difficulties. He was a strong character, but he was
noted for his charm, which earned him many friends; he was
uncompromising and ruthless towards his opponents, however, and
sometimes caused offence by offering unsought advice to his
contemporaries.[20] With hindsight it is apparent that a harmonious
relationship between Fletcher on the one hand and Moulton and
Wright on the other was going to be difficult to achieve. Once Fletcher
assumed the position of full-time secretary the main initiatives
associated with the committee came from him. The other members
were forced to assume a secondary consultative and critical role.

By 1914 Wright was bombarding the committee with suggestions
and demands. On 4 June he proposed that a council be created for the
Central Institute at Mount Vernon with himself as chairman to
safeguard the rights of the heads of departments and their staff in such
matters as the allocation of rooms. On 10 June he wrote a letter to
Lord Moulton, which was discussed at the meeting of the committee
on the following day.[21] He laid out his requirements as follows:

- He wanted the title of 'director of bacteriological research'.
- He accepted the salary (£2000) but wanted an assurance that he
  could carry on in the post until the age of 65 years (the proposed
  retiring age for those at the new Institute was 60 years).
- He wanted three months' annual leave.
- He wanted to undertake remunerative work — private practice, for
  example.
- He required complete liberty with regard to publication and public
  speech.
- If at any time a director general of the Institute was appointed he
  should have a major say in the appointment.
- He wished to have direct access to the committee.
- He wished to be consulted as to his staff and any changes to it.
- He wanted as many beds as possible in the hospital.
- He wished to be chairman of the Institute council, the setting up of
  which he had proposed.
- He wanted to stay at St Mary's until beds at Mount Vernon were
  available.
- He wished his secretary, Mr Hamblin, to be taken on to the staff as
  his private secretary.

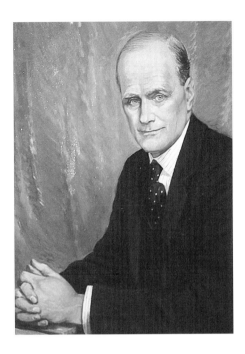

Figure 24
Sir Walter Morley Fletcher, the first
Secretary of the Medical Research Council.
(Medical Research Council, London)

The committee was somewhat nonplussed at these demands. Wright was in a strong position at this time. He was celebrated for his work on typhoid; vaccine therapy was at the height of its popularity and he had friends in high places; and Moulton was a firm ally. Wright was also being asked to take a substantial cut in salary — at the time he was earning £6000 a year in private practice, a very large sum for those days. At their meeting on 2 July the committee devoted their entire time to discussing Wright's demands. They did not object to the title of director of bacteriological research, but they were hesitant about guaranteeing his employment until the age of 65 years. As to his enjoying three months' leave a year and continuing in private practice they were adamant that these requests should be refused. In the matter of appointments, and in particular the appointment of an over-all director, they asserted that these had to be made solely by the committee after due consultation. On the other matters they adopted a flexible and conciliatory policy. No doubt fearful that at this early stage there might be a full-scale and damaging disagreement, the committee asked Fletcher to smooth matters over. This Fletcher did in a series of talks with Wright, followed up by a firm but tactfully worded letter.[22] He wrote that there was no objection to the title Wright wanted but as regards retirement age the committee would find it difficult to give, in advance, one member of their staff an 'exceptional and unconditional undertaking' to retain him in office beyond 60 years. The Committee did, however, have the full power to extend service beyond the age of 60 and 'they hoped you will recognise that the power would be exercised ... when the extension of service was advantageous in the view of the committee to the advancement of medical research.' The letter was explicit on the matter of prohibiting private practice and Wright seems to have acquiesced in this decision; in any case it was an aspect of his work he did not enjoy. The committee refused three months' annual leave but would readily grant special leave to visit other laboratories or research workers. They were not prepared to give a definite undertaking to employ his secretary, but when secretarial appointments were made they undertook to attach very great weight to Wright's recommendation. Finally Fletcher pointed out that they were not contemplating the appointment of a general director for the Institute but that the committee 'retained complete liberty in this matter'.

Wright's reply to this letter is not recorded but he must have accepted the terms. The evolution of the laboratories at Mount Vernon along the lines now agreed was, however, knocked out of shape by the onset of war. The committee placed its services at the disposal of the army and many of those who were to have been employed enlisted. Wright and members of his staff, as we have seen, left for France and set up the laboratory in Boulogne. Throughout the war the Medical Research Committee agreed that any difference in pay between staff salaries and military pay should be made up from committee funds. This applied to Wright and in addition, up until 1917, St Mary's Hospital received £2500 a year to fund his research beds.

When Wright returned to London after the war it was assumed that he would take up his appointment at the new Institute that was being built at Mount Vernon. But the whole situation at the MRC had altered. Fletcher was now very much the driving force and he had been exceedingly irritated by Wright's memorandum to Derby, mentioned in Chapter 9, in which he had used the name of the MRC without authority. Even more significant was the displacement of Lord Moulton from his position of chairman — cessation of funding for Wright's research beds had quickly followed this. Moulton had taken a special interest in medical research and had played a key role in establishing the Medical Research Committee. All the early meetings had taken place at his house and business had been conducted in a largely informal and unconventional manner surprising in a lawyer. Thus the minutes of previous meetings were not circulated but merely read out by the chairman at the next meeting.[23] There was also a strong suspicion that his close friends, and these included Wright, had undue influence with him. None of this appealed to Fletcher and, under circumstances that are far from clear, when the chairman's appointment came up for renewal in 1916 Moulton was not chosen and the position was given to Waldorf Astor. (It is highly likely that Fletcher himself played a significant role in engineering Moulton's dismissal. Henry Dale, the head of the biochemistry department at the MRC laboratory, in a letter written on 16 December 1916, congratulated Fletcher on deposing Moulton and thus ridding the committee of 'dirty intrigue'.[24]) Moulton was furious but perhaps this was unreasonable because at this time he was director general of explosive supplies at the Ministry of Munitions. It was thought that chairing the MRC might direct his energies away from this work.

Wright was 56 at the end of the war and his personal life was in turmoil; he had separated from his wife, had no house of his own and had to take rooms at 34 Bruton Street above the surgery of a dentist friend, W B Sansom. To make matters worse he had fallen in love with a woman who did not return his affection with equal ardour (see Chapter 11). He was a man who liked to get his own way, and his dominating personality combined with an aggressive manner in discussion was unappealing to Fletcher. It was apparent that the two would find it difficult to work together. The war had done nothing to curb Wright's fertility in firing off demands. Colebrook records in his diary that Wright wanted 'effective representation of the workers on the governing committee'. He also proposed a scheme for educating men who joined the research service. He considered that such men would run research departments in hospitals and universities returning from time to time to the Central Institute to keep up to date. That this is approximately how matters developed is less significant in this context than that the committee resented the ideas coming from Wright. As the historian of the MRC relates: 'The committee was finding it very difficult to deal with this eminent scientist as a man of affairs'. It was with some relief therefore on 14 March 1919 that the Committee received a handwritten letter from Wright asking to be allowed to remain at St Mary's. His request was granted with alacrity that same day. Wright resigned from the post of director of bacteriology at the Institute on extremely advantageous terms.[25]. He was allowed to retain his salary and he continued to receive this until the age of 66. It is unpleasant to record that he did not always acknowledge this generosity and referred to it in only one of his publications. Furthermore it is ignored by both of his previous biographers, Leonard Colebrook and Zachary Cope.

Perhaps it is unsurprising that after the upheavals of the war all was not sweetness and light at St Mary's. Many of the staff, and especially

Fleming and Colebrook, who had enjoyed a new-found independence in the army, felt uncertain as to their future. Colebrook wrote in his diary that Wright had returned from France in a 'very combative vein wanting to oust King Fletcher'. In this he was singularly unsuccessful. Colebrook clearly thought Wright unwise not to go to Mount Vernon on the MRC's terms as the accommodation at St Mary's was 'very uncomfortable'. Douglas, who had supervised the laboratory there all through the war, was thoroughly dissatisfied with this position; and he now decamped to Mount Vernon, where he was appointed to the post vacated by Wright.

This was a great gain to the MRC; Douglas laid the foundations of a department of bacteriology and virology that was to achieve an international reputation. His departure was a loss to St Mary's where at this time the inoculation department under his guidance was making a clear profit of £500 a month (more than £10,000 in today's values). Wright himself was undoubtedly becoming more difficult: even his disciple Colebrook found him so. In April 1919 Colebrook wrote of 'difficulties in personal contact' and that Wright was finding him too critical. Discussions between Wright and Fletcher led to Colebrook being given no option but to transfer to the MRC at Mount Vernon with Douglas. He viewed this move with equanimity because, as he records in his diary, he was becoming more and more conscious that he and Wright could not continue to work well in harness together. Colebrook did return to St Mary's in 1922, but as an external worker for the MRC, before departing some years later to the Bernhard Baron Memorial laboratories at Queen Charlotte's Hospital. There he obtained dramatic results in the treatment of streptococcal puerperal infections with the newly discovered sulphonamides.

To the outside world there were few signs that Wright's star was on the wane. In 1919 he was made a Membre de l'Institute de France and at home he became a Companion of the Order of the Bath and the order of Knight Commander of the British Empire was conferred on him. He also received the Serbian Order of St Sava first class and, from the Queen of Montenegro, the Order of Danilo. (The Prince and Princess of Montenegro were to visit the laboratory at St Mary's on 24 October 1929.) In 1920 he became the first recipient of the gold medal of the Royal Society of Medicine in recognition of his distinguished service to medicine during the War. The meeting at which the award was announced was on Armistice Day 1920 and was followed by a lecture from Wright on 'Medical research, and the conditions that are indispensable to the achievement of new knowledge'. The vote of thanks was given by Keogh who said that

Figure 25
The visit of the Prince and Princess of Montenegro to the inoculation department on 24 October 1929. The Mayor and Mayoress of Paddington (Mr and Miss Snell) and the Town Clerk, Mr Abbiss, are on the left of the picture, the Prince and Princess in the centre and Wright in the background. The others are unidentified. (Alexander Fleming Laboratory Museum, St Mary's Hospital, London)

they had been associated 'for a good many years, had very violent disagreements, but we retain our friendship'. It seems that this particular friendship had lasted, and did so until Keogh's death in 1936. In 1921 Wright's contribution to the treatment of war wounds was again publicly acknowledged. Sir John Bland Sutton, one of the greatest surgeons of the time, in a address to the Royal Society of Medicine described Wright's fitness for the gold medal in recognition of his contributions to military medicine and surgery during the Great War as indisputable.

At St Mary's amicable relationships were not so forthcoming in resolution of problems between the inoculation department and the hospital and medical school, or within the department itself. The position of the department was anomalous, as it was an independent self-financing unit within the curtilage of the hospital. Rent was paid to the hospital for the use of its premises but the finances of the department itself were obscure — and have remained so; no accounts have been traced. The medical school paid a small salary, between £100 and £300 per annum, to some of the members who took part in undergraduate teaching; but this was augmented in many cases by private practice and by money the department made from sale of vaccines — a revenue that was to continue throughout the inter-war years.

The arrangement with the hospital and medical school was administratively untidy. Matters were not made easier by general academic unrest following the war. There was a mistaken notion that there were too many doctors; and for a while it was doubtful if a small, poorly endowed school such as St Mary's could survive. Fortunately it both did and prospered. This was largely due to the efforts exerted by the dean. Charles McMoran Wilson (later to become famous as Churchill's physician and better known as Lord Moran[26]) had been a student at St Mary's, qualifying in 1908 at the same time as Alexander Fleming. In 1914 he was medical registrar at the hospital but enlisted at once. He had a distinguished war record, and gained the MC at the battle of the Somme. Returning to St Mary's as assistant physician he was appointed sub-dean on 3 February 1920 and promoted to dean on 7 December the same year. He devoted the next years to establishing St Mary's as one of the leading medical schools in the country. This was accomplished by careful selection of students and staff and by obtaining substantial sums of money from influential friends and patients, notably Lords Beaverbrook and Revelstoke. Wilson was a powerful personality and clearly relations with someone as aggressive as Wright were likely to be strained though, as already related, they were united in their view that St Mary's should cease to admit women medical students.[27] One of Wilson's first tasks on becoming dean was to inform Wright that the medical school would not bear half the cost of converting a room into a bacteriological laboratory. On 1 November 1921 he again had to deny Wright money to defray the increased cost of the chemical pathology work.

From the point of view of the dean the inoculation department was the proverbial sore thumb. It was a renowned research establishment embedded in the hospital and medical school complex, yet he had no authority over it. Wright's position as bacteriologist to the hospital and professor of experimental pathology in the University of London, as well as being a research worker with an international reputation, made him virtually unassailable. A compromise was reached. A new Institute of Pathology and Research was established with Wright as its principal. It embraced the medical school departments of anatomy, chemical pathology, systematic bacteriology, clinical bacteriology, general pathology and experimental physiology. The inoculation department was assimilated into this Institute but continued to be administered by its existing house committee and remained financially independent; it continued to generate considerable sums of money from the sale of vaccines. The Institute was nominally under the control of a committee with Wright as its chairman and Wilson, dean of the medical school, as its secretary; it consisted of the heads of all the departments. The idea seems to have been that Wright and his disciples would be outnumbered and thus brought under some control. Wilson reckoned without Wright's force of personality in pursuing his aims. The committee met twice a year, mainly for the purpose of allocating research funds. These funds were supplied by the inoculation department, which ensured that, from 1920 onwards, £1000 (equivalent to at least 20 times that sum in today's values) was available annually for distribution among the departments.

Yet the arrangement between the inoculation department and the medical school, anomalous though it was, became of great financial advantage to the latter. In 1928, when it was decided to rebuild the medical school and laboratories, the inoculation department contributed £20,000 from its reserves on condition that they could occupy their laboratories rent-free. The building took some time to complete and, as is usual in such cases, cost more than originally estimated. The inoculation department came to the rescue with grants of £1300 on 22 October 1931, £5250 on 18 February 1932 and then in 1933, just before the buildings were to be opened, Mrs Romanes (whose son had married Dolly Wright) gave £3000 to ensure that the lecture theatre would be completed on time. Some idea of the financial success of the activities of the inoculation department may be gleaned from the balance of the reserves in 1947, just before the advent of the National Health Service, when they stood at over £196,000.[28]

In the early 1920s a problem exercising Wright was that of his successor. Here he behaved with uncharacteristic foolishness. The two longest-serving men in the department were John Freeman and Alexander Fleming. Freeman was the senior and indeed had persuaded Wright to recruit Fleming in 1906, though mainly it seems because he wanted him for the hospital rifle club. Fleming was a first-class shot and the hospital was anxious to carry off the honours at Bisley which, with Fleming's help, they did. The appointment was of course a brilliant success. Fleming's technical genius proved invaluable to the department. His work on war wounds had been outstanding and there is no doubt that Wright would have achieved little without Fleming's expertise in the organisation and performance of experiments. Although documentation is scanty, it appears that Wright had promised *both* men that he would back them to succeed him as head of the department.[29] Such behaviour was not conducive to a good working environment. As early as 1919 Colebrook was writing

in his diary that the friendly atmosphere of prewar years had
disappeared and he feared the 'the Old Man is going to have a poor
house and an unhappy one to work in for his latter days.'[30] Yet
whatever his faults Wright was a tireless fighter on behalf of those in the
department. Thus he secured official status in the hospital for senior
members of the Institute. Both Freeman and Fleming achieved this
and using today's terminology were given positions equivalent to
honorary consultants on the staff. Fleming was appointed assistant
director of the Institute and given charge of the department of
systematic bacteriology. Freeman was bacteriologist to the hospital and
was also in charge of the allergy clinic, which he had started before the
war with Leonard Noon, where patients with hay fever and asthma
were desensitised by prophylactic injections with grass-pollen extracts
and other allergens.

Freeman and Fleming were poles apart in temperament. Freeman
was tall, vivacious, handsome and socially agile but mercurial; he was
easily upset if any of his ideas were opposed. In the words of one
contemporary, 'He blew in, blew up and blew out'.[31] Fleming was
small and, though friendly and fond of company, calm and taciturn.
Yet before the war they had enjoyed an amicable relationship, indeed
Fleming's consulting-room for his private patients was in Freeman's
house at 30 Devonshire Place. It was only after the War, in 1921, when
Fleming was given the title of assistant director that ill feeling was
generated. Matters were not improved when Fleming was promoted to
professor of bacteriology in the University of London in September
1928. This was a title seldom used by Fleming as he wished to spare
the feelings of Freeman, who by this time must have felt himself
superseded although he was the senior man. There is a strong
suspicion that Wright's approach towards his two colleagues was a
policy of divide and rule. Normally he would have retired on reaching
the age of 65 years in 1927, but because of the extraordinary position
of the independently financed inoculation department he remained as
director until 1946, when he was 85 years old. Much to his annoyance
his Medical Research Council grant was terminated by Fletcher in
1927; even though Balfour, the former Prime Minister, had made a
war-like protest on behalf of Wright it was to no avail.[32] Throughout
the remainder of his time he paid himself a salary out of money
obtained by sale of vaccines. Thus the two senior men were kept in the
department, each believing that he would shortly become the director
when Wright retired.[33] This disgraceful policy did have one advantage
in that it enabled Fleming to pursue his researches during the years
between the wars unhindered, to some degree, by the burdens of

administration; though Wright came increasingly to rely upon him to undertake many of the routine chores associated with running the department and in particular the provision of vaccines, which was essential to keep it financially viable. It was during these years that Fleming made his two great discoveries, lysozyme and penicillin, with which his name will be forever linked. He had, however little influence on fundamental policy; thus he was unable to persuade Wright to allocate money for chemical research into penicillin.[34]

How did Wright occupy himself? His research continued, but at a much slower pace. While at Boulogne he had initiated studies on leucocyte function in connection with wound healing, and was also one of the first to realise the importance of disturbances in acid–base balance in patients suffering from shock and wound infection. The latter was controversial work and hampered by lack of available suitable biochemical techniques. His energy and enthusiasm were both some-what diminished, not surprising in a man of 56 who after four years of war was not in the best of health; he had angina of effort. In the 28 years before 1920 he had published 126 scientific papers but in the next 27 years there were only 22 publications in his name. This is only partly explained by his age: his interest and energy were turning towards philosophy. The major part of his later scientific writings was concerned with modifications of various technical methods he had devised; in collaboration with Colebrook he brought out a second edition of his book *The technique of the teat and capillary glass tube* in 1921.

Two of his post-war papers are of considerable interest in that they pointed the way to future developments in immunology. They were ignored by the medical establishment largely because they were extremely lengthy, each occupying three numbers of the *Lancet*, and because the terminology used was obscure. Wright was obsessed with language and had an irritating practice of inventing new words. In his view: 'The store of short and simple native words has long since been exhausted'; so he proceeded to invent his own based on longer composite Greek words.[35] Prominent examples of this are to be found in the many derivations which resulted from the word *phylactic* in reference to guarding against infection. Thus the leucocytes, or white blood cells, are *phylactic* agents; *ecphylactic* is employed when guardian agents are rendered impotent, *epiphylactic* when guardian agents are reinforced and so forth. Few of these terms have survived and indeed there is no evidence that they were ever widely used. In the early 1920s there is the occasional hesitant insertion of one of these Wright-coined words into a paper or lecture by Fleming and Colebrook, but this soon ceased and outside the St Mary's circle they were never employed.

The papers in the *Lancet* where these terms were repeatedly used were published lectures delivered at the Royal Society of Medicine on 30 November 1922[36] and at the Medical Society of London on 27 October 1930[37]. Both were given before audiences of between 120 and 150 composed of established and well-known practitioners, and each lecture lasted well over an hour. The introduction of new words and much of the subject matter must have tested the attention span of these worthy gentlemen (there were few women among medical consultants in those days). The tragedy is that there were important concepts buried in Wright's verbiage, the significance of which was not to be realised until after the Second World War. Ostensibly both lectures were concerned with immunisation and vaccine therapy. At this time the terms *antibody* and *antigen* were used freely. Antibodies were known to be substances that could neutralise antigens in the form of bacteria, or toxins such as diphtheria or tetanus toxin, but there was no knowledge as to which cells produced antibodies. If an antigen, in the form for instance of dead typhoid bacilli, was injected into a human or an animal, then some days later serum taken from that human or animal could be shown to contain antibodies that would specifically bind to the injected antigen and neutralise it. This process is now known to be extremely complex and to involve subtle and elaborate molecular systems, but antibody production is still a key part of the process. At the time that Wright was working no one had any idea as to the site of antibody production. He had the aim of producing antibodies *in vitro*, that is outside the body, in a test tube or in his slide cells — small chambers he built on to glass microscope slides. He claimed that by inoculating blood placed in these small chambers with pathogenic bacteria he could elicit an antibody response. This did not occur if the leucocytes, the white cells of the blood, were killed. After a series of such experiments he wrote in 1923:

> 'We are inevitably conducted to the conclusion that the bactericidal elements found in vaccinated blood are derived from the leucocytes, and that leucocytes can, under the influence of a vaccinating dose of microbes, instantaneously export their antibacterial elements into the surrounding body fluids.'[38]

Wright's 1930 lecture emphasised the importance of treating infection by enhancing the natural defences of the body. He pointed out that surgical excision of an infected focus often resulted in dissemination of the infection by introduction of the infecting organism into the blood-stream during surgical manipulation. He reiterated Fleming's experiments on antiseptics to illustrate their inefficiency in treating wounds and their harmful effects on phagocytes. Significantly, in view of his attitude in later years, he paid tribute to 'my friend and fellow-worker' and referred to 'Fleming's marvellously simple and ingenious experiments'. He was scathing in his review of chemotherapy, but his views were coloured by the unfortunate experience he had had when using optochin in the treatment of pneumonia in South Africa; a side-effect of the drug was development of severe visual disturbances, including blindness. The only drug he considered of practical use was salvarsan for treatment of syphilis. The main thrust of his lecture was again to emphasise the role of leucocytes. He stated quite categorically: 'Conclusive evidence has been obtained of the elaboration of anti-bacterial substances by leucocytes.' It is extraordinary that he does not seem to have carried this insight any further or to have encouraged one of his assistants to do so. Furthermore he uses the term 'leucocyte' to embrace all white blood cells, making no attempt to distinguish between their various forms. It is not clear that he gave serious thought to this matter, and only once does he mention the various types of white cell — -neutrophils, eosinophils, basophils, monocytes and the lymphocytes. Yet from reading his papers it is apparent that he was aware that separation of these various forms was to some extent possible by differential centrifugation. Implicit in much of his writing is the assumption that he was dealing with neutrophils, yet he knew that these cells were phagocytic and destroyed bacteria by ingesting and digesting them. This new property, which he claimed for white cells, of manufacturing and secreting anti-bacterial substances, ie antibodies, might have been thought to be the function of the other prominent white blood cell, namely the lymphocyte, which makes up 20 per cent of the total white cell population. Free discussion of this matter with his colleagues at one of his famous tea-parties might have generated some fruitful ideas, but by 1930 Wright was becoming intellectually more isolated. Colebrook was working at Queen Charlotte's Hospital on the problem of puerperal fever and its conquest by the use of sulphonamides, and Fleming was fully occupied with his own studies on lysozyme and penicillin.

Wright, along with other immunologists of the period, was obsessed with antigen–antibody reactions in the test tube. They largely ignored cellular reactions that took place in the tissues following inoculation with antigen. It was not until 1945, when Harris and his colleagues[39] showed that, following injection of dead typhoid bacilli into the footpad of a rabbit, there were striking changes in the lymph node draining the area, that the problem was further elucidated. They demonstrated that a considerable quantity of antibody was present in the lymph leaving the node, thus providing a firm indication that lymphocytes were essential for antibody production. Yet even in 1950 Arnold Rich,[40] writing on the pathology of the lesions in tuberculosis, where lymphocytes are a prominent feature, noted that: 'The lack of more adequate information regarding the function of the lymphocyte is one of the more lamentable gaps in medical knowledge.' During the next two decades, after Wright's death, the interests of immunologists turned sharply towards cellular aspects of their subject with the classical studies of Gowans[41] on the recirculation of the lymphocyte, the introduction of immunofluorescent techniques allowing identification of individual antibodies within cells and the clinical necessity of understanding the role of the lymphocyte in the pathology of organ transplant rejection.

The 1920s also witnessed Wright unwisely entering the field of physical chemistry. During the war when treating wounds with hypertonic salt solution he noted there was a copious flow of lymph into the wound cavity. He attempted to study this phenomenon *in vitro* and concluded, erroneously, that when albuminous fluids and salt solutions come into contact forces in addition to diffusion are involved. He considered that mixing took place more rapidly than could be explained by known physical mechanisms and that some other force must be involved. This new force he described as 'intertraction'.[42] In fact all his observations could be explained by simple diffusion but Wright, being of a contrary and argumentative nature, refused to accept this. A polemical discussion followed in the *Proceedings of the Royal Society* reminiscent (though of a less vituperative nature) of his correspondence with Watson Cheyne on the subject of antiseptics. Two physicists, N K Adams and G Jessop[43] vigorously rejected Wright's concepts and explained his findings without invoking any new force. Fortunately the Royal Society rejected any further papers by Wright on this subject, and the scientific world was saved any further embarrassment. Colebrook met Sir James Jeans, at that time one of the secretaries of the Royal Society, while on a Scandinavian cruise in 1929 and received short shrift when he approached him on the matter. Jeans described Wright's work as sloppy and said that two further papers by Wright had been turned down. It was an unhappy episode providing ammunition for those who, behind his back, referred to 'Sir Almost Wright' and 'Sir Always Wrong'. Wright admitted to Colebrook on more than one occasion that many of his ideas were misconceived; yet he affirmed that this was true of many great scientists and mentioned by way of illustration Newton's belief in alchemy. One concept he was forced to discard was his view, first put forward in 1900[44], that scurvy was caused by acidosis! He was only convinced that lack of vitamin C was the cause after one of his assistants at St Mary's, the biochemist L C Holt, had carried out appropriate experiments and demonstrated that pure crystalline ascorbic acid cured the condition in experimental animals.[45]

Aside from research, Wright was exercised by the whole question of medical education. In the first decade of the 20th century there was disquiet among politicians and men of science about the large number of routes a person might take to become a qualified medical practitioner. The Royal Colleges in England, Scotland and Ireland, the Society of Apothecaries as well as the universities in the British Isles, all issued registerable qualifications. Standards required by these various examining bodies differed widely. A similarly chaotic state of affairs existed in the United States, but there the situation had been brought into sharp focus by a report on medical education, published in 1910, by Abraham Flexner. He was not a medical man although his brother Simon, a friend of Wright's, was a bacteriologist who became director of the Rockefeller Institute. Abraham Flexner graduated from Johns Hopkins University in 1884 and became a school-teacher, but after a few years undertook graduate studies in psychology at Harvard and then studied comparative education in Berlin. In 1908 he published *The American college*, a book on higher education that so impressed Henry S Pritchett, head of the Carnegie Foundation, that he commissioned Flexner to investigate the teaching of medicine. In 1910 his report, *Medical education in the United States and Canada*, created a sensation. It revealed that many medical schools were extremely lax in the standards required for entry and in those needed for qualification; they were obsessed by the profit motive, and their main interest was not in teaching but in extracting money from the students. As a result of this report some fifty medical schools were closed. In October of that year Flexner travelled to England as the first step in conducting a similar investigation into medical education in Europe. His visit coincided with the setting up of a Royal Commission on London University. He was warmly received by Sir William Osler, Regius professor of medicine at Oxford, and later by Sir William McCormick, secretary to the Carnegie Trust in Scotland and a member of the Royal Commission. Osler was especially concerned that British medicine was lagging behind Germany and the United States in medical laboratory methods and research.

Two other important figures that Flexner met were Lord Haldane who, as chairman of the Royal Commission on London University, had not intended to include medical schools in his investigation, and Robert Morant, secretary to the Commission. It was Morant who urged Flexner to be brutally frank in his criticisms;[46] this he was, declaring that in Britain there was no encouragement for the scientific study of medicine and that teaching was of incidental importance to honorary hospital consultants, who were primarily concerned with earning a living in private practice. He favoured a system of university education on the German pattern as had been adopted at Johns Hopkins, where there were full-time professors and teaching staff who had no private practice but were paid an adequate salary. Such men should form special university units within teaching hospitals. This view was strongly supported by Osler (he had been professor of medicine at Johns Hopkins) and indeed by Wright. These opinions did not receive universal support from the entrenched London consultants, however. Flexner's lack of any medical qualification was a source of irritation. Sir Henry Morris, a former President of the Royal College of Surgeons, sneered, 'I am not aware that Mr Abraham Flexner is either a clinician or science teacher.'[47] Reporting back to Pritchett, Flexner wrote of 'the certain hostility of the local profession'.[48] He did acknowledge that the British medical teaching had one great strength: the actual clinical training 'on the wards' was superior to anything either the United States or the continent of Europe could offer. What was lacking was a scientific background in a world where laboratory investigation and diagnosis were to play an increasingly important role.

In their final report, published in 1913, the Royal Commission largely reflected Flexner's views and recommended the creation of medical and surgical units under the direction of full-time professors in the London teaching hospitals. Negotiations were started between the University and the hospitals but were put back many years by the onset of the Great War.

During his time at Netley and in his early years at St Mary's, Wright was known as an inspirational lecturer. Attendance at his lectures was such that extra seats often had to be provided. It was his fine performances on these occasions that enabled him to attract such able men to his staff. His lectures were lengthy — they often exceeded the conventional hour — but any tedium was relieved by elegant practical demonstrations of his various laboratory techniques. Later in his fifties, after four years of war, his enthusiasm for teaching undergraduates waned and Ida Mann, who was one of the war-time intake of female medical students and went on to become an internationally renowned eye surgeon, described him as 'refusing to teach except for a few statutory lectures.'[49] Yet his ability to enthuse an audience did not diminish; in June 1926 after a discourse by Wright on 'Aims and methods of therapeutic research' at the Royal Institution, Sir Arthur Keith, Fullerian professor of physiology, said it was the best experimental lecture he had heard.[50] Much of the routine instruction in bacteriology to undergraduates devolved on Fleming and Freeman and, in 1926, on Colebrook. Wright's weariness with routine undergraduate teaching did not extend to broader aspects of medical education and in particular the question of continuing medical education. There was a widely accepted view among the medical profession and the general public that once a man had achieved a medical degree he was qualified to undertake any medical procedure that he judged appropriate. This was a most dangerous concept, but only a few enlightened doctors challenged it. There was little acknowledgement that education and training were a lifelong commitment. One notable exception was T P Teale who, in giving an address at the opening of the Leeds School of Medicine in 1831, said that 'so far from the act of receiving a diploma being considered the completion of your medical education you must regard it as being the very threshold — the whole life of a medical practitioner is one continued course of pupillage.'[51] This was also a view firmly expressed by the various official enquiries and commissions into medical education that took place in the 19th and 20th centuries. It was still a prime concern of the Royal Commission on Medical Education that reported in 1968; they condemned the assumption 'that at the end of a few years training the emergent doctor could be sufficiently experienced in medicine, surgery and midwifery to set himself up in independent practice'.[52] They went on to recommend substantial postgraduate professional training. They were only reflecting opinions expressed in earlier reports and in particular that of the Interdepartmental Committee on Medical Schools, the Goodenough Committee, which reported in 1944. Yet it was only in the last two decades of the 20th century that such recommendations were implemented.

In 1920 Wright saw clearly the need for such continuing education and, together with Charles Wilson (later Lord Moran) attempted to rectify the situation with regard to those qualifying at St Mary's. Once a marriage settlement had been reached between the inoculation department and the hospital, and the Pathological Institute had been inaugurated, at least in name, Wright with money from the sale of vaccines founded two scholarships, open initially to those qualifying at St Mary's, to enable them to spend a year training in one of the branches of pathology. Wright realised that no institute could survive without recruits, but he was also keen that a much greater understanding should be built up between the medically qualified laboratory worker and the practising clinician. A good way of achieving this was for the latter to spend some time in the laboratory; moreover some of those taking up the scholarships might return to purely clinical work with a greater realisation of the problems of laboratory investigation for diagnosis. It is ironic, given Wright's views on the female sex, that two of the first three scholarships were awarded to Ida Mann and Joan Ross. Both women were to become celebrated in their chosen specialities, Mann in ophthalmology and Ross as a well-known morbid anatomist. Wright's reaction to these awards — he must have played a part in their allocation — is not recorded. Ida Mann recorded in her autobiography[53] that the award was given only on the condition that she confined her activities to the anatomy department and 'did not set foot in the hallowed masculine territories of the Institute itself'. In 1925 one of the scholarships was given to Ronald Hare. He later worked in the department and then went to Queen Charlotte's with Colebrook. In later years he became professor of bacteriology at St Thomas's and wrote several articles highly critical of both Wright and Fleming. He seems to have been a man who was concerned more with developing a hostile critical faculty than with evolving any creative ability of his own. He referred to Wright's work in attempting to determine the site of antibody formation and to produce antibodies *in vitro* as 'sheer concentrated tomfoolery'.[54]

In order to foster better understanding between laboratory and clinical practitioners Wright started a series of lectures, open to all members of the profession, on recent research in medicine. A variety of prominent medical scientists was invited to talk on topical subjects of their own choosing; they were each given a fee of ten guineas. These lectures were started in 1920 and were enthusiastically received. By 1924 the editor of the *St Mary's Hospital Gazette* noted that nearly all Fellows of the Royal Society with an interest in medicine had been asked to lecture. Wright always gave the first talk but there was a wide-ranging series of subjects, as can be gauged from the list for 1924 which included A V Hill on the function of haemoglobin in the body, Major Greenwood on 'Is the statistical method of any value in medical research?', Gordon Holmes on 'The ductless glands and personality'; Wilfred Trotter on 'The sensibility of the skin in relation to neurological theory'and William Bateson (director of the John Innes Horticultural Research Institute) on 'Determination of sex'. These lectures were extremely popular — when Henry Dale in 1923 talked on the physiology of insulin more than 150 people were present, filling the adjacent corridors as well as the lecture room. Nor were all the lectures specifically oriented towards the laboratory. In 1923 Bernard Hart gave an address on 'The development of psychopathology as a branch of medicine' ; he had been much concerned with the understanding and treatment of shell shock during and after the War. James Mackenzie, famed for his studies on cardiac rhythm, was another friend of Wright's who was recruited to lecture to the postgraduates. A blunt Scot, he had started in practice in the Lancashire town of Burnley, but such was his ability that he later became consultant physician to the London Hospital with an extensive private practice. He was one of the few men who could match Wright in an argument and was known on occasion to tell him he was talking through his hat.

Wright did not cease to give thought to the undergraduate course. On 11 March 1925 he gave a lecture to the Medical Society at St Mary's on 'Medical education'.[55] He began by drawing attention to the alarming fact that, after five years of study, 66 per cent of candidates failed the final examination at their first attempt. This in itself indicated a major defect in medical education. He did not think a deficiency of brain power or poor selection of students was the cause. Rather it was the result of overloading the student's mind with useless details — something that disturbed the Royal Commission 40 years later. This was true of all preclinical and some clinical subjects but in particular he abhorred the teaching of excessively detailed topographical anatomy and obscure branches of specialist surgery; much of what was learned was never of use and forgotten immediately after the examination. His solution to this problem was ingenious but, unfortunately, has rarely been practised. He proposed that if medically qualified staff of the preclinical departments of anatomy, physiology, pathology and biochemistry devoted some time to the study and care of patients, with an adequate salary for their work, they would then cease teaching useless details and concentrate on facts that were clinically relevant. His own department, it will be remembered, had some research beds and undertook care of both outpatients and inpatients. There remained the problem, then as now, that much of what students were taught and learned became obsolete in a few years. Disease patterns change. (For example, smallpox, diphtheria and typhoid were of great importance in the early part of the century, and pneumonia was a frequent life-threatening illness at all ages until the 1940s; but these were replaced by neoplastic and cardiovascular diseases as the main causes of disability and death by the end of the century.) Wright appreciated this, hence his obsession with continuing education; but he considered that as well as recognising the changing pattern of disease it was as important that the qualified doctor should be able clearly to distinguish relevant from misleading information much of it coming as advertising material from pharmaceutical companies as well as from imperfectly refereed articles in the popular medical press.

Views almost identical to those of Wright's were vividly expressed by Wilson in 1932 in a celebrated article in the *BMJ* entitled 'The student in irons'. He wrote:

> 'The one purpose of the student's years is, it seems, not to train and test habits of thought, but to collect and store a set of facts, as squirrels hoard nuts on which they hibernate. These facts are his capital, and he must perforce live on it throughout his working life, for he has not been put in the way of adding to his possessions as time goes by'.[56]

He pointed out that ten years after qualification the medical practitioner remained in much the same state of knowledge as when he obtained his diploma or degree. Lacking a disciplined and critical mind he was liable 'to fall a victim to every passing fashion and live among the credulous'. He was bombarded by much pharmaceutical literature and unable to evaluate useful therapeutic agents from quack medicines. Wilson and Wright were both in favour of an honours degree in medical science for London medical students aimed at fostering the power of scientific reasoning, much on the pattern of the honours degrees offered at Oxford and Cambridge. Wilson outlined a proposal for this to the Rockefeller Foundation, which he hoped would finance the project.[57] Alas, nothing came of it. To inculcate this critical ability Wright proposed that all medical students should be given a course in logic 'which taught how to elucidate facts and how to make inferences from them'. It is sad that this idea was never taken up, but this did not deter Wright from attempting to expound a system of logic of his own during the remaining 20 years of his life.

Notes

1 Burdon-Sanderson J. *Lancet* 1885; **ii**: 747.
2 Waynflete professor of physiology at Oxford (1882–95) and from 1895 to 1903 Regius professor of medicine at Oxford.
3 Porter R. *The greatest benefit to mankind* p529. London: HarperCollins, 1997.
4 Ibid.
5 Tansey EM. The funding of medical research before the Medical Research Council. *J Roy Soc Med* 1994; **87**: 546 This article gives a full account of scholarships available at this time.
6 Sims Woodhead became professor of pathology at Cambridge in 1899.
7 Collier LH. *The history of the Medical Research Club 1891–1991* (privately printed). CMAC SA/ MRC/4.
8 Quoted by Thomson AL. *Half a century of medical research* vol 1 p11 *et seq*. HMSO, 1973.
9 Moulton HF. *The life of Lord Moulton* [Preface]. London: Nisbet & Co, 1922.
10 Ibid p115.
11 CMAC RAMC 563. Leishman papers p176.
12 Thomson AL. *Half a century of medical research* vol 1 p2. HMSO, 1973.
13 Shock M. *DNB 1951–1960*.

14 There was a separate privately financed cancer research fund of which Sims Woodhead was a member.
15 Thomson AL. *Half a century of medical research* vol 1 p109. HMSO, 1973.
16 Ibid p115
17 CMAC RAMC 563. Leishman papers p167.
18 Ibid p166.
19 Thomson AL. *Half a century of medical research* vol 1 p29. HMSO, 1973.
20 Munk's Roll vol 4 p558. London: Royal College of Physicians, 1955.
21 CMAC RAMC 563. Leishman papers p154.
22 Ibid p145.
23 Thomson AL. *Half a century of medical research* vol 1 p30. HMSO, 1973.
24 PRO FD/86.
25 Ibid p116.
26 To the medical profession as a whole he was better known as 'Corkscrew Charlie'.
27 Grainger JS. 1998 The Great Experiment: the admission of women students to St Mary's Hospital Medical School. *Med Hist* 1998; **42**: 68.
28 The detailed accounts are not available but these figures can be found in the minute books of the House Committee of the Inoculation Department at St Mary's Hospital archives. WF1.
29 Hughes WH. Br Lib Add MSS 56214.
30 Colebrook L. Diary entry for 13 November 1919. CMAC.
31 Hughes WH. *Alexander Fleming and penicillin* p21. London: Priory Press, 1974.
32 Colebrook L. Diary entry for 3 July 1927. CMAC.
33 Macfarlane G. *Alexander Fleming, the man and the myth* p113. London: Chatto & Windus, 1984.
34 Hughes WH. *Alexander Fleming and penicillin*. London: Priory Press, 1974.
35 Wright AE. *Lancet* 1919; **i**: 489 *et seq.*
36 Wright AE. *Lancet* 1923; **i**: 365, 417, 473.
37 Wright AE. *Lancet* 1931; **ii**: 225, 277, 333.
38 Wright AE. *Lancet* 1923; **i**: 365,417, 473.
39 Harris TN, Grimm E, Mertens E, Ehrich E. *J Exp Med* 1945; **81**: 73.
40 Rich A. *The pathogenesis of tuberculosis* 2nd edn p600. Oxford: Blackwell Scientific Publications,1951.
41 Gowans JL. *Brit J Exp Pathol* 1957; **38**: 67.
42 Wright AE. 1921 *Proc Roy Soc* 1921; B **92**: 118; ibid 1927; A **114**: 576; ibid 1929; A **125** 587.
43 Adams NK. Ibid 1925; A **108**: 324.
44 Wright AE. *Lancet* 1900; **ii**: 65.
45 Holt LC. University of London, 1937. MSc thesis. Quoted in Lewis HE. *Proc Roy Soc Med* 1972; **65**: 39.
46 Bonner TN. *Med Hist* 1989; **33**: 472.
47 Royal Commission on University Education in London, Reports vol. 5 pp21–5. HMSO, 1910–12. Quoted in Bonner TN *op. cit.*
48 Quoted in Bonner TN *op. cit.*
49 Mann I. Autobiography p154. MSS in St Mary's Hospital Archives.
50 Colebrook L. Diary entry for 24 June 1926. CMAC
51 Quoted by Anning ST, Walls WKJ in *A history of the Leeds School of Medicine* pp18–19. Leeds, 1981.
52 Royal Commission on Medical Education p22. HMSO, 1965–1968.
53 Mann I. *The chase* p69. Fremantle: Fremantle Arts Centre Press, 1986.
54 CMAC PP/HAR/A12 Letter to Professor RI Greaves
55 *St Mary's Hospital Gazette* 1925; **31**: 33.
56 Wilson CM. *BMJ* 1932; **i**: 485.
57 CMAC PP CMW/A8/3/1.

Chapter 11

Family, Friends and Philosophy

Wright's relationships with his wife and children were turbulent. When he moved to St Mary's from Netley he rented 6 Park Crescent, but his wife spent a considerable time in Ireland, where she owned a property, with their crippled son Edward. Until the outbreak of war he let one of his assistants keep him company; up to 1907 this was John Freeman and afterwards Leonard Colebrook. Lady Wright did not accompany him on his holidays, usually taken in Switzerland or France. Instead he went with Colebrook. In 1911 they visited Lugano, Grenoble and Zermatt looking for a suitable place to take his children, Jack and Dolly, then aged 16 and 18; Colebrook found this pathetic.[1] During their holidays there was much discussion of women and marriage; Colebrook was anxious to find a wife and their conversation often revolved round the subject. As noted in Chapter 7, viewed from today Wright's opinions on women seem (to put it politely) eccentric. He recommended Colebrook to 'marry a fool who knows she's a fool'. From reading his diaries the suspicion arises that Colebrook was contemplating an approach to Dolly, Wright's favourite offspring, but this was firmly discouraged, Wright maintaining that Dolly was clever but had a bad mind with no sense of proportion.[2]

By 1912 the situation between Wright and his wife had deteriorated to such an extent that there was a formal separation. Strains must have been accentuated by the condition of Edward who, in spite of his disability, was studying in Dublin. At this stage he was growing weaker, spending most of the day lying in bed 'as any attempt at getting up caused him pain and distress'.[3] When Wright visited Belfast to receive the freedom of the city he took the opportunity to search for a suitable house in the west of Ireland that would provide holiday accommodation for his son and where the rest of the family could visit him. Nothing came of this. Matters were not improved by Wright's letter to *The Times* in 1912 on women's suffrage and the publication of his book on the subject a year later. In 1913, at the age of 24, Edward suffered severe injury from a self-inflicted revolver wound to the chest. Wright, cancelling a lecture in Edinburgh, hastened to Dublin to be at his son's bedside when he died. He was deeply affected and, according to Colebrook, he remained 'under a very dark cloud'; it was some time before his enthusiasm for laboratory work returned. Far from bringing husband and wife closer together, however, this tragedy only served to drive them farther apart. Lady Wright, in a letter to Mrs Fawcett informing her of a bequest from her son to the WSPU, indicated the fractious state of her marriage.

During the next year Lady Wright consulted a lawyer about instituting divorce proceedings. It was at this time that Jack, their other son, approached his father and asked for, and obtained, £4000 to help Lady Wright. When Wright found out about the legal consultations he was furious and his relationship with Jack never resumed its former cordiality. Matters were made worse when Jack refused to join the armed forces during the war. In December 1914 Wright came back on leave from Boulogne. He vacated 6 Park Crescent, his wife took all her belongings and although there was no divorce they went their separate ways thereafter.

Early in 1918 Dolly married the son of the distinguished writer and scientist G J Romanes, founder of the Romanes lectures in Oxford. John Romanes was an officer in King Edward's Horse. Wright had only corresponded with him, yet the poor man seems, according to Colebrook, to have made a bad impression. Wright refused to go to the wedding but sent a beautiful and expensive necklace as a present to the bride. The wedding was a grand society event. It took place at St Ann's Church in Dublin and the Archbishop of Dublin officiated. Many of the great and the good attended including Field Marshal Sir Henry Wilson, a relative of Lady Wright. The Baden-Powells and Mr Fawcett were present, as were Sir David and Lady Bruce. It is possible that inclusion of the last-named couple was a factor influencing Wright's decision to absent himself. Further ill-feeling was generated when Lady Wright told her mother-in-law that Almroth had refused to give Dolly a dowry; in fact he had offered one, which had been declined.[4] Happily Wright mellowed towards his son-in-law when the two met. By 1929 he was telling Colebrook that he considered John a saint with a good mind and Dolly 'was quite unworthy of him'.[5]

After the war many of his friends and family, including Dolly, Colebrook and a Mrs Vaughan of Eton, urged Wright to make up with his wife. This he refused to do.[6] He maintained that their quarrel involved a moral reprobation by his wife concerning his conduct; he had not the least intention of resuming any relationship until she made a full repentance. Neither of two such strong characters was likely to

Figure 26
Lady Wright in 1920, holding her grandson. (Giles Romanes)

submit. Yet they were at last partially reconciled when in 1924 Lady Wright developed a malignant tumour on the cheek — pathologists differed as to the precise diagnosis — which was resistant to treatment. She went, accompanied by her husband, to Paris to undergo radiotherapy. It was all to no avail and the cancer continued its remorseless growth. Wright, who was always deeply moved by any illness, visited her regularly throughout this time, taking her flowers and writing her poetry. They talked like old friends. She died early in 1926.[7]

Although Wright had a fractured family life he was not short of friends. By July 1919 he had taken a pleasant four-storey Georgian house in London, 6 Pembroke Square, complete with a studio which

Figure 27
'Southernwood', the house built by Wright at Farnham after the First World War. (Giles Romanes)

he used as a study. There was an annex in the garden to accommodate guests. In addition he purchased four acres of land and a cottage in Parson's Wood, Farnham. The cottage, 'Southernwood', was extensively rebuilt with the plans being drawn up and the work supervised by Wright's brother Henry, a Major-General in the Royal Engineers. Colebrook and his wife Dorothy took a keen interest in the work, but the only detail with regard to the house with which Wright showed any concern was the location of the back staircase for the use of the servants — he did not want to meet them.[8] On one occasion he told his maid and the cook that they could have the freedom of his house so long as they did not expect to enjoy his company. In contrast he took a close interest in the planning and planting of the garden, where he grew a fine selection of his beloved alpine flowers. The cottage and adjacent land was of great concern to Colebrook as Wright had indicated that he would leave the land to him; this, however, he did not do.

Wright entertained colleagues and friends regularly both at Pembroke Square and at 'Southernwood'. In turn he was invited by grand ladies of his acquaintance to dinner parties; he refused wine but would drink a glass of pale ale. If the company was of an intellectual nature he could be the life and soul of the party but there were occasions when he put a damper on proceedings. Once, at dinner, Wright appeared to be getting on well with his hostess when a sudden

Figure 28
Almroth Wright and his brother, Major-General Henry Wright. (Giles Romanes)

cold silence developed between them. After the ladies had retired his host asked Wright what had occurred. 'Oh nothing,' he replied 'I just told her there are no good women, only those who have lived under the influence of a good man, and no wise women, only those who have lived under the influence of a wise man.'[9] Yet it would be a mistake to consider him a woman-hater. The Hon Mrs Alfred Lyttelton wrote in *The Times* after his death: 'as one of his considerable number of women friends, I should like to record that no more charming, sympathetic, and helpful friend of the individual creature — woman — ever existed.'

During the war he formed a firm friendship with Lady Gordon Lennox, who played an important role in the Red Cross; and besides being a guest at her home, he went to stay with her in 1920 on the island of Capri. He was frequently to be found at dinners given by Lady St Helier and Lady Johnstone. Yet all these took second place to one who was the greatest, unrequited love of his life.

At a gathering at Fontainbleau in 1917 Wright met Mildred Bliss. She was the wife of a rich American diplomat, Robert Woods Bliss, at that time Counsellor at the United States Embassy in Paris. A man of considerable charm and influence, he frequently deputised for the ambassador and acted as an intermediary during President Wilson's efforts in 1916 to bring about an end to the war in Europe. In this he was aided by his wife. The evidence for the attachment between Wright and Mildred Bliss is in the correspondence which he had with her over the next 30 years.[10] Unfortunately only his letters to her survive — her letters to him were destroyed with many of his other papers by Dolly. The Blisses had no children and much of their considerable wealth was spent on collecting Columbian, medieval and Byzantine art.[11] In 1940 they donated their entire collection together with their library and Dumbarton Oaks estate in Washington DC to Harvard University. This estate eventually served as the venue for a conference that outlined the need for the formation of the United Nations. Mildred Bliss was a physically attractive woman. She was also rich being, ironically in view of Wright's views on the subject, heiress to a fortune derived from the sale of patent medicine. She was meticulous in her dress and took infinite pains in charity work. She shared with Wright a passion for gardening. She and her husband shared a reputation for generous hospitality to all the allied forces, giving parties to which both officers and other ranks were invited.[12]

It may be that Wright was introduced to Mrs Bliss by his friend Harvey Cushing. Certainly Cushing knew her well. He had dinner with the Blisses on 4 July 1917, after which he described Mildred as 'a trump' because she had promised to supply his surgical unit with a 'Ford ambulance with French trimmings'.[13] Wright was smitten at their first meeting, and on 11 November 1917 wrote to her expressing his feelings and including a poem translated from the Chinese:

'For thy two pearls I send back two tears,
Tears that we did not meet in earlier years'.

He concluded 'I feel as if we are going to be fast friends.' Wright assumed that Mildred Bliss was interested in things of the mind. By

21 December he was revealing his project to her, writing 'I am at work on ethics — that simply means trying to find out the way of happiness. I want you to help there.' Perhaps he was uncertain how his romantic overtures would be received, because he concluded with the words 'bis repetitia docent' ('things that are twice repeated teach') and then goes on, 'I suppose it means if a man doesn't put his meaning clearly the first time, a kindly lady lets him just try a second time.'

When Wright returned to London in 1918 he was undecided about his future. His inclination was to use his remaining years in writing up his philosophical concepts. His friends, and in particular Moulton and Balfour, advised him to leave this alone and to devote himself to laboratory work.[14] He had even been asked to stand for Parliament as the member for Dublin University[15] but, mercifully, declined — his obscure verbosity, accompanied by his endless invention of new words, would have tried the patience of even that most loquacious of debating chambers. The medical profession, at that time not receptive to new ideas or tolerant of anyone who did not conform to accepted standards of behaviour and thought, considered him an impractical visionary. These dilemmas as to his future no doubt aroused the sympathy of Mrs Bliss but their meetings were infrequent, though she did come to London in January 1919 on account of her health. She suffered from bronchitis and Wright was quick to provide a vaccine. He sent instructions to her own doctor, a man named Beauchamp, as to how it should be administered. He was encouraged in his affections by a request for a photograph and wrote, 'we are going to be special friends'. The vaccine, not surprisingly, did not improve her health and by February Wright was suggesting that, as Dr Beauchamp was not performing the injections himself but leaving them to an assistant, she should go elsewhere. His arch conclusion to this letter was: 'I send you always my affectionate regards — there is a much used monosyllabic word which would express that much more shortly'.

This love affair remained an essentially long-distance operation; on his side it was no less passionate for that. He sent her poems, sometimes via a third party. Thus a mutual acquaintance was entrusted with:

'Light of heart is she
I think she is the most beautiful lady
That ever came from your vast countrie'

— words that conveyed his meaning even if their metrical arrangement was faulty. On 19 July 1919 Wright invited her and her husband to stay at 6 Pembroke Square — in 1918 Bliss had been temporarily posted to the Hague as chargé d'affaires at the United States delegation. Bliss was unwell, however, and early in 1920 was recalled to Washington where he became chief of European affairs at the State department. Mrs Bliss returned to England alone in July of that year for a short visit. Wright was ecstatic at the prospect and entertained her at his house. He took great care over choosing the other guests for a dinner party in her honour. Arthur (now Lord) Balfour was unable to accept the invitation and in the end Bulloch, professor of bacteriology at the London Hospital, and the actor manager Granville Barker (who had played Dubedat in the original production of *The doctor's dilemma*) came, together with their wives.[16] The evening was a great success, and when Mildred returned to New York in August she wrote immediately asking him to come over. This invitation he declined on the grounds that he would have to give lectures, something he did not want to do. She came back to England in 1921 but they did not meet as he was at his cottage in the country; she telephoned his London home and failed to make contact. His letters became more and more concerned with philosophy, a subject of limited interest to a fashionable American hostess. Yet he bombarded her not only with details of his social life — he had entertained the American ambassador to dinner — but with neologisms he had invented for his book on logic, as well as sending her his latest scientific paper on immunology. These strangely stiff *billets-doux* failed to cause Lawrencian stirrings in Mrs Bliss.

In 1923 Bliss was appointed envoy extraordinary and minister plenipotentiary to Sweden and remained there until 1927. Mrs Bliss visited England rarely during this time but she did go to 'Southernwood' to see Wright's garden; afterwards he wrote that he deeply regretted that they only had hours and not days together. Their correspondence continued, and Wright made a strong appeal for Mildred's sympathy. In one letter he wrote:

> 'If only one lives long enough and energy does not flag, why one gets to one's end very tired; and especially tired if one has not beside one's work a life of affection. My family have gone as completely out of my life as if they had never existed. I had no conception such a thing was possible.'

His letters were now punctuated with premonitions of death and there were references to 'the horse hooves of eternity beckoning', a phrase he constantly repeated to Colebrook. These feelings were no doubt magnified by his wife's illness, of which he wrote to Mildred in 1924.

In 1927 Bliss's long service in the world of diplomacy was rewarded by his being appointed ambassador to Argentina. They both came to see Wright at his home on 28 April before their return to the United States. Mrs Bliss asked him to go with them. Wright refused but hoped 'that in another world we will see more of each other'. A visit to London in April 1930 was the occasion of another dinner party at Pembroke Square. His correspondence was full of details of his immunisation *in vitro* experiments, which she must have found as incomprehensible as did most of the medical profession, and his ramblings on philosophy. He was hoping to publish 'the skeleton of a *Dictionary of principles* — a set of tables — a classification of knowledge and the way we came at it'; not the material with which to evoke romantic vibrations in an attractive middle-aged lady. Yet Mildred Bliss had deep concern for the welfare of suffering humanity. In answer to a query from her about unemployment Wright replied: 'Of unemployment I know nothing. I know by report that it is terrible, but you would walk up and down the streets of London without seeing any signs of it.' Such statements might have conveyed the impression that Wright, while obsessed with logic and pursuit of the truth, had little in the way of a social conscience. This impression would be false: he had deep concern for individual suffering, as was evident in his attitude towards the wounded soldiers in the war and his constant anxiety about patients suffering from infections in the wards at St Mary's.

In May 1931, when he was 70, Wright was asked by the Colonial Office, probably as the result of a request by Robert Bliss, to visit Buenos Aires as one of the British delegates to the meeting of the Argentine National Medical Association (the other was Lord Moynihan). Wright took John Freeman as a companion and, on 17 July they sailed on the liner *Darro*. Wright was uncertain whether Mr and Mrs Bliss would be in the Argentine, as they usually visited Europe at that time of year. But they were there to receive the party and Wright stayed with them at the embassy, though the others were put up at an hotel. They had 15 days ashore, Wright giving two lectures and some laboratory demonstrations with which Freeman assisted. Wright reported to Colebrook that from a scientific point of view the meeting was not a success, being poorly attended. This contrasted with the social side, which was hectic: lunch at the Yacht Club, dinner at the Jockey Club and receptions at the embassy. Wright read the lessons in the Protestant cathedral on Sunday. The relationship with Mrs Bliss seems to have prospered and his letters on his return were more frequent and intimate. On 26 August the

Figure 29

The visit to Buenos Aires in 1931. From left to right: Mr Bliss, John Freeman, Mildred Bliss, Wright, an unknown Argentinian and Berkeley Moynihan. (The Wellcome Library, London)

party sailed for home on the *Cobanza*. On arrival in England Wright sent Mildred a book of photographs of Greek sculpture as 'a present for his stay in Buenos Aires'.

The visit represented the high point in their liaison. In 1933 Robert Bliss retired, and they met again only once, in 1935, before the outbreak of war. Although Wright wrote to her she seems to have replied only with the occasional cable. At times he was distraught and his letters were filled with reproaches: 'You don't know how often you are in my thoughts. But I never have a line from you and I feel it badly' — 'You might sometimes let me see your handwriting' — 'I think I write you pretty often, setting you a very good example you don't follow'. He seems to have been completely unaware that the contents of his letters were not such as to stimulate a long reply. In one letter he outlined a work he proposed to publish (he never did) entitled *Fascicle no 1 of operations of Mind*'. Clearly he thought the subject riveting, and he told her it was concerned with 'cognitional operations which lay the foundations upon which we build our edifice of knowledge'. Again he listed a set of new words derived from the Greek, many of which are to be found in the appendix to his posthumous book, *Alethetropic logic*, published by Giles Romanes[17];

few have reached the Oxford Dictionary. At the conclusion of this letter he became incoherent in contemplation of publication and ended, 'Things we feel but are not pictures — states of our central nervous system or intimate ego or soul. These are what really matter. I call them neuronic fruition and neuronic distress.' It is no surprise that Mrs Bliss could think of no suitable reply.

The declaration of war in 1939 made correspondence difficult. Letters often went astray and as all mail between the USA and Britain was conveyed by sea there was the ever-present danger of ships being sunk by U-boats. Nevertheless in July 1941 he 'was watching the post everyday' for a letter. By now he had an additional reason for wanting to hear from her. He needed financial help. He planned publication of his collected works on the physiology and pathology of wound healing, which encompassed all his experience in the Great War. Paper was scarce and publishers were reluctant to undertake such work without financial backing. He needed £1200 as a subvention to the publishers and an application to the Royal Society for this sum was turned down, so he asked if funds were available in the United States. He received no reply to this request. After the end of the war in 1945 the Blisses came to England on a goodwill visit and met Wright. They were distressed by much that they saw in Europe and on returning home sent food parcels to friends, including Wright. He was not interested in food but was himself disturbed by news from Germany where academic friends were in real difficulties, and he wrote urging Mildred to send such parcels to 'a friend in Innsbruck'.

Wright's health since 1920 had not been good. He suffered from increasingly severe angina[18] and had an indolent varicose ulcer, which on occasion became infected and gave him much pain.[19] In August 1937 he contracted an acute paranasal sinus infection while on a visit to France. On return, he went to Scotland to visit Dolly and her family, who were spending a holiday in Ullapool; here he developed pneumonia. While still desperately ill, he was driven 60 miles to a nursing home in Inverness. His condition was complicated by cardiac and renal failure. It was indicative of the affection in which Wright was held by his colleagues that many rushed up to Scotland to attend what was thought to be his deathbed. Freeman, Colebrook and Keith Rogers all thought the end had come. He recovered, however, and three weeks later he was back in his cottage 'Southernwood'.[20]

This severe illness moderated his temperament and, at least for a time, he became less intolerant of the views of others. His recovery seemed complete and a year later he had resumed his sacred ritual of working at home on his philosophy book in the mornings, appearing in the laboratory in the afternoons and staying there late into the night. In 1940 he suffered another setback when he developed an acute gall bladder infection. The gall bladder was drained but he was left with a discharging sinus, which did not close for 15 months. All this illness made him increasingly conscious of his mortality. To Colebrook he spoke of a fear of leaving baggage on the quayside. The baggage was his proposed work on logic.

Although he had first contemplated the work on philosophy before 1914 he had, in spite of his wide acquaintance, few friends with whom he could discuss it. Fletcher Moulton, whom he regarded as the cleverest man he had ever met, died in 1921 — 'I miss him dreadfully,' he wrote to Mrs Bliss. Moulton had provided essential advice and help in the early days of the inoculation department and the two of them had been intimately concerned with establishing the Medical Research Council. But Moulton was a mathematician and Wright was not interested in new avenues in mathematical branches of logic, so their discussions on the subject never progressed. Another close friend was Arthur Balfour — he was one of those whom Wright went to see about the setting up of a medical intelligence unit during the war. Balfour shared Wright's interest in such matters as the nature of belief, which Wright thought had a physical basis. Even before going to Netley in 1892 he had been fascinated by the relationship between emotions and the visceral sensations associated with them.[21] Balfour at first encouraged Wright in his philosophical endeavours; indeed at one time they contemplated collaboration on a book. Wright, with his passion for new words suggested they should define every abstract word they used. Balfour replied 'One need never define one's terms; for if one employs words sufficiently often, everyone will understand what one means.' Wright rebelled against this because each reader would put his own interpretation on the words and not a few 'would feel quite sure that any interpretation which happened to please them was the correct one'. Wright added tartly, 'That is what used to happen in the case of most of Lord Balfour's political pronouncements!'[22] Although from widely differing backgrounds, the two men had much in common. Both were placed in the second class in the Cambridge tripos; the memoir in the *Dictionary of national biography* concluded that Balfour's 'mind was perhaps too independent for a curriculum'. In his Gifford lectures Balfour declared, 'My business was with the ground work of living beliefs: in particular with the goodness of that scientific knowledge whose recent developments had so profoundly moved mankind.'

In the 1920s Balfour was still absorbed in politics but found time to dine with Wright. In a letter to Mrs Bliss, Wright recounted that the two of them had 'a really good enjoyable row' over the projected book on morals — confusingly, the subject title of Wright's *magnum opus* changed from time to time. By 1924 Balfour seems to have lost faith in Wright's ability to produce a book on either logic or morals and, as it was causing so much mental anguish, he advised him to 'stick to science'. Indeed, there was something reminiscent of Casaubon's search for the key to all mythologies in *Middlemarch* about Wright's despairing search for the true logic. Yet Balfour remained a firm friend and, according to Colebrook, he wrote Morley Fletcher a 'belligerent letter' when the Medical Research Council terminated Wright's grant in 1927.[23] This is not quite correct. Balfour wrote to Fletcher on 3 May 1927 asking him to lunch to discuss 'a rather tiresome matter' and added 'it concerns Sir A Wright'.[24] There is no record of their conversation but Balfour certainly held Wright in high regard; in a later letter to Fletcher on the question of raising funds for St Mary's, he wrote 'I am not sure you have quite so high opinion of Wright's work as I have.'[25]

Balfour died in 1930 and with his passing Wright lost his most critical friend, at a time when his scientific work was in decline and his mind increasingly occupied with philosophical matters. Others of his acquaintance on whom he might have tried his ideas had, like William Osler, died or were abroad, as was Harvey Cushing, or were unsympathetic to such intellectual matters, like the surgeon Berkeley Moynihan. There remained George Bernard Shaw. Their friendship had matured since the latter's visit to the inoculation department in 1906 when the idea for *The doctor's dilemma* was conceived. Colebrook has stated there was little warmth in their relationship;[26] this is difficult to believe. There were times when Shaw wrote about Wright in a flattering, even fulsome, manner. Certainly, Wright was corresponding with Shaw as late as 1942 saying how overjoyed he was to receive a letter about his recently published book — *The prolegomena to the logic which searches for truth* finally saw the light of day in January that year. It was one of the longest letters Wright wrote and ended 'yours affectionately', hardly words one associates with two men who find each other's company distasteful.[27] Both Shaw and his wife were visitors to 'Southernwood' and when Charlotte Shaw was dying Wright sent her flowers and a poem. Shaw himself was deeply touched by Wright's condolences.

Yet it would be true to state that the two men disagreed about almost everything. Wright was irritated by his portrayal as Ridgeon in *The doctor's dilemma*; he walked out in the interval. Conversation or dialogue can seldom have taken place during their meetings. Both men were verbose and each so absorbed in his own soliloquy that they had no inclination to listen to the other. Yet they got on well. This was nowhere more evident than on the occasion when Shaw visited Wright in 1917 in his house in the Boulevard Daunou. The two men were sitting in the drawing-room discussing the place of philosophy in the solution of scientific problems when the chimney caught fire and belched smoke into the room. The two men were quite impervious to the alarms and chaos raised around them, and continued talking.[28] It was during one such discussion that Shaw suggested that the title of Wright's proposed work on philosophy should be *Morals in the melting pot.*

The position of women in society was a subject on which the two men were vehemently at odds. At a luncheon early in 1914 Wright asserted that men and women could not profitably and comfortably work cheek by jowl. Shaw disagreed and Wright countered with 'Everybody knows what you are, Shaw.' Later, at the same meeting, Shaw declared that the art of good living lay in a diet of cold vegetables to which Wright made the celebrated retort: 'God help the women of England, Shaw, if you ever have a mutton chop.'[29] Wright harboured doubts as to Shaw's sexual inclinations, as he did about those of John Stuart Mill and A J Balfour. (His doubts may have been fuelled by Shaw's pleading with him to use his influence to obtain a bed at St Mary's for Lord Alfred Douglas. Douglas recovered without an operation 'after undergoing washing by a nurse and other indignities'.[30]) Wright considered them 'not to be he-men', presumably a code term for homosexual though there is no evidence to support this view. Wright always maintained that his book when written 'would be directed at only those with a complete human equipment'.

One matter on which both men were agreed was on the absurd pretensions of the medical profession, especially those who practised in Harley Street. Wright's letter to the *Liverpool Daily Post* in 1905 pointed to the lack of facilities and interest in medical research in England and this, together with his continual denigration of much medical practice in his lectures and writings, had not endeared him to those in the higher reaches of the profession. He stood by his opinions and refused the Fellowship of the Royal College of Physicians of London, at that time a singular honour for a bacteriologist, when it was offered to him in April 1922.[31] He only accepted it in 1938 when his colleagues at St Mary's remonstrated with him on the matter.[32]

Shaw's views on medicine, as opposed to those on some medical practitioners, were frankly potty. Yet there was just a little reason in his madness. He maintained that the real cause of illness and disease was poverty and economic maldistribution, and that to focus on medical matters would deflect attention from this. Insofar as most people's health has improved because of improved living standards rather than by medical intervention, he was right.[33] But he did not believe in smallpox vaccination or in Wright's anti-typhoid vaccine. His views on bacteriology were as perverse as those of Florence Nightingale — she was unconvinced by the germ theory of disease. Yet he was fascinated by Wright's work on opsonin and bewitched by the wonder of the phagocytes. In 1923 he contributed two long but ill-informed articles to the *Nation*. The first appeared on 3 February and was entitled 'Jenner'. He wrote: 'To call him [Jenner] a man of science nowadays would be like calling Old Moore an astronomer.' But Shaw had no understanding of science — he refused to believe that there were five million red blood cells in a cubic millilitre of blood, or that the Sun was 98 million miles from the Earth. In the article he maintained that the decrease in incidence and death from smallpox was unrelated to vaccination, seemed to confuse the disease with syphilis and praised Parliament for passing a bill enabling magistrates to exempt children from vaccination if their parents conscientiously objected to it.

The second article, published on 10 February, entitled 'Almroth Wright', was both fatuous and misguided. It had the well-intentioned aim of extolling Wright's work; it did nothing of the sort, however. Shaw began with a compliment: 'When we pass from Jenner and Pasteur to Almroth Wright we mount from one intellectual category to another and obviously a keener one.' This was not at all obvious to scientists or the general public then or now — Pasteur and Jenner will remain two giants in scientific achievement and, although Wright's contributions have been seriously undervalued, they cannot be considered to surpass those of these two men. Shaw continued with a general condemnation of the medical profession reiterating arguments that had been formulated in the *English Review* and in the preface to *The doctor's dilemma,* and which were to be repeated at a later date in *The Times.* He accused Jenner, Pasteur and Lister of loading their successors 'with a heavy burden of malpractice that was eagerly adopted by the General Medical Council (a body almost perfect as an example of everything that is pernicious in trade unionism)'. He condemned the system whereby private doctors are paid only when people are ill, thus giving them a vested interest in ill-health. But he also damned the profession for embracing prophylactic procedures, such as vaccination, as this enabled doctors to obtain money from perfectly healthy people. He then praised Wright for 'blowing the reputations of Jenner, Pasteur and Lister to smithereens' (Wright had done no such thing) and commended him for his work on war wounds. Unfortunately Shaw's comments were punctuated by many factual errors. Thus, he asserted that following the advent of Listerian antiseptics surgical wounds failed to heal for up to a year, allowing the surgeon to dress them daily and pocket the appropriate fee, whereas, he ludicrously claimed, before their introduction wounds had healed in a fortnight. He referred to Wright as one in the first rank as a scientific investigator and inventor and applauded his introduction of routine blood tests. He confused typhoid and paratyphoid, and maintained that diphtheria anti-serum caused diphtheria.

The article had the reverse effect of that intended. Wright was embarrassed and annoyed. His medical colleagues were much displeased and it was only the fact that his entry in the *Medical directory* stated that he was no longer in private practice that prevented serious repercussions; in those days any form of advertising could bring a doctor before the General Medical Council disciplinary committee. There was much hostile correspondence in the *Nation*. Shaw was severely criticised for using technical terms that he did not understand and for being out of touch with recent advances in medicine and biology—he had misquoted statistics on smallpox vaccination. His views on the medical profession were castigated as demonstrating 'the essential vulgarity of a mind which invariably imputes the vilest motives to persons whose views are disliked'. His opinions were classed as 'sanctimonious, self-righteous and "bad form".' The remarks on Lister were regarded as unworthy sneers at human fumblings towards the truth.[34]

Yet the most severe criticism was directed at Wright who was described in sarcastic terms, one correspondent writing: 'Even the divine Almroth Wright, according to his publicity agent, sometimes nods.'[35] The article was indeed potentially very damaging to Wright's reputation and his colleagues in the inoculation department were incensed, urging him to reply. Reluctantly he did so in a short but cogent letter repudiating Shaw and pointing out that such ill-informed articles were bound to be written 'as long as mankind accepts as instructors in medicine those who are prepared to teach without adequate study, without sense of responsibility, without equipment of intellectual morality and without reverence for the work of Pasteur and gratitude for that of Lister and Jenner'.[36] It was an unfortunate episode and Wright did well to keep a low profile and not to enter into a lengthy debate.

What of the work on philosophy? By 1940 it was clear to Wright, now 80 years old, that if he did not publish his ideas soon they would indeed be left on the quayside. He considered that although the complete treatise was not ready he must put something into print so, in 1941, he published *The prologomena to the logic which searches for truth*. In writing this he had the assistance of an able and long-suffering secretary, J Hector Dare. Long-suffering indeed, because Wright indulged in much rewriting; in some sections as many as 60 drafts in barely decipherable handwriting were prepared. Wright's attitude to this work bears some comparison with that of others in the late Victorian and Edwardian era. Arthur Sullivan was convinced that his true *métier* lay in grand opera, whereas he is chiefly remembered for his comic operetta collaboration with W S Gilbert. Conan Doyle was convinced that his literary talent lay in the historical novel, but his name is forever associated with Sherlock Holmes — a creation he grew to hate. So with Wright, whose claim to fame rests on his anti-typhoid work, his contribution to the revolution in treatment of war wounds and his foundation of the sciences of clinical bacteriology and immunology, but who hoped to be remembered for his philosophical outpourings. The assessment of this work requires the services of a professional philosopher, which the present author most certainly is not. Yet much of Wright's writing on the subject was directed at the lay reader and in particular the medical student and practitioner.

He often tried out his ideas, both scientific and philosophical, initially on colleagues in the laboratory and on the Medical Society at St Mary's Hospital Medical School. In 1921 he addressed a packed audience on 'Morals'. No typescript of his talk survives but the *St Mary's Hospital Gazette* carried an amusing commentary on the lecture by Dr Charles Wilson (later Lord Moran) entitled 'Wright on wrong'[37]. At this period Wright's philosophical talk and writing focussed on two main areas, morals and religion. He proposed that morals should be learned from an experimental approach. What precisely this entailed is not clear, but at that time the memories of the horrors of trench warfare were fresh in everyone's mind, indeed had been experienced by many in his audience. Wilson in commenting on the lecture wrote that the ultimate practical experiment in moral behaviour took place in Flanders, being an examination in 'unselfishness and the final test of that, a willingness to go "west"'. Wright drew a picture of himself as a moral pirate and, according to Wilson, mocked at such concepts as unselfishness and working for others. This was, of course, nonsense. Wilson saw Sir Almroth 'as getting prizes for attendance and good conduct in his youth, as being perfectly free from the blemishes of indolence and worse that blot our own records'. He added that he was attracted by Wright's anxiety 'to cover up his good deeds' for which he was well known. Wright had explained this away by claiming that he experienced epicurean pleasure from his work and good deeds — he was celebrated for helping those in need — and thus they did not merit the accolade of moral rectitude. Wilson attributed much of Wright's thinking and behaviour to his Celtic origins: the use of exaggeration and his splendid oratory. This he contrasted with the habitual understatement of the Anglo-Saxon. To illustrate it he mentioned the Duke of Devonshire, who claimed the proudest moment of his life was when he won the first prize for a pig at the Skipton agricultural show.

Yet in ascribing Wright's views to his Celtic ancestry Wilson was only partially correct. A greater influence was surely his strict Calvinist upbringing, with its belief in the absolute truth and literal interpretation of the Bible. As with many sons of fathers who practised an evangelical and fundamentalist religion — one thinks of Edmund Gosse — he revolted against it in adult life. His conversations with Colebrook, who was himself a believer and had contemplated life as a missionary, although no doubt designed to shock were nevertheless an indication of his true state of mind. Nowhere was this more so than when discussing marriage and the family. Wright claimed the 'family was an abominable institution 'a man is always pleading the support of family instead of the good of the State — the State should look to the family.'[38] His division of moral law into four departments provides an indication of the provocative nature of his views[39]. His four departments were:

> *Truth:* it is not enough to speak the truth, we ought also to diligently seek to find it before we speak.
> *Property:* possession must not be possession for all time. We must get rid of the idea that it is theft to take away what should not really belong to another man. So if England holds Gibraltar it is not defensible except it is agreed it makes for the happiness of the world.
> *Force:* this must remain to maintain conditions for the happiness of the world.
> *Adultery:* 'thou shalt not commit adultery' must be superseded by the idea that there can be no property in wives or husbands.

These concepts no doubt surprised the conservative audience at the meeting at St Mary's and perhaps it was fortunate they were not published in that hospital's *Gazette* at the time.

In the preface to *The prolegomena to the logic which searches for truth* Wright set out his aims. Firstly, the student of logic must learn which of the ideas and propositions that assail his ears he may properly accept, which he should reject as erroneous, and which he should regard as dubious. Secondly, and this was a strong reaction against his religious upbringing, he 'put it to men of religion that they should when they are enunciating transcendental dogma, or referring to the wonder stories which have been linked up with these, avoid suggesting that the things they are talking of are actually true or proved or logically verified'. A reviewer in the *Times Literary Supplement* described Wright's work as 'being endowed with originality and with considerable philosophic force'.[40] Wright's description of the evolution of transcendental ideals in Greek literature was greatly admired. He used his classical learning to good effect in discussing the Greek plays and their relevance to transcendental values. In his commentary on the *Alcestis* and the *Antigone* he gives his prejudices on the female sex full rein. He wrote 'Alcestis takes it upon herself to die as proxy for her husband, she does so not out of any romantic affection (in the play there is absolutely no word of that) but because she, like every decently brought-up woman in Greece (or indeed anywhere) was persuaded of her essential inferiority to man.'[41]

Yet Wright's main invective was reserved for the Christian religion and especially that of the Roman Catholic Church—here at least he was in agreement with his father. He considered that Christ in his own person 'would probably have not persuaded any appreciable numbers of mankind to accept his ideals' and it was St Paul who played the premier role in the warfare of 'belief against critical employment of the intellect.'[42]. He complained that Paul's fine writing, unsupported by proof, had been incepted as truth. Alarmingly, he compared Paul with Hitler and Stalin and thought one of Paul's most pernicious arguments was fear of the day of judgment as a reason for good behaviour. He pointed out that the inferiority of Paul's moral principles came 'clearly into view' when one considered that in all civilised countries an overwhelming majority of intelligent persons who have no belief in biblical 'wonder stories' do not make disbelief an excuse for practising vice. He deplored that Christianity had been 'left in possession of the field for so long', discouraging all intellectual enquiry and diversity of opinion; from 500 to 1500 AD 'Gothic darkness had settled' on the world. Miracles were a pet aversion of Wright's. He was particularly sceptical about the birth of Christ but, somewhat surprisingly considered that: 'The portion of the story which is incredible to every intelligent man is that which imports that a star can, by standing in the zenith, function as a pointer to a particular house.'[43] There is no discussion of the virgin birth. Much of the remainder of the book is concerned with aspects of reasoning traditional to logicians. Thus he asserts that: 'To prove a proposition means to ordinary mortals to furnish evidence that the proposition is true. But logicians when they speak of a conclusion do not mean that it is true. All they mean is that the conclusion follows from the premises. A logical conclusion ought to count as proved even if the premises from which it has been deduced are indubitably false.'[44] It is unsurprising that these thoughts, often written in impenetrable prose, did not galvanise the minds of medical students at St Mary's, occupied as they were with the distressing and baffling problems encountered in clinical practice.

Wright's posthumous work, *Alethetropic logic*, was a much longer and more ambitious project. Its main thrust was related to the nature of belief and disbelief. It is couched in language so obscure that an extensive glossary of terms was needed as an appendix. The four main sections of the book are:

- Prelogical operations of belief
- The grammar of logic
- Logical operations proper
- The critical evaluation of the criteria for truth.

There are in addition 16 appendices dealing with subjects as varied as miracles, the Gospel parables, the physiological element in emotion and conscientious objectors. These last, and here he included Christian Scientists and anti-vivisectionists as well as pacifists, were particular *bêtes noires* of Wright's. Detailed criticism of this work really requires the services of a professional philosopher, but it would seem this has not been undertaken. A search of the main philosophical journals of the period fails to reveal any critical reviews. The work was ignored, and sales did not repay the costs of publishing the book — costs that were nobly borne by Giles Romanes, Wright's grandson. The reader, if he is sufficiently persistent to arrive at the halfway mark, will find a revealing reference to a conversation between Wright and Balfour.[45] They had been discussing the architectonics of exposition and Balfour said that before they talked further on the matter Wright should read some fifty pages of a book that Balfour had written. Wright then said: 'Ought I to expect to understand what you write down when I have arrived at the end of each sentence, or should I bide my time till I have arrived at the end of a paragraph? Or again should I, ere I could hope to understand, read to the end of the chapter, or to the end of the book?'

'Do you know,' said Balfour, 'that is an extraordinarily good question.'

'I know,' said Wright, and went on to point out that it was not the first time he had put the question to Balfour but had never had an answer. Balfour replied that he was not surprised! Such a conversation might have taken place, had he lived, between Wright and a reader of *Alethetropic logic* without any satisfactory answer.

In the first section Wright seems to equate belief and imagination and points to the essentially personal nature of belief, contrasting it with knowledge, which is never the personal possession of one man. He maintains that believing is by no means always a pleasurable experience; he cites the fact that there is pain mixed with pleasure in every form of higher sexual love as there is always some call to self-sacrifice. Mainly, though, he is concerned with the evils of religion and deplores the part that both suggestion and belief have played in the world. He blames ethnic suggestion deliberately brought into application in Germany and Japan. He quotes from Lucretius: 'So much harm has religion been able to persuade man to do.' Wright thought that such religious beliefs implanted by suggestion could not be eradicated by reason — the only method was to set against such fallacies an innumerable array of conflicting facts.

He is critical of minds that cannot think in the abstract, referring to the disability of the eiconic mind. ('Eiconic' he defines as meaning mental image whether visual, kinaesthetic, auditory or olfactory.) These are minds incapable of thinking without mental pictures, unable to conceive broad concepts or things in what Bertrand Russell refers to as universals. He cites the example of Bishop Berkeley who could not apprehend a triangle in the abstract — he always visualised a triangle of a particular size or shape. Newman, whom he admired as a man, is condemned as unwholesome for believing in the Biblical Adam rather than Darwinian evolution.

Aside from his swipes at religion Wright's principal polemic is directed at John Stuart Mill, whom he characterised as having a theoretical mind that recoiled from the concrete and 'was so taken up with generic resemblances that it is fatuously blind to quite important specific differences'. He dismisses Mill on three grounds. Firstly, as regards logic he finds the 'Canons of Induction' entirely unhelpful because Mill has no practical acquaintance with either crucial or statistical experimentation. Secondly, with regard to Mill's work on political economy, which encompassed the epitome of Victorian liberalism, Wright's criticisms were ill-informed. He considered that political economy was concerned only with the acquirement of wealth. Wright's interpretation was that Mill saw the state simply as a collection of individuals who were supposed to work as entirely independent units and to be influenced only by the desire for gain. He wrote: 'Human beings of this sort are, of course, merely creations of

Mill's imagination.' These are not opinions that would be shared by historians today. Mill was anxious that the franchise should be extended not only to all male householders but also to women of wealth and education, as well as to women householders. He proposed that the vote should be given on the basis of intelligence. Such views were abhorrent to Wright and formed the basis for his harshest and lengthiest criticism of the third aspect of Mill's work, namely his support for the feminist cause. Mill's contention that men and women have equal brain power was, according to Wright, wholly false. Furthermore he thought that Mill's opinion that, if men and women were harnessed into intellectual partnership, then the intellectual output of humanity would be doubled was fallacious. According to Wright, Mill held that 'the reason why women have so far not received the honour which he thinks should have accrued to them as original thinkers is because their original ideas have always been purloined by their husbands and brothers, who have brought them out as their own.' These contentions of Mill were not likely to appeal to a man who maintained all his life that there were no good women, only those who had lived under the influence of a good man. Wright's discussion of the relative merits of the brain power of males and females is unconvincing. He quotes dubious examples from the animal kingdom, claiming at one point, on very inadequate evidence, that male dogs are more intelligent than bitches—something with which few dog-owners would agree. Women's successes in examinations, particularly medical examinations, he dismisses as the result of their battening on to textbooks; he thought they were hopelessly incompetent when it came to applying knowledge in practice. These anti-female opinions were further elaborated in a chapter devoted to female psychology which reiterated many of the arguments first put forward in his book *The unexpurgated case against woman suffrage*. At the end of the chapter he quotes 58 epigrams, all of which belittle the mental ability of females.

It is fortunate that this work was published posthumously. Thick-skinned though he claimed to be, Wright would have been hurt, not by severe criticism to which he would have enjoyed responding vigorously, but by the total indifference with which it was received by the intellectual public.

Notes
1   CMAC PP/Col Diary entry for 5 June 1911.
2   Ibid 22 June 1911.
3   Ibid 1912.
4   Ibid 10 February 1918.

5 Ibid 26 September 1929.

6 Ibid 25 October 1923.

7 Ibid 12 January and 2 May 1926.

8 Ibid 21 May 1924.

9 CMAC PP/Col/C11 Snippets. Attributed to Ross G (of Toronto).

10 CMAC GC70. This correspondence consists only of Wright's letters to Mrs Bliss. Her replies were probably destroyed after his death.

11 *Smithsonian Magazine* 31 May 1996 p4.

12 Cushing H. *From a surgeon's journal 1915–1918* p278. Boston: Little, Brown & Co.1936.

13 Ibid p149 *et seq.*

14 CMAC PP/Col Diary entry for 28 November 1918.

15 CMAC PP/Col Loose foolscap page in diary dated 28 November 1918.

16 Granville Barker came with his second wife. His first wife had divorced him and he had married Helen Huntington, the divorced wife of Barker's financial backer Archie Huntington.

17 Wright AE. *Alethetropic logic: a posthumous work* (presented by GJ Romanes) pp33–69. London: William Heinemann, 1953.

18 CMAC PP/Col Diary entry for 16 February 1923.

19 Ibid 26 October 1919.

20 Ibid 28 September 1937.

21 Wright AE. *Brain* 1895; **18**: 217.

22 Wright AE. *Alethetropic logic: a posthumous work* (presented by GJ Romanes) p169. London: William Heinemann, 1953.

23 CMAC PP/Col Diary entry for 3 July 127.

24 PRO 5D5/63.

25 Ibid.

26 Colebrook L. *Almroth Wright: provocative doctor and thinker* p193. London: William Heinemann Medical Books, 1954.

27 Shaw letters in Manuscript Collection, Trinity College, Dublin 9888/2/1-34.

28 Colebrook L. *Almroth Wright: provocative doctor and thinker* p72. London: William Heinemann Medical Books, 1954.

29 Ibid p238.

30 Letter from Shaw to Wright, dated 14 July 1938. Manuscript Collection, Trinity College, Dublin 9888/2/1-34.

31 Letter from the Registrar, The Royal College of Physicians, London, dated 5 April 1922. Ibid 9888/1.

32 Ibid. Letter from Charles Newman dated 28 April 1938.

33 Waller PJ. Personal communication.

34 Roberts H. *The Nation* 17 February 1923 p749.

35 Ibid.

36 Ibid 24 February 1923 p783.

37 *St Mary's Hospital Gazette* 22 January 1922 p5.

38 CMAC PP/Col C11.

39 Ibid.

40 *Times Literary Supplement* 8 February 1941.

41 Wright AE. *Prolegomena to the logic which searches for truth* px *et seq.* London: William Heinemann, 1941.

42 Ibid pxxviii.

43 Ibid p7.

44 Ibid p11.

45 Wright AE. *Alethetropic logic: a posthumous work* (presented by GJ Romanes) p171. London: William Heinemann, 1953.

Chapter 12

The Final Years

Most men on reaching the age of 65 years are only too glad to retire. Not so Wright. When his personal MRC grant of £2000 per year stopped, he showed no inclination to resign his directorship of the Pathological Institute. He received no pension from the MRC, but this made little difference because he continued to draw a salary of £2500 from the inoculation department, using funds supplied by Parke Davis from the sale of vaccines.[1] He resumed a little private practice — Lady Gordon Lennox remained a patient of his. Any hopes entertained by members of the Institute that one of their number might succeed him were thwarted, though there is no evidence that such thoughts were in their minds in 1926; certainly there is no mention of anything of the sort in Colebrook's diary.

Yet Wright's relationships with his colleagues did afterwards become more difficult. On 12 December 1933, the new medical school buildings and the new Pathological Institute with its inoculation department were opened by the King and Queen. The dean, Moran, announced to the chairman of the hospital, Mr H G Verey, that he alone would receive their Majesties. Wright at once declared that unless he received them, as it was his Institute that was to be opened, he would lock its doors and disappear into the country. Verey was at a loss and retired to his club to consider the matter.[2] No sooner had he settled into his armchair than a taxi ejected Wright, who appeared, tapping the side of his head and exclaiming 'Megalomania, my dear Verey, megalomania.' Verey calmed him down, reassured him that he would be included in the reception party and dispatched him in another taxi. No sooner had this been achieved than a car disgorged Moran who declared, 'Senile decay, my dear Verey, senile decay.' He too was reassured and in the end the chairman of the hospital, Moran, and Wright, 'like the three incomprehensibles in the Athanasian creed . . . almost hand in hand received their Majesties'.[3]

By 1936, when Wright was 75 years old, colleagues and friends decided that the time had come to give him a strong hint that retirement should be considered, or at that least he might give up the directorship of the Institute. A party was arranged and on 24 March in the medical school library he was presented with a portrait bronze bust, the work of Donald Gilbert, and an 'engrossed' address signed by 250 subscribers to the testimonial. The address mentioned his outstanding work in immunology, vaccine therapy and the establishment of the inoculation department, as the Pathological Institute continued perversely to be labelled, at St Mary's. It concluded, perhaps unwisely, by wishing him continued health and vigour so that he could continue 'to enrich those branches of medicine with which your name will ever be linked.'[4]

Wright, when asked whom he would like to present the bust, had replied: 'The man of my choice, the one I have most reverence for in science, is my friend Dale.'[5] He cannot have known of the letter Dale wrote to Fletcher in 1916.[6] Dale, in making the presentation, spoke of the admiration and affection for Wright felt by his colleagues and friends and paid tribute to his work on typhoid vaccination which 'effectively put out of action' that weapon in 'death's armoury' during the Great War. Yet he balked at any direct mention of retirement. Instead Dale spoke of Sir Almroth being 'well set'. A nostalgic note was added when he expressed regret that Stewart Douglas was not present at the ceremony — he had recently died — as he had played a major role in Wright's early work. Wright was clearly moved by the proceedings. Always conscious of his mortality he concluded his reply with a quotation from Bunyan where Mr Valiant-for-Truth, standing at the brink of the river of death, declares: 'I leave my sword to him that shall succeed me in my pilgrimage, my courage and skill to him that can get it.'[7] Yet he exhibited no signs of desiring to make the bequest at that time and continued work as usual.

Wright did his reputation no favour by continuing to preside over the department. His interest in laboratory work was becoming less intense, his mind being occupied by the enigmas posed by philosophy. His colleagues found his routine of arriving in the department after 3 pm and staying until eight o'clock in the evening or later increasingly antisocial. At the age of 65 Wright had learnt to drive a car and when he stayed late in the laboratory often gave his assistant a lift home. Dr Keith Rogers described this as a terrifying experience. Wright appeared to ignore all other traffic in his pertinacious attempt to arrive at his destination in the shortest possible time.[8] The day-to-day running of the laboratory and its finances was left to Fleming, who habitually departed for the Chelsea Arts Club around 5 pm; thus contact between the two men was limited.

Wright's attitude to Fleming has been the subject of much comment. André Maurois, in his biography of Fleming, considered that Wright was largely responsible for the failure to develop penicillin production at St Mary's. The main figures in the department were turning more and more to the study of anti-bacterial substances, whereas Wright's thoughts were entirely concerned with improving and enhancing the natural defences of the body. He remained hostile to chemotherapy for infections and to the employment of antibiotics. It seemed that his unfortunate experience with optochin in 1911 had induced an irreconcilable revulsion against such drugs. Unfortunately this attitude separated him from his colleagues. His closest disciple, Colebrook, whose disposition towards his chief until the late 1920s fell little short of worship, gradually became disenchanted. With the coming of war in 1939 they saw less and less of each other. In 1945 Colebrook recorded that their former happy association had ceased and that 'the Old Man seemed determined to keep up the barrier' between them.[9] He felt that the advent of sulphonamides and penicillin had been a considerable blow to Wright since he had expected the future in the management of infections to lie with immunisation. In this, of course, he may well have been correct, though in the heady days of 1945 when antibiotics first came into general use and such hazards as antibiotic resistance and hypersensitivity were still minute clouds on the horizon, it was not a view likely to carry weight. Today opinion is swinging more in Wright's direction.

In 1942, when the public first became aware of penicillin following its purification and early bulk production by Florey and his team in Oxford, Wright wrote on 28 August to *The Times*: 'In the leading article on penicillin in your issue yesterday, you refrained from putting the laurel-wreath for this discovery round anybody's brow. I would, with your permission, supplement your article by pointing out that, on the principle of *palmam qui meruit ferat*, it should be decreed to Professor Alexander Fleming of this research laboratory. For he is the discoverer of penicillin and was the author of the original suggestion that the substance might prove to have important applications in medicine.' Colebrook commented that Wright had been obliged to support penicillin as it came from St Mary's, but added that he had never shown any interest or done any work on it.[10] He became unreasonably critical of the work of others while any self-criticism he had, and it was never very great, receded. Colebrook was now regarded as a 'renegade' because of his enthusiasm for chemotherapy. Discussion between the two on the rare occasions they met, usually at 'Southernwood', became heated and brought on Wright's angina.

Colebrook would then lapse into silence; this infuriated Wright even more, so the visits became increasingly rare. On 13 December 1945 Colebrook recorded in his diary that he spent a night with Wright which was 'not a success' as 'all the Old Man's grievances flared up again'. Matters were not made easier as Wright had by now become rather deaf so could not, or would not, understand what Colebrook was saying. Finally, Colebrook lost his temper. At 84 years of age, Wright still refused to talk of retirement. Colebrook concluded his diary entry on this occasion, 'I must not go and see him again — it is too painful and futile.'

From 1939 onwards, relationships at St Mary's had deteriorated further. Fleming had to administer the department without any authority. Wright maintained absolute power over hiring and firing staff. He summarily dismissed a close associate of Fleming's, a Dr McLean, who had had day-to-day charge of vaccine production, while Fleming was absent and Wright refused to reinstate him in spite of Fleming's pleading on McLean's behalf.[11] (The grounds for McLean's dismissal are not recorded.) By then Wright was exhibiting the petty-minded jealousy which, regrettably, can be a feature in the aged who refuse to give up the reins at work. Fleming's manual dexterity and technical ingenuity were legendary and, while Wright had ideas, it was often Fleming who put them into practice. The two complemented each other, a fact that Wright in his later years refused to acknowledge. In 1944, when Fleming had achieved world renown, Wright still refused 'to give him his head'.[12] The strains in the department were apparent to the junior members. Wright was by nature generous with money but in his later years there were episodes of uncharacteristic parsimony. Thus Clayden, who had joined Wright's staff in Boulogne and was the key technician in production of vaccines, the main source of departmental finance, asked Wright for a salary increase but obtained one only after Fleming had persistently interceded on his behalf.[13]

On the day on which Fleming's knighthood was announced in 1944 Wright arrived in the laboratory and presided over the afternoon tea-party. He appeared bad-tempered. He spoke to no one until Fleming arrived, then he turned his back on Fleming and proceeded to launch into a diatribe, lasting for 20 minutes, on the demerits of chemotherapy and the virtues of immunisation; he stopped only when he ran out of breath. Throughout this time Fleming maintained his renowned poker face, not exhibiting any sign of anger or amusement. When Wright paused Craxton, the institute secretary, handed him some paper concerning a financial matter. Wright snapped at him, 'Don't bother me with such trivial things, *Doctor* Fleming will deal with them.' Fleming held out his hand for the papers and left the room without a word.[14] That Fleming is never recorded as having expressed resentment at such treatment indicates not only his extraordinary equanimity and great loyalty, but also the awe in which Wright was held by his staff. That evening, after Wright had left at an unusually early hour, Fleming gave money to Clayden and told him to go out and buy beer and gin, after which he gave a party to all the laboratory staff. The award of the Nobel prize must have irritated Wright even more than Fleming's knighthood did, but no record exists of his reaction. Maurois thought that Wright expected to receive the prize himself.[15]

In the early 1940s, before the introduction of the National Health Service, the inoculation department had become a largely geriatric institution. There was no retiring age and no superannuation scheme for provision of pensions. Several colourful personalities were employed there, but they were long past doing any useful laboratory work. One, Dr John Mathews, had sailed round Cape Horn; another, F C Martley, who had been mentioned as a possible deputy for Wright in 1911, spent his old age playing chess for Ireland and working for the Medical Sickness Society. He died in 1941. The impending advent of the National Health Service made many of the staff anxious about their future employment prospects.

There is evidence from the minutes of the house committee of the inoculation department that pressure was brought to bear on Wright to retire by the chairman, Sir Andrew Duncan, who was not at all happy about the circumstances attending the dismissal of Dr McLean, mentioned above, who had given 22 years of service to the department. His disquiet was echoed by the other lay members of the committee. McLean did find another post and the matter was not pursued further. On 24 June 1946, Wright finally did retire from the post of director and was given a sum of £5000 and a pension equivalent to his salary, £2500 a year! It was agreed that Fleming would succeed him, and the older-established members of the department feared that the new director would clear out much of the dead wood. But Fleming was in demand as a lecturer overseas and, during one of his absences, Wright had been persuaded by the other members of the department to arrange that they should have tenure. This singularly mean and selfish act resulted in Fleming being left with only one post to fill, that of reader in bacteriology, when he assumed his new office. Once again there is no record of his reaction to this, but Fleming was not easily moved to temper.[16] He was also very

Figure 30
Visit of Queen Elizabeth on 9 August 1944 to St Mary's. Wright and the Queen are standing next to each other. Lord Moran's head can just be seen appearing over the left shoulder of the Queen. (Alexander Fleming Laboratory Museum, St Mary's Hospital, London)

magnanimous; when he gave an address after receiving an honorary degree at Harvard University he paid tribute to Wright, describing him as 'one of the great men of this world whose work as a pioneer has never been sufficiently recognised.'[17]

Visits by members of the Royal Family provide an insight into some aspects of Wright' personality. On 9 August 1944 the Queen made a surprise visit to St Mary's to discuss celebrations for the hospital's centenary, which was to fall in the following year. There was the usual jockeying for position. A photograph of all the distinguished members of the board of management with the Queen shows Sir Almroth nudging his way to the front and dwarfing the diminutive Lord Moran. One of Wright's last acts as head of the inoculation department was to welcome the Queen on 28 June 1945 when she visited St Mary's. The occasion was what was known as a 'Big Day' to capitalise on the discovery of penicillin and raise much-needed money for the hospital and medical school. In his diary Colebrook lamented that too much of the exhibition was devoted to the work of Florey and his associates in Oxford. The Queen was very friendly towards Wright, who made a speech which was a summary of his work ethic. This was well received. He spoke as the oldest member of staff and asked the forgiveness of

Her Majesty for saying something personal. Drawing attention to the untiring work of the Queen during the war — she had undertaken 7700 public engagements — he extolled her example. To the young members of the audience he said, 'If you find yourself when you go to bed not really tired you should get down on your knees and pray to God to forgive you for wasting your day.' He emphasised that the older one became the harder it was to work and advised getting 'one's harshest work' done when young. He ended on a theme that had characterised his own conduct with regard to charity. He quoted a passage from Marcus Aurelius, which he considered one of the most profitable sayings of antiquity: 'When you have done an act of kindness to a fellow-creature, what more would you have? You have acted in accordance with your nature so you must not speak of any recompense for this. Does the eye want to be rewarded for seeing, or the feet for walking?'[18] This was a principle by which he had lived and in earlier days Colebrook, who came from a humble background, and many others benefited from his kindness. During the 1930s he had supported a penniless Dutchman who was unable to find a scientific post, paying him out of his own pocket to sort out his scientific papers — a task which was never completed.[19]

When in 1946 Wright eventually did resign, he spent most of his time at 'Southernwood' working on his philosophy book, although he returned occasionally to the department. Outside his work he was surrounded by lady friends and admirers. Before and during the war Grizel Hartley, the wife of an Eton housemaster who was away in the services, was in constant attendance. Wright's visits to the Hartleys were not always appreciated by the other guests. Janet Adam Smith recorded that he was rather worse than Billy, the Hartleys' notorious dog, and that he passed the time with denunciations of all women. This infuriated the ladies present, who considered him 'a terrible old man', yet Grizel was very fond of him and the feelings were reciprocated. One guest thought her affection may have been related to the fact that Wright received the Buchanan medal of the Royal Society, an award founded by Grizel's grandfather Sir George Buchanan.[20] This seems unlikely; in spite of all protestations to the contrary Wright was attractive to many women and was attracted to them. This susceptibility was apparent from the reasons he gave for excluding them from the laboratory: 'Ugly women annoy men; carefully groomed and good-looking women disturb them'. He used to add, 'I much prefer them a bit sinful.'[21]

Wright had several times been a patient in St Mary's, as when he underwent a gall bladder operation and when he was admitted for

Figure 31
Wright in his garden at 'Southernwood' shortly before his death.
(Giles Romanes)

episodes of heart failure. Sister Bloss, who cared for him on these occasions, had nothing but happy memories, reporting that he was a very good patient and the 'nurses loved him'. He never forgot to send her flowers, mainly gentians and heathers from his garden.[22] He was admitted for the last time in April 1947 following a myocardial infarct. Everyone expected him to die but he recovered sufficiently to return to 'Southernwood', where he died early on the morning of 30 April.

He was cremated at Golders Green on 3 May but surprisingly few turned up to do him honour — Colebrook, Fleming, Freeman and Zachary Cope of the St Mary's staff together with the inoculation department staff, but none of the St Mary's consultants. The service was conducted by Canon J O Hannay, better known as the author George Birmingham, an old friend whom he first met when they were both schoolboys in Belfast. His ashes were scattered in his garden at 'Southernwood'. A memorial service was held at Holy Trinity church, Prince Consort Road on 8 May, also conducted by Hannay. This was better attended, and the congregation included the Earl and Countess of Iveagh, Lord and Lady Moran, Anthony de Rothschild and Fleming; it was described by Grizel Hartley as a 'terribly sad affair'. Surprisingly Colebrook was not present, giving the rather lame excuse that he and his wife had booked a holiday in Scotland.

Wright's reputation declined rapidly after his death. Few recognise his name today and those that do chiefly recall his opposition to women's suffrage. Yet his life marked a watershed in medicine between the pragmatic approach to illness and the scientific basis of treatment. When he qualified the age of Listerian surgery was under way, but treatment for diseases associated with infection, which comprised the majority of fatal illnesses, consisted of bed rest in a well-ventilated room, plenty of fluids by mouth and, like as not, violent purgation. Blood-letting was still practised. Even aspirin was not available until 1896.[23] Digitalis could be used for heart failure, quinine was available for malaria and mercury was employed in the treatment of syphilis. There was little else. Preventive medicine was in its infancy and there was no public finance for medical research. By the time of Wright's death the whole pattern had been transformed. The advent of sulphonamides and antibiotics had revolutionised treatment of infections such as lobar pneumonia, puerperal fever and syphilis. Effective preventive measures had been introduced to reduce drastically the incidence of the enteric fevers. The necessity of funding medical research from government as well as private resources had been accepted and the Medical Research Council was fully established. In all this it can be claimed that Wright played a seminal role. Yet his achievements are largely unacknowledged or forgotten.

There is an unfortunate tendency among members of the medical profession to decry or forget progress made by their immediate predecessors. Retrospective judgments of past scientific work in the light of present-day knowledge are all too often unduly harsh. Wright's struggle to have anti-typhoid inoculation accepted illustrates this to a nicety. The concept that injection of a dead pathogenic bacillus might induce immunity to disease caused by that bacillus when alive might seem commonplace today; at the end of the 19th century, when even the bacterial origin of infections was denied by some established members of the profession, it was revolutionary. That acceptance of preventive inoculation against typhoid was slow to be adopted by the army was due to a variety of reasons. Wright himself noted at the end of his life that: 'New discoveries in science, in spite of being published in scientific journals, may be long overlooked, discarded or disbelieved if they contradict widely held popular belief.'[24] Eventually they are, albeit reluctantly, conceded and finally they are dismissed as obvious and it is agreed that anyone could have made the observation or discovery. The original struggle for acceptance is conveniently forgotten.

One factor in Wright's failure to obtain acceptance for his ideas lay in his personality. He was by any standard an extremely clever man, fluent in French, German and Spanish and possessed a profound knowledge of both modern and classical literature. Dante was his first love. He claimed to be able to remember 250,000 lines of poetry and was known to recite Milton for half an hour at a stretch on long motor journeys during the First World War.[25] When he was over 75 he taught himself Russian[26] and at the age of 80 began to study Eskimo. But clever men are not always popular with their contemporaries; especially was this so in the medical profession in the first half of the 20th century. Wright did not improve matters by at times being unnecessarily argumentative and blunt-spoken. Like his friend Mackenzie, the cardiologist, he was authoritative in his speech and opinions but had a deep distrust of authoritative statements made by others. He had a particular aversion to the Harley Street practitioner who, at the beginning of the 20th century, was the acknowledged source of medical wisdom. Wright never missed an opportunity to deride these men, yet it was upon their goodwill that ultimately he depended for implementation of his recommendation for the management of infections. It says much for the tolerance of the Royal College of Physicians of London that, in spite of his polemics against them, they were the main body that gave support to his advocacy of anti-typhoid inoculation.

It was a similar story during the 1914–18 war, when he and his colleagues realised all too clearly the damage that was being perpetrated by the antiseptic treatment of wounds. The surgical establishment, led by the President of the Royal College of Surgeons, Sir W Watson Cheyne, was reluctant to accept Wright's experimental evidence. In dealing with this situation, and with defects he perceived in the organisation of the RAMC, he approached matters in a tactless and insensitive manner, employing his friendships with politicians and the intelligentsia over the heads of the military and medical authorities. It was not until the war was nearly over that his views were grudgingly accepted, though his contribution was not openly acknowledged.

The major part he played in formation of the Medical Research Council is forgotten today. His letter to the *Liverpool Daily Post* in 1905 (see page 201), lamenting the lack of facilities and career opportunities in medical research, was given a hostile review by the *Lancet* but ultimately he persuaded Lord Moulton and his other influential friends in the political world to take action. It was unfortunate that the war intervened to direct his energies away from this project. That he played a relatively minor role after the war was in large part due to the antagonism that existed between him and Morley Fletcher.

As with other men of genius — and Wright was a genius acknowledged by men opposed to his views, for example the celebrated medical statistician Major Greenwood[27] — some of his ideas were hare-brained. One of the most perceptive comments on Wright was made by Metchnikoff:[28] 'He is the sort of man who has very good original thoughts but he also has many thoughts which are only original.' Nowhere was his eccentricity more apparent than in his attitude to women. His implacable opposition to granting them the vote now seems absurd but, in the debates in 1912, it did not appear so unreasonable. He had strong support not only from a good many men but also from some prominent women. He was no misogynist, as is apparent from his close female acquaintances. Furthermore, although he was much in demand at dinners given by society ladies, such as Lady St Helier and Lady Gordon Lennox, he was no snob. One day during tea in the laboratory, an assistant came into the room to inform Wright that there was a Mr Mackenzie to see him. 'Does he look like a patient or a gentleman?' asked Wright. 'A gentleman, sir,' was the reply. 'Oh well, give him a seat even if he is a gentleman,' was Wright's instruction.[29] On another occasion John Freeman told of a splendidly dressed society physician 'complete with frock coat, top hat, gold-tipped malacca cane and lavender gloves' who came to the laboratory and explained that he had just been appointed physician to a member of the royal family and he would like Wright to tell him 'all about immunity'. Wright failed to show interest and continued to look down his microscope while the physician went on talking. Then sounds of hobnailed boots were heard on the stairs and a 'grizzled old working man' entered the room saying 'I dunno, Governor, if I ought to be here by rights....' Wright immediately turned to him, saying, 'What may I have the pleasure of doing for you, my friend?' The society physician wilted and backed out of the laboratory.[30]

One of Wright's most important and lasting contributions to medicine was the promotion of clinical pathology, with its subdivisions, as a separate and definitive branch of medical science. His insistence that diagnostic pathologists should enjoy the same status within the hospital as the physicians and surgeons brought about major change. The concept of the bacteriologist as a man confined to the laboratory was anathema to him. He insisted, and indeed was the first to do so, on having charge of a ward in which he could establish the diagnosis in patients with infections and observe the results of treatment. And it is not only in the matter of status that pathologists owe him a debt. He was a great pioneer of laboratory technique. His creation of methods whereby testing of a variety of changes in blood and serum could be investigated using drops of blood obtained by pricking the fingers, at a time when venepuncture was a primitive and uncertain operation, opened up a new era in the scientific investigation and monitoring of disease processes. His books *The principles of microscopy* and *The technique of the teat and capillary glass tube* are classics of their kind and remain monuments to human ingenuity, illustrating how much can be achieved with the simplest home-made apparatus.

Wright's persistent promotion of vaccine therapy was at the time misplaced; but in recent years, with widespread resistance to antibiotics and the possibility of inducing immunity to tumour viruses, development of vaccines has once again become a subject of wide importance. It was unlucky that in Wright's day knowledge of bacteriological and virological antigenic structure was insufficient to allow effective development of this form of preventive treatment.

Throughout the last 45 years of his life Wright remained steadfastly loyal to St Mary's Hospital and in his turn inspired intense loyalty in those who worked with him. He had founded a great research centre and his assistants had served him well — Fleming with his discoveries of lysozyme and penicillin, and Colebrook with his important contributions to the treatment of burns and to the combating of hospital cross-infection. In 1946 the inoculation department was renamed the Wright–Fleming Institute, but the title was dropped in 1967 when final merging with the medical school took place — there is still an Almroth Wright ward and lecture theatre. But for the introduction of the National Health Service, St Mary's might have remained the main centre for clinical laboratory research in England.

Wright's great mistake was overstaying his time as head of his department. Had he retired at 65 or even 70, the memory of his achievements would have been accorded more respect at the end of his life and afterwards. He died out of tune with the generation that succeeded him as he had been out of tune with his own. It is best to forget the pettiness of some of his actions in old age and remember him in his early years. Then he might be found alone late at night, at the gas-lit bench in the laboratory, trying to unlock the secrets of nature — a somewhat dishevelled, stooping, bear-like man with large head, hands and feet, yet performing the finest manipulations, miracles of skill, with his enormous fingers.[31]

Notes

1   CMAC PP/COL Diary entry for 28 April 1930.
2   Another to be put out on this occasion was the house governor of the hospital, Colonel Walter Parkes. He considered that the Dean, Wilson, was claiming credit for Parkes's efforts in fund-raising.
3   Letter from HG Verey to J Freeman. TCD Archives 9890.
4   *St Mary's Hospital Gazette* 1936 p47.
5   Ibid.
6   See Chapter 9.
7   Ibid.
8   Rogers K. Personal communication.
9   CMAC PP/COL Diary entry for 23 September 1945.
10 Ibid September 1945.
11 Ibid.
12 Ibid December 1945.
13 Br Lib Add MSS 56214.
14 Br Lib Add MSS 56214. Letter from Dr WH Hughes.
15 Maurois A. *The life of Sir Alexander Fleming.* London: Jonathan Cape, 1959.
16 Rogers K. Personal communication.
17 Maurois A. *The life of Sir Alexander Fleming* pp203–4. London: Jonathan Cape, 1959.
18 TCD Archives 9888/4/4.
19 CMAC PP/COL Diary entry for 30 October 1930.
20 Lawrence PSH, ed. *Grizel: Grizel Hartley remembered* p193. London: Michael Russell, 1991.
21 Colebrook L. *Almroth Wright: provocative doctor and thinker* p237. London: William Heinemann, Medical Books, London, 1954.
22 TCD Archives 9890.
23 Porter R. *The greatest benefit to mankind* p674. HarperCollins, London.
24 Wright AE. *Alethetropic logic: a posthumous work* (presented by GJ Romanes) p266. London: William Heinemann, 1953.
25 Freeman J. *St Mary's Hospital Gazette* 1952 pp 94–100.
26 CMAC PP/COL Diary insertion 1945.
27 *Lancet* 1947; i: 656. [Obituary notice.]
28   *St Mary's Hospital Gazette* 1936 pp 47–8.
29 CMAC PP/COL Diary entry, 1913.
30 Freeman J. *St Mary's Hospital Gazette* 1952 pp 94–100
31 Ibid.

Index

264